PHYSICS
STUDENTS' GUIDE 2
UNITS H to L

Revised Nuffield Advanced Science

**General editor,
Revised Nuffield
Advanced Physics**
John Harris

Consultant editor
E. J. Wenham

Editors of Units in this *Guide*
Stephen Borthwick
Peter Bullett
David Chaundy
John Harris
Wilf Mace
Jon Ogborn

The Nuffield–Chelsea Curriculum Trust is grateful to the authors and editors of the first edition:

Organizers: P. J. Black, Jon Ogborn; **Contributors:** W. Bolton, R. W. Fairbrother, G. E. Foxcroft, Martin Harrap, John Harris, A. L. Mansell, A. W. Trotter.

PHYSICS STUDENTS' GUIDE 2

UNITS H to L

REVISED NUFFIELD ADVANCED SCIENCE
Published for the Nuffield–Chelsea Curriculum Trust
by Longman Group Limited

Longman Group UK Limited
Longman House, Burnt Mill, Harlow, Essex CM20 2JE, England
and Associated Companies throughout the World

First published 1971
Revised edition first published 1986
Second impression 1988
Copyright © 1971, 1986 The Nuffield–Chelsea Curriculum Trust

Design and art direction by Ivan Dodd
Illustrations by Oxford Illustrators Limited

Filmset in Times Roman and Univers
Produced by Longman Group (FE) Ltd
Printed in Hong Kong

ISBN 0 582 35416 1

Cover

Silicon solar cells. Many of these cells go to make up a solar panel for the direct generation of electricity from solar energy.

Paul Brierley

CONTENTS

H

I

J

K

L

FOREWORD

When the Nuffield Advanced Science series first appeared on the market in 1970, they were rapidly accepted as a notable contribution to the choices for the sixth-form science curriculum. These courses were devised by experienced teachers working in consultation with the universities and examination boards, and subjected to extensive trials in schools before publication and they introduced a new element of intellectual excitement into the work of A-level students. Though the period since publication has seen many debates on the sixth-form curriculum, it is now clear that the Advanced Level framework of education will be with us for some years in its established form. That period saw various proposals for change in structure which were not accepted but the debate to which we contributed encouraged us to start looking at the scope and aims of our A-level courses and at the ways they were being used in schools. Much of value was learned during those investigations and has been extremely useful in the planning of the present revision.

The revision of the physics course under the general editorship of John Harris has been conducted with the help of a committee under the chairmanship of K. F. Smith, Professor of Physics, University of Sussex. We are grateful to him and to the committee, whose other members were W. F. Archenhold, J. Bausor, Professor P. J. Black, Professor R. Chambers, A. E. De Barr, Roger Hackett, John Harris, Wilf Mace, Robert Northage, Professor Jon Ogborn, A. J. Parker, and Maurice Tebbutt. We also owe a considerable debt to the Oxford and Cambridge Schools Examination Board which for many years has been responsible for the special Nuffield examinations in physics and to the Assistant Secretary of the Board, Mrs B. G. Fraser, who has been an invaluable adviser.

The Nuffield–Chelsea Curriculum Trust is also grateful for the advice and recommendations received from its Advisory Committee, a body containing representatives from the teaching profession, the Association for Science Education, Her Majesty's Inspectorate, universities, and local authority advisers; the committee is under the chairmanship of Professor P. J. Black, educational consultant to the Trust.

Our appreciation also goes to the editors and authors of the first edition of Nuffield Advanced Physics, who worked with Jon Ogborn and P. J. Black, the project organizers. Their team of editors and writers included: W. Bolton, R. W. Fairbrother, G. E. Foxcroft, Martin Harrap, John Harris, A. L. Mansell, and A. W. Trotter. Much of their original work has been preserved in the new edition.

I particularly wish to record our gratitude to the General Editor of the revision, John Harris, Lecturer at the Centre for Science and Mathematics Education, Chelsea College, and a member of the team responsible for the first edition. To him, to E. J. Wenham, Consultant Editor of the revision, and to the editors of the Units in the revised course – all teachers with a wide experience of the needs of students and of the current state of physics education – Roger Hackett, Nigel Wallis,

David Grace, Mark Ellse, Charles Milward, Trevor Sandford, Paul Jordan, Peter Harvey, Maurice Tebbutt, David Chaundy, Wilf Mace, Stephen Borthwick, Peter Bullett, and Jon Ogborn, we offer our most sincere thanks.

I would also like to acknowledge the work of William Anderson, publications manager to the Trust, his colleagues, and our publishers, the Longman Group, for their assistance in the publication of these books. The editorial and publishing skills they contribute are essential to effective curriculum development.

K. W. Keohane,
Chairman, Nuffield–Chelsea Curriculum Trust

INTRODUCTION

This is the *Students' guide* for the second year of the Revised Nuffield A-level physics course. It covers Units H, I, J, K, and L. An introduction to the whole course, and an explanation of the way in which the *Students' guides* are organized is given under the heading 'About the course and about this book', in *Students' guide 1*.

ACKNOWLEDGEMENTS

One of the pleasantest aspects of the development of *Revised Nuffield Advanced Physics* has been the willing way in which so many people have contributed and become involved in the work. Above all, teachers have helped in many ways, and the very number who have done so makes it impossible to acknowledge the contribution of each individual. Many have offered suggestions at meetings or have written in with ideas for questions, demonstrations, and so on. We have tried to consider carefully all the suggestions put forward and, inevitably, it is impossible to give proper credit to the source or origin of every idea we have used. One who has made a particularly valuable contribution in this way is Colin Price. To him and the many others whose contributions go unacknowledged, we offer our sincere thanks.

Other teachers have helped by conducting trials of some of the more radically changed parts of the course, and of a major innovation – the 'Dynamic modelling system'. The trial schools are: Aylesbury Grammar School; Beechen Cliff School, Bath; Bexley–Erith Technical High School, Bexley; Bishop Hedley High School, Merthyr Tydfil; Cheltenham College; Esher College; Forest Hill School, London; Godolphin and Latymer School, London; The Grammar School, Batley; The Greenhill School, Tenby; Haverstock School, London; Heathland School, Hounslow; Henbury School, Bristol; Highfield School, Wolverhampton; Howell's School, Llandaff; King Edward VI College, Nuneaton; Kingsbridge School; Lady Margaret High School, Cardiff; Malvern College; Marlborough College; Netherhall School, Cambridge; North London Collegiate School; Northgate High School, Ipswich; Oulder Hill Community School, Rochdale; Richmond-upon-Thames College; Royal Grammar School, High Wycombe; Rugby School; Samuel Ward Upper School, Haverhill; and Sutton Manor High School.

We are grateful to the Inner London Education Authority for trying some of our material on electronics in their 1983 Summer School for sixth-form students at the North London Science Centre.

Mark Ellse has read and commented on much of the draft material, and has made particularly useful suggestions about the up-dating of some experiments and pieces of equipment.

Thanks are due to a group of teachers, convened by Bob Fairbrother, who met several times to discuss assessment. Their suggestions led to some changes in the structure of the examination.

Others, as well as teachers, have helped, of course. While he was working as a technician at the Centre for Science and Mathematics Education, Chelsea College, Phil Webb found time in a busy schedule to try out ideas for demonstrations and experiments, and to suggest ideas for new apparatus.

CLEAPSE School Science Service reviewed all the suggested experiments and demonstrations and made useful suggestions on the safety aspects of some of them.

Industry has helped too, and, among others, we are indebted to Rank Xerox, Amersham International P.L.C., and the CEGB for technical help and information.

Examination questions in the *Students' guide* are reprinted by permission of the Oxford and Cambridge Schools Examination Board. All are taken from Oxford and Cambridge Nuffield A-level Physics papers. Where guide lines for answers to examination questions are provided it must be understood that these are not the Examination Board's responsibility.

The Consultative Committee have, I believe, been asked to work harder and contribute more than is usually expected of such a group. As well as attending many meetings they have read and commented in detail on draft manuscripts – sometimes in a far from ideal state – and they have done all this most willingly.

It is a pleasure to acknowledge E. J. Wenham's help and sound advice. Much of what is written in these books has benefited from his knowledge and experience as teacher and author.

All of us who have contributed to these books owe a great debt of gratitude to Nina Konrad and her colleagues in the Publications office of the Nuffield–Chelsea Curriculum Trust for their thorough and painstaking work in preparing our manuscripts for the printers and our sometimes quite inadequate drawings for the artists.

Finally, I would like to express my sincere thanks to Paul Black and Jon Ogborn. Their help and support has been invaluable. During a period when both have been particularly busy, they have still found time to give advice both on general matters and on points of detail. They were, of course, the chief architects of the original Nuffield Advanced Physics course. Their willingness to be involved with what must at times have seemed like a severe distortion of their original plans, says much about their generosity of spirit.

John Harris

Unit H
MAGNETIC FIELDS AND A.C.

David Chaundy
Malvern College

H

SUMMARY OF THE UNIT

INTRODUCTION

Magnetic fields are more complex than either electric or gravitational fields. The strength of a magnetic field when iron is present is difficult to calculate. This is why the treatment here is largely practical rather than theoretical, and why it is aimed at showing how to make magnetic fields and how to apply them effectively.

Perhaps the most important applications are to be found in the generation of alternating current supplies for the mains distribution system and, at much higher frequencies, for use in radio communication and television. The Unit is also concerned with some applications of a.c. which are not possible with d.c.

Section H1

MAGNETIC FIELDS

Dry cells, solar cells, and fuel cells do not depend on magnetic fields. However, they are incapable of providing the amounts of energy upon which our industry, commerce, agriculture, transport, and our homes depend. For this we need electrical generators capable of transforming vast amounts of energy derived from the combustion of fossil or nuclear fuels. All such generators depend on electromagnetic induction in strong magnetic fields. This Section will show how electric currents produce magnetic fields, how these fields are measured, and how they are used to handle atomic particles.

Forces on currents

DEMONSTRATION H1
Forces on currents;
forces between currents

Two long flexible conductors attract one another if they carry currents in the same direction (as if they were trying to become one wire). They repel each other if the currents are in opposite directions (figure H1). These forces are very small compared, for example, with those needed to drive an electric train.

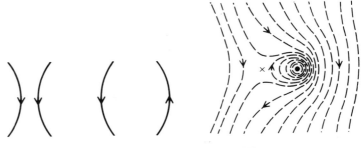

Figure H1
Forces on currents.

Figure H2
The catapult field.

OPTIONAL DEMONSTRATION H2
The catapult field

A wire carrying a current is pushed aside when there is a magnetic field at right angles to the wire. The 'catapult field' demonstration shows how the magnetic field due to the current in the wire and the external field combine (figure H2).

DEMONSTRATION H3
Forces on induced currents

An explanation of the 'jumping ring' demonstration (figure H3) also involves the magnetic forces between currents.

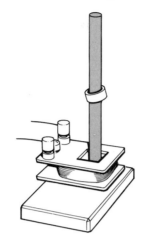

Figure H3
The jumping ring.

Gravitational field strength is given by

$$g = F/m$$

and the force acts in the direction of the field.

Electric field strength is given by

$$E = F/Q$$

and the force acts in the direction of the field.

DEMONSTRATION H4
Directions of forces in magnetic fields;
measuring magnetic fields

The strength of a magnetic field is given by

$$B = F/Il$$

and the force acts in a direction *perpendicular* to both the current and the field, given by the left hand rule. See figure H4.

g is measured in $N\,kg^{-1}$; E is measured in $N\,C^{-1}$; B is measured in $N\,A^{-1}\,m^{-1}$ or tesla (T).

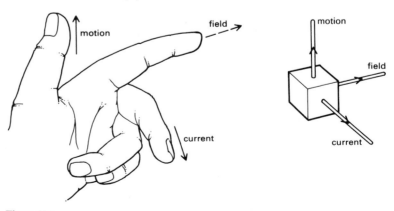

Figure H4
Force–direction rule.

The strength of a magnetic field may be measured by putting a wire of length *l* in the field, sending a current *I* through it, and measuring the force, *F*, on the wire. *B* is also called the flux density of a magnetic field. Like *g* and *E*, *B* is a vector quantity.

QUESTIONS 1 to 5

The force on a moving charge

QUESTION 7 From $F = BIl$ it can be shown that the force on an individual particle carrying charge *Q*, moving with velocity *v* at right angles to a magnetic field of strength *B*, is

$$F = BQv$$

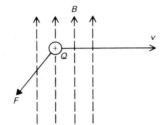

Figure H5
$F = BQv$.

QUESTIONS 8 to 10

READING
Electromagnetic flowmeters
The 'Hall-effect' flowmeter (page 18)

DEMONSTRATION H5
Hall effect; Hall probe

In a demonstration of the Hall effect in a semiconductor the magnetic force on a moving charge is balanced by the electric force on it. The electric field is V/d and so the electric force is QV/d.

Thus $BQv = QV/d$, giving the Hall voltage $V = Bvd$.

A Hall probe can therefore be used to compare magnetic fields by comparing voltages provided that the speed of the charge carriers, *v*, is kept constant. This means that the current in the Hall probe must be kept constant.

Measurement of *e/m*

QUESTIONS 6, 11

DEMONSTRATION H6
Measuring the specific charge
for electrons

A beam of electrons can be bent into a circular path by a uniform magnetic field at right angles to the electrons' direction of motion. A fine-beam tube contains gas at low pressure which is ionized by the electrons. The ionized gas glows, enabling us to see where the electron beam is. Combining the formulae for centripetal force (mv^2/r), magnetic

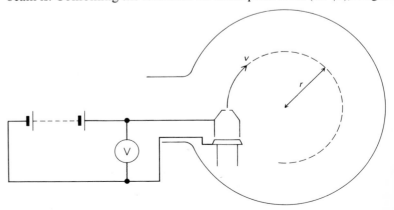

Figure H6
Measuring the specific charge of an electron.

force on an electron (*Bev*), and for energy of an electron accelerated through a p.d. V ($\frac{1}{2}mv^2 = eV$) leads to an expression for the specific charge (that is, charge per unit mass) for the electron:

$$\frac{e}{m} = \frac{2V}{B^2 r^2}$$

For an electron, $e/m = 1.76 \times 10^{11}\,\mathrm{C\,kg^{-1}}$. The charge on the electron is known to be $1.60 \times 10^{-19}\,\mathrm{C}$ (from Millikan's experiment), giving a value of $9.1 \times 10^{-31}\,\mathrm{kg}$ for the electron's mass.

Magnetic fields are used in many devices and experiments involving atomic and sub-atomic particles. They are used to separate particles according to their charge-to-mass ratio, as in the mass spectrometer, and so to identify isotopes, and to identify particles from their curved tracks in cloud and bubble chambers. They are used to deflect electrons in the cathode-ray tube of a monitor or television set, and to control the motion of sub-atomic particles as they are accelerated to very high energies, as in the cyclotron and synchrotron.

H

QUESTIONS 12 to 16

Fields near currents

EXPERIMENT H7
Fields near electric currents

The field strength near a long straight wire can be shown to be inversely proportional to the distance from the wire and proportional to the current flowing in it.

Thus

$$B \propto I/r$$

The ampere is defined as that current which, if maintained in two infinitely long conductors of negligible diameter, placed 1 metre apart in a vacuum, would give a force between the conductors of $2 \times 10^{-7}\,\mathrm{N}$ per metre length. The ampere is the basic unit from which all other electrical and magnetic units (coulomb, volt, tesla, etc.) are derived.

The constant of proportionality is written as $\mu_0/2\pi$, so

QUESTIONS 17 to 22

$$B = \frac{\mu_0 I}{2\pi r}$$

and it follows from the definition of the ampere that

$$\mu_0 = 4\pi \times 10^{-7}\,\mathrm{N\,A^{-2}}$$

The constant μ_0 is called the permeability of free space.

The formula for the field of an infinitely long solenoid (N turns in length l) is

QUESTION 19

$$B = \mu_0 \frac{N}{l} I$$

The formal definition of the ampere does not provide a practical way of making a measurement: a force of $2 \times 10^{-7}\,\mathrm{N}$ is much too small to measure accurately in this situation. Instead, the larger forces between solenoids are measured using instruments for calibrating ammeters, like that shown in figure H7.

Figure H7
National Physical Laboratory current balance.
National Physical Laboratory, Crown Copyright.

Section H2   ELECTROMAGNETIC INDUCTION

About 150 years ago Michael Faraday found that there were many ways in which an e.m.f. could be *induced* in a circuit without any electrical contact with the circuit. All that was needed was some movement or some change of a magnetic field.

One very important use of electromagnetic induction is in generators, which move coils or magnets to produce electricity. It is also used in transformers, where nothing can be seen moving, and in induction motors, which have no electrical connection to the rotor. Another example is an inductor, where the e.m.f. is induced in the circuit which is itself producing the magnetic field.

DEMONSTRATION H8
The e.m.f. induced in a moving wire

The force which acts on a charged particle moving in a magnetic field leads to an induced e.m.f. in a conductor moving through a magnetic field. If a length of wire l is perpendicular to a magnetic field B and moves at right angles to both its length and the field at a speed v, the magnetic force on each electron is Bev (figure H8). Electrons begin to move along the wire and there is a separation of charge leading to a potential difference between the ends of the wire. This p.d. is called the *induced e.m.f.*, $\mathscr{E}$. If the length of the wire is l, the electric field in it is $\mathscr{E}/l$ and the electric force on each electron is $e\mathscr{E}/l$. When the electrons are in equilibrium the electric and magnetic forces balance:

$$e\mathscr{E}/l = Bev$$

QUESTIONS 23 to 25 $\mathscr{E} = Bvl$

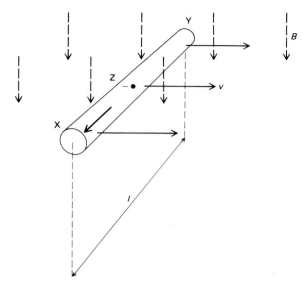

Figure H8
Conductor moving across a magnetic field.

Direct current generators and motors

DEMONSTRATION H9
Inducing e.m.f.s in a motor/dynamo

When the rotor of a generator is turned, the rotor coils move through a magnetic field. An e.m.f. proportional to the rate of rotation is induced. If an external circuit is connected a current will flow.

The torque of a motor is the couple produced by the rotor. From $F = BIl$ it follows that, for a given motor, the torque is proportional to I, the rotor current. Small motors use permanent magnets so the field, B, is fixed. Larger motors use iron-cored coils to produce the field, so B and hence the torque increase with the current in these field coils.

In a motor, the turning rotor is a conductor moving in a magnetic field. So when it rotates an e.m.f. is induced in it which is proportional to the field, B, and to the rate of rotation. The current in the circuit is driven by the applied p.d., V, and opposed by the e.m.f., $\mathscr{E}$, induced in the rotor. The rotor current is therefore given by

$$V - \mathscr{E} = IR$$

where R is the resistance of the rotor coils.

QUESTIONS 26, 27

If R is small, $\mathscr{E}$ is almost as big as V. If the load on the motor is increased more torque is needed and the rotor current I must increase. The rotor slows down, $\mathscr{E}$ is reduced, and I grows.

The equation $V - \mathscr{E} = IR$ leads to

$$VI = I^2 R + \mathscr{E}I$$

DEMONSTRATION H10;
OPTIONAL EXPERIMENT H11
Behaviour and efficiency of motors

VI is the total power taken from the supply. $I^2 R$ is the power which heats the rotor and it is wasted. $\mathscr{E}I$ is the power transferred to the load, used to overcome mechanical losses (for example in the bearings), etc.

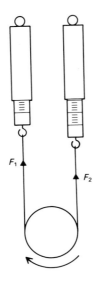

The mechanical power delivered by a motor to a band brake of radius r is $2\pi rn(F_2 - F_1)$. F_2 and F_1 are the tensions on the two sides of the band (figure H9) and n is the rate of rotation of the rotor (in revolutions per second). Power can also be found from the rate at which the motor raises a load.

Figure H9
Band brake on pulley.

Flux

QUESTIONS 28, 29

The flux, Φ, through any circuit is the product of B and the area A of the circuit. If the flux links with N turns of wire the total flux linkages are NBA. The unit of flux is the weber (Wb). Since $B = \Phi/A$ the magnetic field strength is also the flux per unit area or *flux density.*

Faraday's Law of electromagnetic induction

DEMONSTRATION H12
Moving wires and changing flux

DEMONSTRATION H13
A continually changing field

STUDENT DEMONSTRATION H14
Induction using a.c.

Lenz's rule

READING
Electromagnetic flowmeters
The turbine flowmeter (page 16)

It is useful to know Faraday's Law in two slightly different forms:

When a conductor cuts magnetic flux, the e.m.f. induced is equal to the rate at which flux is cut.

When the flux linked with a circuit changes the e.m.f. induced is equal to the rate of change of flux linkages.

The magnitude of the induced e.m.f., $\mathcal{E}$, is given by $\mathcal{E} = N d\Phi/dt$.
The direction of the induced e.m.f. is such that it tends to oppose the motion or change causing it. This must follow from the conservation of energy.

The effect of iron

Inside a toroid (figure H10) the flux density is the same as in an infinitely long cylinder with the same number of turns per unit length

$$B = \mu_0 \frac{N}{l} I$$

If the toroid has a cross-sectional area A, the flux inside it is

$$\Phi = BA = \mu_0 \frac{N}{l} I A$$

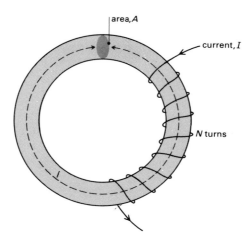

area, A

current, I

N turns

l

Figure H10
A toroid.

DEMONSTRATION H15
The effect of iron in a solenoid

When the toroid is filled with iron the flux is increased by a factor μ_r, the relative permeability of the iron, giving

$$\Phi = \mu_0 \mu_r \frac{N}{l} I A$$

μ_r may be as high as 1000 for soft iron; it varies greatly as the flux in the iron changes. The equation can be rearranged to give

$$\Phi = \frac{NI}{(l/\mu_0 \mu_r A)}$$

The product NI is often referred to as 'current turns', and the quantity $l/\mu_0 \mu_r A$ is known as the *reluctance*. The equation

QUESTIONS 31 to 35

flux = current turns/reluctance

can be compared with

current = potential difference/resistance.

EXPERIMENT H16
Increasing the iron in a
magnetic circuit

When a solenoid has an iron core with an air gap, the two reluctances (iron and air) are first added like resistances in series, and then the flux can be calculated using the formula above. High flux densities ($\Phi/A = B$) are needed if an electromagnetic machine (motor, generator, or transformer) is to be efficient, which is why they contain a lot of iron with only small air gaps.

Inductance

DEMONSTRATION H17
Mutual inductance of two coils

A varying current in one coil sets up a varying magnetic field which can induce an e.m.f. in a second coil nearby (figure H11). This induced e.m.f. depends on the rate of change of current in the first coil.

$\mathscr{E} \propto \mathrm{d}I/\mathrm{d}t$

The constant of proportionality is called the *mutual inductance*, M,

QUESTION 36 $\mathscr{E} = M \dfrac{\mathrm{d}I}{\mathrm{d}t}$

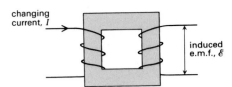

Figure H11
Mutual inductance.

DEMONSTRATION H18
Self induction
DEMONSTRATION H19
Measurement of self inductance

M depends on the geometry of the coils and any iron present.

A varying current in a single coil causes changes of flux which induce an e.m.f. in the coil itself, so every coil has a *self inductance, L*. The e.m.f. induced in a coil by a changing current in the coil is given by

$$\mathscr{E} = L \frac{dI}{dt}$$

When a steady p.d. is connected to a circuit with resistance and inductance (figure H12),

$$V = IR + L \frac{dI}{dt} \qquad \text{(compare the equation for a motor)}$$

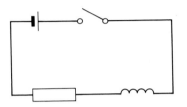

Figure H12
LR circuit.

QUESTIONS 37 to 41

When I is very small, $dI/dt \approx V/L$, and the initial rate of rise of current depends only on V and L. A steady applied p.d. produces a current which initially grows at a uniform rate.

When the current has stopped rising, dI/dt is zero and so $I = V/R$: the final current depends only on V and R. See figure H13.

If the current is switched off suddenly, dI/dt is very large and a very big e.m.f. is induced.

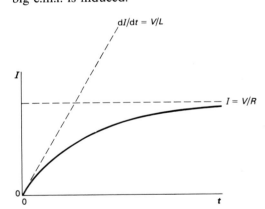

Figure H13
Growth of current in *LR* circuit.

Section H3 ALTERNATING CURRENT

An alternating current will do things which a direct current will not do. If a steady p.d. is applied to a circuit containing a capacitor there may be a short-lived pulse of current – but no steady current is possible. However, if an alternating p.d. is applied to such a circuit, an alternating current will be maintained as long as the p.d. is applied. And since the flux due to an alternating current is constantly changing, an a.c. will induce e.m.f.s continually in an inductor, whereas with steady d.c. the induced e.m.f.s occur only when the current is switched on or off.

READING
The generation and transmission of
electric power (page 20)

Large commercial generators are a.c. machines. The economical distribution of electric power at high voltage on the National Grid depends on step-up and step-down transformers.

QUESTION 48

Transformers

EXPERIMENT H20
Investigation of transformer action

In a perfect transformer, with N_p turns on the primary winding and N_s turns on the secondary, the e.m.f. induced in the secondary ($\mathscr{E}_s$) is related to the p.d. across the primary (V_p) and the primary and secondary currents (I_p, I_s) by

QUESTIONS 42 to 47

$$\frac{\mathscr{E}_s}{V_p} = \frac{N_s}{N_p} = \frac{I_p}{I_s}$$

H

In practice there are losses of energy both in the windings (due to the resistance of the wire) and in the iron core, so that these equations do not hold exactly. In a real transformer the primary current is a little greater, and the number of turns on the secondary needs to be higher.

Eddy currents

DEMONSTRATION H21
Eddy currents

When the flux in a solid piece of iron changes, an e.m.f. is induced in the iron, causing large eddy currents and loss of energy. To reduce such eddy currents the iron core of a transformer is made of laminations which are insulated from each other (figure H14). Eddy currents can also occur in direct current machines, such as motors, if the flux in the iron is changing, and so their iron cores are laminated too.

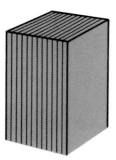

Figure H14
Laminated transformer core.

Alternating current in a resistor

DEMONSTRATION H22
Power in a resistive circuit

When a direct current is adjusted to make a lamp glow at the same brightness as with a sinusoidal a.c., the steady p.d. across the lamp is rather more than half the peak value of the alternating p.d.

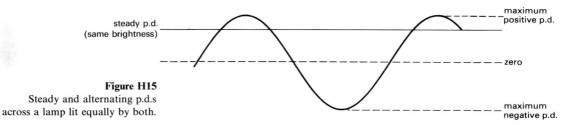

steady p.d.
(same brightness)

maximum
positive p.d.

zero

maximum
negative p.d.

Figure H15
Steady and alternating p.d.s
across a lamp lit equally by both.

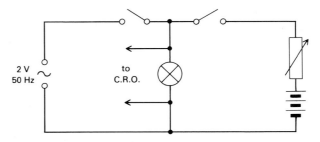

Figure H16
Comparing the brightness of a
lamp lit from a.c. and d.c.

QUESTION 49

When current flows through a resistance R and the p.d. across the resistor is V, the power dissipated at any moment is V^2/R. For an a.c. with a sinusoidal waveform, V^2 will vary with time as shown in figure H17: V^2 varies with twice the frequency of V. Because power $\propto V^2$ the total energy is proportional to the area under the graph of V^2 against time. Since this graph is symmetrical about $\frac{1}{2}V_0^2$, the mean power is $\frac{1}{2}V_0^2/R$. Hence the effective voltage is $\dfrac{1}{\sqrt{2}}V_0$, which is called the root

$$V_{\text{r.m.s.}} = \frac{V_0}{\sqrt{2}} \approx 0.707\,V_0$$

mean square (r.m.s.) voltage. This is the value shown by the line labelled 'steady p.d.' in figure H15.

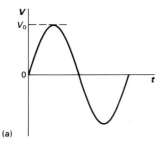

(a)

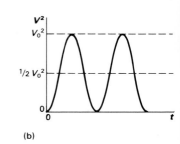

(b)

Figure H17
Variation of (a) V and (b) V^2 with time.

Capacitors in a.c. circuits

DEMONSTRATION H23
Slow a.c. in a circuit containing a capacitor

Positive current in the circuit of figure H18(a) charges the capacitor positively, as shown in the graph – figure H18(b). When the current falls to zero the capacitor has its maximum positive charge and the p.d. across it has reached its maximum positive value. The negative current first discharges the capacitor and then charges it negatively and so, when the current has risen to zero again, the p.d. across the capacitor has its maximum negative value. The current through the capacitor thus leads the voltage by one-quarter of a cycle (90° or $\pi/2$). See figure H18(b).

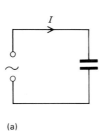

(a)

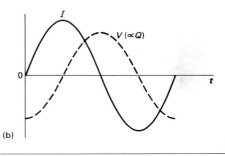

(b)

Figure H18
Current, p.d., and charge for a capacitor.

To reach the same maximum p.d. at a higher frequency, the same charge must flow in a shorter time, and so the current is greater.

With a larger capacitance at a given frequency, more charge is needed in the same time and so more current flows, for the same p.d. This means that $I \propto fC$.

Power in a capacitor

The power at any instant is given by VI and is alternately positive and negative (see figure H19). When a circuit containing capacitance only is connected to an a.c. supply, no net energy is taken from the supply: energy which is taken from the supply while the capacitor is charging up (either positively or negatively) is returned when the charge drops to zero.

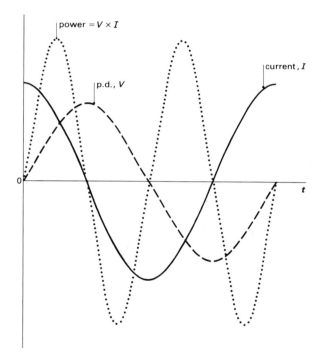

Figure H19
Variation with time of current, p.d.,
and power in a capacitor circuit.

Alternating current in an inductor

An applied p.d., V, equal to $L dI/dt$ is needed to maintain an alternating current in an inductor. Figure H20 shows that V reaches its extreme values when I is changing most rapidly. The current in an inductor lags the applied p.d. by a quarter of a cycle. In practice an inductor always has some resistance and so V is greater than $L dI/dt$, and the phase lag is less than $\pi/2$.

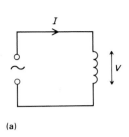

(a)

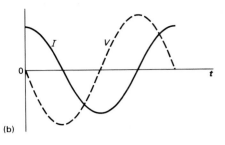

(b)

Figure H20
Current and p.d. for an inductor.

At a higher frequency a smaller current can give the same rate of change of current and so, for the same p.d., less current flows in an inductor as the frequency is raised.

With more inductance at a fixed frequency a smaller current can produce the same flux and so less current flows for the same applied p.d.

QUESTIONS 53 to 55

These results show that $I \propto \dfrac{1}{fL}$.

No energy is taken from an a.c. supply by a pure inductance with no resistance. The energy which is taken from the supply while the flux is building up is returned when the flux returns to zero.

Capacitor and inductor in parallel

DEMONSTRATION H25
Alternating currents in a circuit
containing capacitance and inductance

In a parallel circuit (figure H21) the current in the capacitor leads the applied p.d. by $\pi/2$ and the current in the inductor lags the applied p.d. by $\pi/2$. At the resonant frequency these two currents have the same magnitude and so the current in one is just right for supplying the current in the other and no current is taken from the supply. In practice there is always some resistance in the circuit, especially in the inductor, and a small current is taken from the supply.

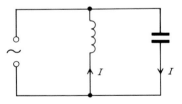

Figure H21
Alternating current in a parallel *LC* circuit.

EXPERIMENT H26
Oscillations in a parallel *LC* circuit

The resonant frequency of such circuits depends on the values of L and C. They can be used as oscillators and as filters to select one particular frequency, as in the tuning circuit of a radio. The lower the resistance of the circuit, the sharper its resonance.

DEMONSTRATION H27
A simple radio

Mechanical analogue of an *LC* circuit

QUESTIONS 56 to 59

'Electromechanical similarities' in the Reader *Physics in engineering and technology*

Electrical oscillations in an *LC* circuit can be compared with the mechanical oscillations of a mass-and-spring system. Inductance, *L*, is analogous to mass, *m*; and $1/C$ (*C* is capacitance) to the spring constant, *k*. The formulae for frequency of natural oscillations of the two systems are:

mechanical

$$f_{\mathrm{nat}} = \frac{1}{2\pi}\sqrt{\frac{k}{m}}$$

electrical

$$f_{\mathrm{nat}} = \frac{1}{2\pi}\sqrt{\frac{1}{LC}}$$

H

Section D4, Forced vibrations and resonance

Resistance in an electrical oscillator corresponds to friction in a mechanical oscillator: both cause the oscillations to die away; both cause broadening of the resonance curve. The *Q* factor is a measure of the width of the resonance peak (figure H22).

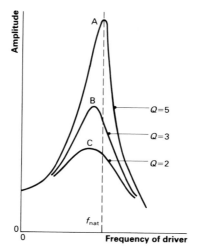

Figure H22
Resonance curves.

READINGS

ELECTROMAGNETIC FLOWMETERS

This reading passage, which is based on articles in *Physics at work* and *Physics principles at work* (both published by BP Educational Service, copyright BP International Limited, and reproduced with their kind permission), describes how the principles of electromagnetism are used in two types of flowmeter which are in day-to-day use at oil refineries and chemical manufacturing plant.

The turbine flowmeter

Twenty-five million tonnes of crude oil entered BP's Grangemouth Refinery in 1979 and accurate measurement is needed for costing and for payment of taxes to the Government (£478 000 000 in 1979).

A totally enclosed method of measurement is needed since fire and explosion risks in a refinery demand strict safety precautions. The oil flow through the pipe drives a turbine fan which has small magnets embedded in the turbine rotor. As the turbine rotates the moving magnetic fields cut the turns of a detector coil inducing an e.m.f. in the coil (see figure H23).

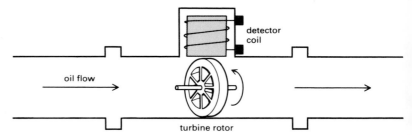

Figure H23
Principle of turbine flowmeter.

One type of flowmeter has a rotor with 8 blades and has 27 magnets embedded in the stainless steel rim (figure H24). The diameter is 203 mm (8 inches).

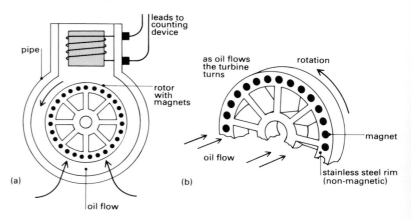

Figure H24
Detail of turbine.

As the rotor turns the magnets are swept past the detector coil (resistance 1850 Ω). The induced e.m.f. is shown in figure H25.

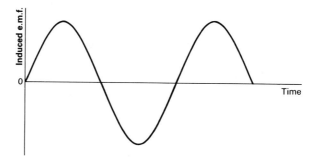

Figure H25
Variation of induced e.m.f. with time.

More magnets produce more pulses per revolution and help to improve the accuracy of the measurements (an important consideration in fiscal/customs measurements).

The signal output is converted into square pulses which are then counted (figure H26).

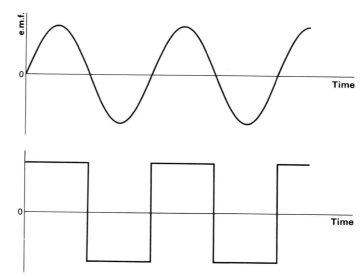

Figure H26

From the number of pulses counted in a given time, the volume flow rate can be obtained (figure H27). Rates of flow between 120 and 1130 cubic metres per hour (about 0.03 and 0.3 m³ s⁻¹) can be measured in this way.

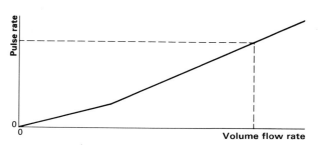

Figure H27
Calibration curve for turbine flowmeter.

The 'Hall-effect' flowmeter

A conducting fluid flowing along a pipe with velocity v, through a magnetic field of strength B and pipe of diameter d, will produce a voltage of value

$$V = Bdv$$

This voltage can be used to measure the volume flow rate.

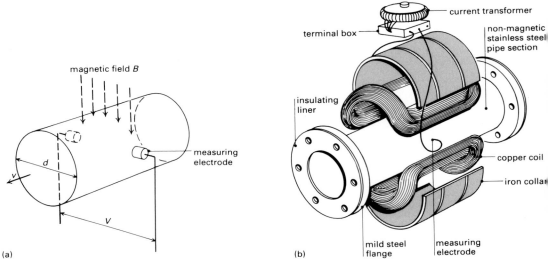

(a)

(b)

Figure H28
'Hall-effect' flowmeter: (a) principle and (b) design.

The magnetic field is provided by field coils which operate using stepped-down mains a.c. The voltage V is thus alternating. The field coils are not simple coils as they are designed to fit the cylindrical pipe as shown in figure H28. (They are similar in shape to the coils controlling the electron beam in a household television tube.) The effectiveness of the field is enhanced by the use of an iron collar as shown in figure H28(b).

Another system uses shaped iron pole-pieces which are magnetically energized using a field coil (figure H29).

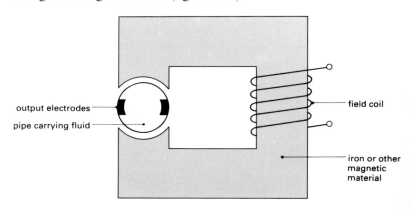

Figure H29

In either system, the pipe close to the measuring device must be non-magnetic and the shape of the electrodes and coil design are very important. The use of a.c. avoids the presence of thermoelectric and electrochemical voltages which affect the measurement. This is important as the size of the voltage between the measuring electrodes is small (about 1 mV), particularly when the conducting fluid is flowing slowly. The percentage accuracy of recorded rates increases with the speed of flow (figure H30).

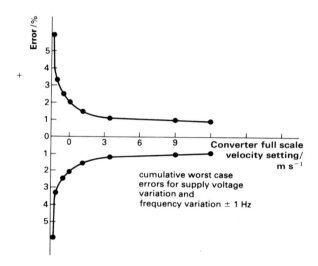

Figure H30
Accuracy curve.

Because the detectors have to be set up with great care, it is recommended that 24 hours be taken to achieve a particular performance. This is no hardship in an industry which operates round the clock.

Magnetic fields of approximately $1 \times 10^{-2}\,T$ are produced using currents of about $1\,A$ in the 1000 or so turns of the coils. The conductivities of the liquids are typically about $50 \times 10^{-4}\,\Omega^{-1}\,m^{-1}$ (engineers sometimes refer to this unit of conductivity as mhos per metre). The liquid has to be sufficiently conducting to allow enough current to operate the voltage detectors.

The above method of measurement has been successfully applied to the measurement of flow in the human body where blood acts as the conducting fluid.

Questions

a Suggest one way of producing the square pulses shown in figure H26 from the smoothly varying induced e.m.f. Why is it necessary to produce square pulses?

b 'More magnets produce more pulses per revolution.' What other effect on the induced e.m.f. would you expect more magnets imbedded in the rim of the turbine to have?

c Explain why the field coils are wound on iron (figures H28(b) and H29).

d Suggest advantages and disadvantages of the two types of flowmeter described.

THE GENERATION AND TRANSMISSION OF ELECTRIC POWER

In industrial communities, it is no longer dark at night. The great majority of people in Britain can sit and read, work, or play games as late as they please, using electricity costing only a few pence. The change from the time when a dim candle or rush light was the only available illumination has occupied several generations, and it is hard to know how to estimate its effect on the quality of life, especially as other changes have at the same time made at least as large an impact

We can, if we wish, spend perhaps 10 to 20 per cent longer in good light than could our ancestors, and so have an 'extra' ten or so years of productive life. At home we also use electricity in all kinds of appliances for preparing and cooking food, washing clothes, and so on – not to mention entertainment. Electrical machinery is essential to the manufacture of many of the goods we buy.

The way we live, and perhaps the kind of people we are, are influenced for good or ill by science and the technologies that grow out of it. The nationwide supply of electricity is a good example of such an influence.

Demand versus amenities

Most of us depend on electricity. The Central Electricity Generating Board (CEGB) now sells about 200 GW h every year in England and Wales, where the population is about 50 million. But few want a power station in the view from their windows, and many are concerned at the effect on the countryside of pylons carrying the overhead lines that bring electricity to their houses. Are underground cables the answer? Could electrical power not be produced by many small, independent generators, with a dynamo in every house? Why do we have large power stations, some producing over 1000 MW each, linked by miles of transmission lines using voltages up to 400 kV?

Why have large power stations?

At first sight, a million one-kilowatt generators would seem to be as good as a single one thousand million watt station. But the effect of making things smaller or larger is not negligible. A large turbine (660 MW is now quite common) turns out to have a smaller capital cost per unit of power produced than the equivalent number of small ones.

Table H1 illustrates the trend towards larger generating sets in Britain. Table H2 gives comparative data for an old and a relatively new power station. Notice that as well as larger generating sets, the newer station operates at higher steam temperatures and pressures.

Table H1
Age and power of steam-driven generating sets.
Data from Central Electricity Generating Board Statistical yearbook 1982–83.

Age (years)	Number of sets		
	Below 100 MW	100 MW up to 500 MW	500 MW and over
0–4	–	–	9
5–9	–	1	11
10–14	1	8	33
15–19	9	25	8
20–24	31	54	–

Table H2
Comparison of two coal-fired power stations. (Note that Battersea power station is no longer in use.)
Data from Central Electricity Generating Board Statistical yearbook 1982–83.

Station	Date	Generator sets	Steam temperature/°C	Steam pressure/Pa	Efficiency
Battersea 'A'	1933	1 × 100 MW 2 × 69 MW	427	42×10^5	16 %
Drax	1974–76	3 × 660 MW	565	160×10^5	37 %

Large turbines and generators are more efficient for several reasons. It would be very difficult to design a one kilowatt turbine with as high an efficiency as can be achieved for a one million kilowatt machine, if only because the smaller machine would have a larger surface area in proportion to its volume, so that heat losses (although smaller) would be a greater proportion of the energy transformed in the boiler and turbine.

Steam at high pressures and temperatures can be used in large turbines. The greater the temperature difference between the inlet and outlet temperatures, the higher the efficiency of the machine. Figure H31 illustrates the association between inlet steam temperature and efficiency for power stations in one of the CEGB's regions.

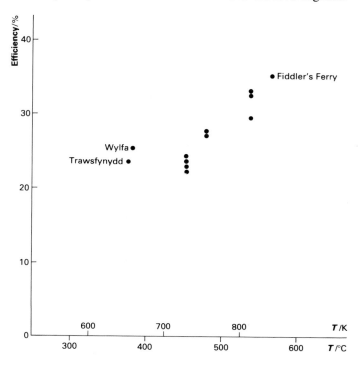

Figure H31
Efficiency and steam temperature for power stations in the North-West Region.
Data from Central Electricity Generating Board Statistical yearbook 1983–84.

Electricity cannot be stored up

Unlike fuels, or water stored behind a dam, electrical energy cannot be stored in quantity. It must be produced on demand. This is another reason why a small domestic plant is not viable: the demand fluctuates widely, and to cope with the occasional use of a cooker, a capacity of ten or a hundred times the capacity needed at other times would have to be installed.

When aggregated, many small fluctuating demands become a total demand of relatively smooth daily profile which can be connected to geographically distributed power stations by a grid of transmission lines. Even so the task is not easy, as the daily demand curve (figure H32) shows.

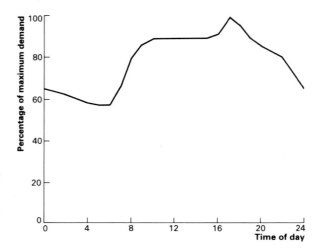

The nationwide demand is quite noticeably affected by popular television programmes, especially in breaks between programmes when large numbers of people boil kettles for tea.

As well as allowing the fluctuating demand to be shared among many power stations, the National Grid of transmission lines makes it possible to site power stations near the sources of the fuels they use, or near available cooling water from a river or the sea, rather than having to build them near the centres of population which use the electricity they generate. Nuclear power plants can be built away from densely populated areas if this is felt to be important.

By sharing out fluctuating demand the system can be run using only half of its full capacity on average. The power stations we actually have differ widely in efficiency, so that it is more economical to run the most efficient stations twenty-four hours a day, transmitting their power over large distances, than it is to run all stations part of the time. This is another reason for having the National Grid linking stations together.

At 31 March 1984 the 90 power stations in England and Wales had a total net capability of 51 028 MW. The maximum demand met in the winter of 1982/83 was 43 802 MW, the average load through the year being 45 % of the average total net capability. As table H3 shows, most of the stations were steam operated. The majority of these, 52 out of 63 used coal as their primary fuel; there were 11 oil-burning stations. Nuclear stations, although shown separately, are also in a sense steam operated since the energy from the nuclear disintegrations in the reactors is used to generate steam to drive turbines, just as the energy from burning a conventional fuel is.

Type	Number of stations	Electricity supplied/GW h
Steam	63	182 000
Nuclear	9	31 000
Gas turbine	9	52
Hydro	7	202

Table H3
Types of power station and energy supplied.
Data from Central Electricity Generating Board Statistical yearbook 1983–84.

One interesting recent development is pumped storage. The same piece of electrical machinery can be used either as a generator or as a motor. When demand is low and there is power to spare it can be used to pump water up to a high-level reservoir. When demand is high the water is allowed to fall down again, driving the machine as a generator and recovering some of the energy used to pump it up.

The National Grid

A generator usually operates at 10 to 20 kV, while users are supplied at 240 V. Power is transmitted at much higher voltages, of 275 kV or 400 kV on the Supergrid, or 132 kV on the old grid system.

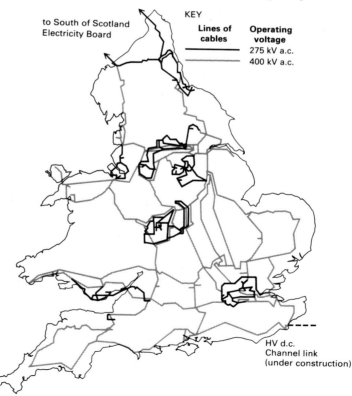

Figure H33
Supergrid system as at 31 March 1984.
From Central Electricity Generating Board Statistical yearbook 1983–84.

The reason for using high voltages is simple: the power losses are smaller, as is shown below.

Two of the 400 kV Supergrid conductors, capable of handling 1000 MW, have a combined resistance of 0.034 ohm per kilometre. (They are made of aluminium on a steel core, cross-sectional area 2.6 cm².)

To make a simple calculation, we treat them as d.c. lines carrying 1000 MW at 400 kV. The current is 2500 A, and a power of 210 kW is dissipated in each kilometre of cable, a loss of 2.1% in a hundred kilometres.

Had the voltage been ten times lower (40 kV), the current would be ten times higher (25 000 A) and the power loss (proportional to the square of the current) a hundred times greater, amounting to 21 MW in each kilometre.

In this much simplified calculation, the lower-voltage lines would be dissipating 21 kW per *metre*, and would be as hot as electric fire elements. (The resistance of the hot line would have risen, invalidating the calculation as it stands.)

In general, for a given power, energy losses for a given cable cross-section, or cross-section for a given loss, vary inversely as the square of the transmission voltage.

It is cheaper to pay for the cost of nearly a thousand transformer substations, connected to 16 000 kilometres of high-voltage cables, than to transmit the power through thicker cables at lower voltages.

High-voltage transmission also allows a significant reduction in the number of circuits required, and therefore of supporting towers.

Figure H34
Bishops Wood 132/275 kV substation near Stourport-on-Severn, Worcestershire.
Central Electricity Generating Board.

Overhead lines versus underground cables

The National Supergrid 400 and 275 kV transmission system has more than 13 000 circuit km of overhead lines. About 70 % of the overhead lines operate at 400 kV. There are also about 900 km of underground cables, mostly in the cities.

Many people would prefer to see fewer pylons straddled across open country. Ultimately, the choice depends on how much one is prepared to pay not to see the overhead lines, assuming that one wants the electrical power delivered.

The CEGB estimates that at 132 kV, underground cables are more than ten times as expensive to install as an equivalent overhead line. They put the capital cost of a double circuit 400 kV underground cable at between £6m and £7m per kilometre, compared with the cost of the equivalent overhead line at some £500 000, a factor of fourteen against the use of cable.

The high cost of underground cables is mainly a consequence of the fact that soil is not a good thermal conductor. Overhead cables are cooled by the air, but buried cables can easily overheat. To avoid this they need to be made thicker and to be cooled, so therefore they are more expensive. A 400 kV cable of 2250 mm² cross-section can, when water-cooled, provide a continuous rating approximately equal to that of two 400 mm² overhead lines operating at 65 °C. The electrical insulation round the cable, which also costs money, adds to the cooling problem.

Figure H35
A 400 kV tower, part of the CEGB's 400 kV Sizewell–Sundon transmission line. *Central Electricity Generating Board.*

H

Choice between a.c. and d.c.

Alternating power supplies are convenient because the voltage can easily and efficiently be changed with transformers.

A cable has some electrical capacitance to earth or other cables nearby, and if the supply alternates at 50 Hz, this capacitance is charged and discharged a hundred times a second. For a 400 kV overhead cable, this requires a charging–discharging current of the order of one ampere, but for a similar buried cable, the current may be nearer 40 A, depending on the construction and length of line or cable concerned. For considerations of this kind, direct currents have advantages at high voltages, especially for underground cables.

An interesting example is the link between the British and French systems. The first link was in use for some 20 years. The first stage of a new 2000 MW d.c. link was commissioned in 1985. The link enables the two systems, which have peak demands at different times of day, to feed each other spare power. This use of d.c. also means that the two sets of generators do not have to be synchronized, as do all the generators in an a.c. linked system.

Electricity and choice

The general availability of electric power means that everyone can do more and for longer than would be possible without it. Choices have to be made, however, about the cost of supplying this power in terms of money and damage to the environment. If we choose to pay the cost of putting cables underground, we must also be prepared to choose from what other desirable things we divert resources.

There has long been concern over the pollution of the atmosphere by flue gases from fuel-burning power stations, although domestic coal fires can be worse offenders in this respect. Our cities are much cleaner now than they were 50 or even 25 years ago thanks to various 'clean air' measures which restrict or control the burning of fuel. On the other hand the problem of 'acid rain' is one that has only been brought to our attention in the last few years.

The large amounts of carbon dioxide produced by burning fuel may slightly raise the average temperature of the Earth by making the atmosphere more like a greenhouse. On the other hand, smoke and dust may reduce the temperature by producing clouds which reflect radiation from the Sun before it reaches the Earth. Quite small temperature changes would have a significant effect: a rise of a few degrees would melt the polar icecaps and raise the sea level by tens of metres, flooding most of the World's large cities.

Clearly, choices will have to be made. They will be better choices if they are made in the light of an understanding of the issues involved. We may have to balance the advantages of having larger-scale energy resources for each person against the consequences of providing them.

Questions

a The 50 million people in England and Wales 'use' about 220 T W h of electrical energy every year. (T = tera = 10^{12})
i How much is this, *per person*?
ii Estimate how much electrical energy you use in an average day, and hence your yearly consumption.
iii A healthy person can work steadily at a rate of about 50 W. For how many hours would you have to work to generate as much electrical energy as you use in a day?
iv Account for any difference between your answers to *i* and *ii*.

b *i* Show that for two objects of the same shape (*e.g.* spheres, or cubes) the ratio of surface area to volume is greater for a small object than for a large one.
ii What shape should an object have to minimize this ratio?
iii Give another example of the importance of size in reducing the (relative) rate at which energy is transferred thermally.
iv Suggest another reason – not concerned with energy transfer – why a large electromagnetic machine may be more efficient than a small one.

c 'Electrical energy cannot be stored up in quantity.'
i Name two systems which *can* be used to store electrical energy, and, for one of them, make an estimate of the energy that could be stored in an installation of reasonable size. Apart from limited capacity, what other disadvantages do such systems have? Where, on the other hand, do they find application?

ii List the factors which determine the capacity of a pumped storage system. Estimate values for them and hence estimate the capacity of such a system.

d Show, algebraically, that 'for a given power, energy loss for a given cable cross-section, or cross-section for a given loss, vary inversely as the square of the transmission voltage.'

e *i* Why should the charging and discharging current for an underground cable be so much greater than that for the equivalent overhead line? (Think about the factors that determine capacitance.)
ii Estimate the capacitance of the cable for which the charging–discharging current at 400 kV, 50 Hz is 40 A.

f Why do all generators in an a.c. linked system have to be synchronized?

LABORATORY NOTES

DEMONSTRATION
H1 Forces on currents; forces between currents

l.t. variable voltage supply
2 Magnadur magnets
mild steel yoke
aluminium cooking foil, 1 cm wide and 1 m long
2 clip component holders
retort stand base and rod
2 bosses
demonstration meter, 10 A d.c.
scissors
leads

H1a Forces on currents

Pass a current of about 2 A through the strip of foil. Where must the magnet be placed to lift the strip of foil off the bench?

Reverse the direction of the current. What happens to the force on it? What other change can you make to lift the foil off the bench?

Draw a diagram showing the relative directions of the current, I, the force, F, and the magnetic field, B (*i.e.* the direction of the force on the North pole of a plotting compass).

H1b Forces between currents

Hang two strips of foil vertically between a pair of clip component holders. The strips should be about 50 cm long and 1 cm apart.

Pass a high current (5–8 A) through the strips. What is the direction of the force between the strips when the currents are in opposite directions? When the currents are in the same direction?

What is the direction of the magnetic field near a long, straight, current-carrying conductor? How is the direction of the force on one conductor related to the direction of the current in that conductor and the magnetic field due to the current in the other conductor?

OPTIONAL DEMONSTRATION
H2 The catapult field

l.t. variable voltage supply
retort stand base
3 retort stand rods
7 bosses
4 nails, 15 cm long
piece of card with hole (see figure H36)
2 Magnadur magnets
iron filings
0.45 mm PVC-covered copper wire
demonstration meter, 5 A d.c.
leads

The large coil of wire in figure H36 is about 20 cm square. It should have at least ten turns of PVC-covered wire. The magnets are set up with unlike poles facing to produce a uniform field between them.

Use the iron filings to show the field due to the magnets alone. Remove the magnets and the iron filings. Pass a current of about 3 A through the coil, and sprinkle iron filings again to show the field due to the current alone.

If both current and magnets are present, what shape would you expect the field to have? Where will the two fields combine to produce a stronger field? Where they are in opposition the combined effect will be a weaker field.

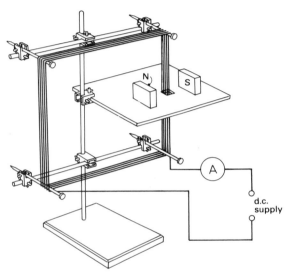

Figure H36
Demonstration of the 'catapult field'.

Now use iron filings to test your prediction for the shape of the field due to both current and magnets together.

Of course there are no invisible stretched elastic bands in the magnetic field, but its 'catapult' shape may help you remember that there is a sideways force on the wire. (You can work out the direction of the force by sketching the two independent fields, and then combining them.) The magnets give a nearly uniform field from N to S. Use the right hand fingers and thumb rule* to find the direction of the circular field around the wire (figure H37). On one side of the wire the two fields are in opposite directions. At one point the combined field will be zero. The magnetic force on the wire pushes it towards this point.

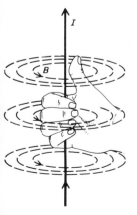

Figure H37

* If the thumb points in the direction of the current, then the curled fingers of the right hand show the direction of the magnetic field.

DEMONSTRATION

H3   Forces on induced currents

l.t. variable voltage supply
coil with 120 + 120 turns
retort stand base and rod (mild steel)
aluminium ring
split aluminium ring
leads

The coil is placed over the retort stand rod. An alternating current of up to 5 A from a 12 V a.c. supply can be passed through the coil for *short periods* without overheating it.

What happens when the aluminium ring is placed over the coil (with the retort stand rod passing through both coil and ring) and the current is switched on? Does the split ring behave in the same way? Feel both rings.

Try to suggest explanations.

DEMONSTRATION

H4a   The directions of forces in magnetic fields

current balance
flat solenoid
4 Magnadur magnets
plotting compass
2 mild steel yokes
bare copper wire, 2 mm diameter, 1 m long
1100-turn coil
2 batteries, 12 V
demonstration meter, 1 A d.c.
demonstration meter, 5 A d.c.
rheostat, 10–15 Ω, 5 A
roll of tickertape
scissors
leads

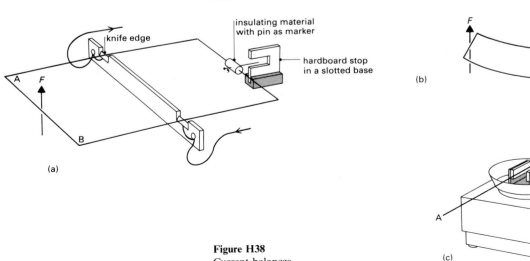

Figure H38
Current balances.

A current balance can be used to detect magnetic fields, and to measure them.

Various designs of current balance are available. Figure H38(a) shows a wire rectangle pivoted on razor blades or brass strips. A current of about 3 A is fed to the wire through the razor blades. Current only passes between the pivots along one side of the rectangle – there is a small gap in the wire on the other side. In figure H38(b) the wire is not pivoted, but any vertical force on it causes it to bend. In figure H38(c) any force on the magnets due to a current in the wire can be calculated from the change in reading of the balance.

In which of the situations depicted in figure H39 is there a vertical force on the wire? Use these observations, and what you know (or can find out using a plotting compass) about the directions of the magnetic fields produced by a pair of magnets, by current in a coil, and by a straight wire, to try to formulate a rule relating the relative directions of current, field, and force (or, if you already know such a rule, to test it).

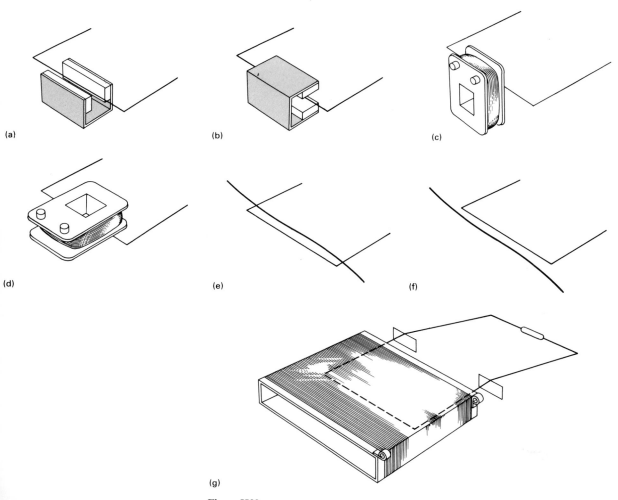

(a)

(b)

(c)

(d)

(e)

(f)

(g)

Figure H39
Forces on currents.

DEMONSTRATION

H4b Measuring a magnetic field

The force on the wire in the current balances shown in figures H38(a) and (b) is measured by adding small pieces of paper or wire to the deflected current balance and adjusting the current until the balance returns to its original position. The magnetic force on the current-carrying wire is then equal to the weight of the paper added to it.

In figure H38(c) the force on the magnets, which (by Newton's Third Law) is equal in magnitude to the force on the wire, is measured directly from the change in reading of the balance. (But remember that balances are used to measure *mass*: the *force* needed in this experiment is the weight of that mass.)

With the current balance and the pairs of magnets it should be possible to test how, for a given magnetic field, the force on a current-carrying wire depends on I, the current in the wire, and l, the length of wire in the field.

The current balance can also be used to measure the strength of the magnetic field inside a flat solenoid, using the definition of magnetic field strength

$$B = F/Il$$

If the strength of a magnetic field is defined in this way, what units should it be measured in?

DEMONSTRATION

H5a The Hall effect in a semiconductor

semiconductor Hall effect demonstration
milliammeter, 100 mA d.c.
cell holder with four cells
sensitive galvanometer
2 Magnadur magnets
rheostat, 10–15 Ω
leads

The sideways force on a current-carrying conductor in a magnetic field is the sum of the forces on all the individual charged particles moving in the magnetic field. These charge carriers are pushed towards one side of the conductor – figure H40(b); this separation of charge leads to an electric field from the back to the front edge of the conductor – figure H40(c). There will be a p.d. between the back and the front of the specimen which can be detected with the galvanometer in the arrangement in figure H41. Suppose the charge carriers in figure H40 were negatively charged. What would be the direction of the electric field?

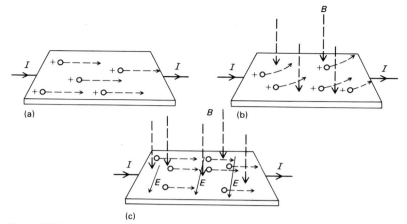

Figure H40
Forces on positive charges moving in a conductor with a transverse magnetic field.

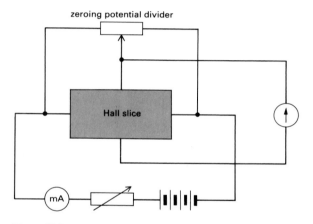

Figure H41
Measurement of Hall voltage in a semiconductor.

You should be able to combine the relevant equations

magnetic force $F = BQv$
electric force $F = EQ$
electric field $E = V/d$
current $I = nAQv$

to obtain an expression for the Hall voltage, V_H, in terms of the dimensions of the specimen (width d, cross-sectional area for current flow A), the magnetic field B, the current I, the density and charge of the carriers n, Q. (See question 9, page 58.)

Use this expression for V_H to explain why the effect is much smaller in good conductors (*e.g.* aluminium, $n \approx 10^{29}\,\mathrm{m^{-3}}$) than in semiconductors (*e.g.* germanium, $n \approx 10^{20}\,\mathrm{m^{-3}}$); and why for a large Hall voltage, the specimen should be thin.

Thin slices of semiconductor material are used in Hall probes, which are much more convenient devices than the current balances for comparing magnetic field strengths.

DEMONSTRATION
H5b Calibrating a Hall probe

Hall probe and circuit box (with suitable meter)
flat solenoid
l.t. variable voltage supply
l.t. smoothing unit
rheostat, 10–15 Ω
ammeter, 5 A d.c.
leads

The Hall probe is calibrated by measuring the voltage produced when it is in a magnetic field of known strength.

The field strength inside a flat solenoid carrying a current of, say, 1 A d.c. is known from measurements of the force on a current balance in demonstration H4.

DEMONSTRATION
H6 Measuring the specific charge for electrons

Safety note: An h.t. supply may be used in this demonstration. It must be used with great care since it is potentially dangerous. Always switch it off before making or altering connections to it. It is advisable to use leads having shrouded 4 mm plugs.

Specific means 'per unit mass'; so the specific charge for electrons is the charge of a kilogram of electrons.

The fine-beam tube contains gas at low pressure. Electrons, accelerated from the cathode, C, pass through a hole in the anode, A. The electrons ionize the gas atoms, which then emit light, so making the path of the electron beam visible.

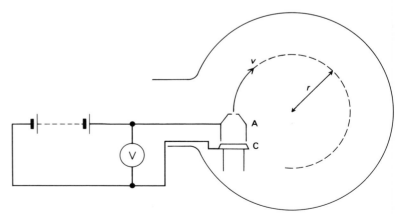

Figure H42
Electron beam bent into circular path in fine-beam tube.

In a uniform magnetic field, perpendicular to their direction of motion, the electrons move in a circle. The experiment consists of measuring the diameter of this circle, and the magnetic field strength, B. The size of the circle also depends on the electrons' speed, v, which can be calculated from the accelerating p.d., V (measured with the voltmeter in figure H42).

The physics involved in this experiment is as follows:

Motion in a circle: centripetal force $= mv^2/r$.

This force is provided by the magnetic force on the electron, Bev.

Energy of an electron accelerated through a p.d. of V volts: $\frac{1}{2}mv^2 = eV$.

It is now simply a matter of algebra to combine these to give an expression for e/m in terms of the measured quantities, B, r, and V.

Which of the measurements (B, r, V) is subject to the greatest uncertainty? Estimate the percentage uncertainty in each of these measurements, and hence calculate the uncertainty in the value for e/m.

EXPERIMENT
H7 Fields near electric currents

A variety of conductors, field-measuring devices, and sources of current can be used for these investigations. See figure H43.

Conductors
either
large Slinky
2 slotted bases
2 wooden strips (*e.g.* rulers) to support Slinky
2 crocodile clips
or
set of solenoids
or
magnetic field board
reel of 0.45 mm PVC-covered wire
or
coil with 120 + 120 turns

Field-measuring devices
either
Hall probe and circuit box
sensitive galvanometer
or
axial search coil
lateral search coil
oscilloscope

Sources of current
either
12 V battery
rheostat, 10–15 Ω, 5 A
ammeter, 10 A d.c.
or
transformer
rheostat, 10–15 Ω, 5 A
ammeter, 10 A a.c.
or
signal generator
ammeter, 1 A a.c.

leads

The Hall probe or a search coil can be used to explore magnetic fields due to currents in straight wires, in coils, in solenoids, and so on. If you use the search coil which responds to a changing magnetic field, then the current in the wire, coil, etc., must be a.c.

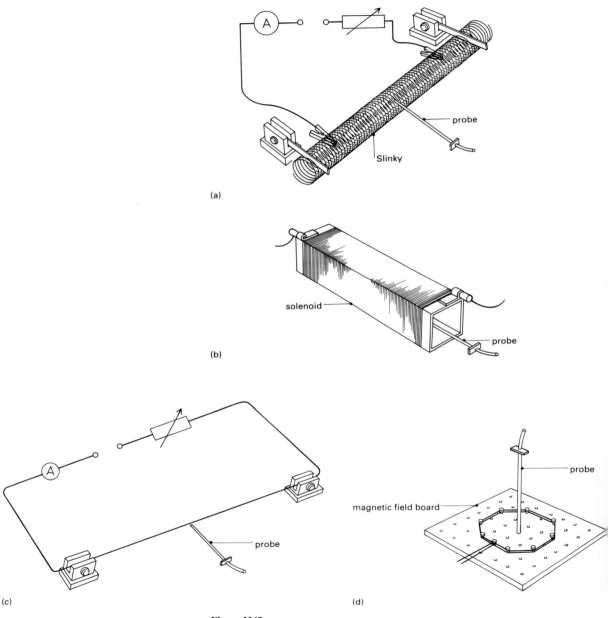

(a)

(b)

(c)

(d)

Figure H43
Measuring magnetic fields near currents. (a) Field in a Slinky solenoid. (b) Field in a solenoid. (c) Field near a long, straight wire. (d) Field of a coil.

Straight wire

The magnetic field near a single straight wire is rather weak, so it is necessary to use as large a current as possible, without overheating (turn off the current whenever you can). Several parallel wires, close together and each carrying a large current, will also increase the field strength. Use the rheostat to control current in the wire.

What orientation of the probe gives a maximum reading for a fixed distance r from the wire?

Theory says that $B \propto I/r$. Do tests of this relationship, and suggest reasons for any departure from it.

Solenoids

A current of 1 to 2 A will be needed.

What orientation of the probe gives the maximum reading? Always use the probe in this orientation.

You should be able to answer the following questions:

Is the field strength constant across the width of the solenoid?

How does it vary along the length of the solenoid?

How does the field strength inside the small solenoid compare with that inside the large one?

How does the field strength depend on current?

How does it depend on the spacing of the turns? (Use the solenoid with closely wound turns and the one with spaced turns, or use the Slinky stretched to different extents.)

Coils

You can make flat coils of various shapes and sizes on the magnetic field board. To get sizeable fields, each coil should have about 10 turns. Use a current of about 5 A.

Some things you can test:

How does the field at the centre of the coil depend on the radius? On the number of turns?

What is the direction of the field at points on the axis of the coil?

For which position on the axis of the coil is the field strength a maximum? You may be able to look up and test a formula for the variation of field strength with distance from the coil, for points on the axis.

How does the field strength vary with position for points in the plane of the coil? How does its value at the centre compare with its value nearby?

DEMONSTRATION

The e.m.f. induced in a moving wire

sensitive galvanometer
2 dynamics trolleys
10 Magnadur magnets
5 mild steel yokes
bare copper wire, 2 mm diameter
reel of 0.45 mm PVC-covered copper wire
clip component holder
adhesive tape
leads

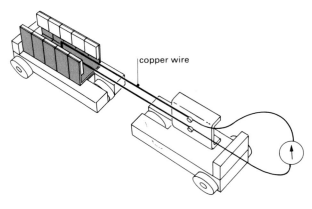
copper wire

Figure H44
Moving wire or moving magnet.

Magnadur magnets with opposite poles facing (figure H44) are used to produce a region of about 15 cm length in which there is a nearly uniform magnetic field.

It is possible to move the magnet past the copper wire, or the copper wire past the magnet. Explore whether either movement produces an e.m.f.

How does the direction of any e.m.f. that is induced depend on the motion of magnet or wire? What factors determine its magnitude?

Is it a magnetic or an electric field that causes a force on an electron in the wire as it moves through the magnetic field? When the magnet moves past the wire we would say that any force on the electrons in the stationary wire must be due to an electric field acting on them. But the demonstration shows that the result is the same whether magnet or wire moves. It is only the *relative* movement of the magnet and the wire that matters.

Einstein was able to link magnetic and electric effects. Coulomb's Law (which applies to charges at rest) and the ideas of relativity theory show that what we call magnetic effects are to be expected from charges in motion, that is, from currents.

DEMONSTRATION
H9 Inducing e.m.f.s in a motor/dynamo

fractional horsepower motor
battery, 12 V
demonstration meter, 1 A d.c.
demonstration meter, 5 V d.c.
2 rheostats, 10–15 Ω, 5 A
geared hand drill
rubber pressure tubing to fit 5 mm shaft, about 10 cm long
steel rod, 5 mm diameter, about 10 cm long
lamp, 12 V, 6 W
lampholder, s.b.c., on base
leads

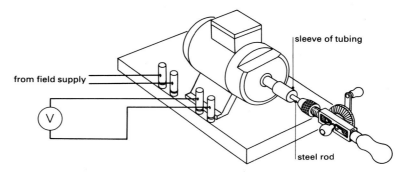

Figure H45
Fractional horsepower motor as a dynamo.

The magnetic field of the motor (figure H45) is provided by a current of about 0.5 A to the field coils. The hand drill is connected to the shaft of the motor by a short piece of rubber tubing. Turning the hand drill makes the rotor rotate.

As the rotor turns, its coils sweep through a strong magnetic field and an e.m.f. is induced.

It should be possible to demonstrate how the induced e.m.f. depends on the rate of rotation, and by varying the current in the field coils, that the e.m.f. depends on the strength of the magnetic field.

When the output of the rotor is connected to a (high-resistance) voltmeter, very little current flows, and so very little energy is transformed. But if a lamp is connected across the rotor terminals it will light, and the rotor is now harder to turn. You should be able to explain this effect firstly in terms of energy (why do you have to work harder to turn the rotor now?); and secondly by considering the fact that there is now a current in the rotor. (Which way will the force on this current in a magnetic field tend to turn the rotor? Why *must* it be in this rather than the opposite sense?)

DEMONSTRATION

H10   Behaviour of a fractional horsepower motor

Not all the electrical energy supplied to a motor is transferred to the load. There are losses due to heating the rotor windings, magnetic losses in the iron core of the motor, and mechanical losses, for example due to friction in the bearings.

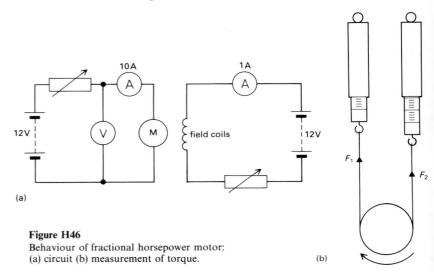

(a)

Figure H46
Behaviour of fractional horsepower motor:
(a) circuit (b) measurement of torque.   (b)

It is easy to measure the resistance of the rotor coils when they are stationary. (Use $R = V/I$.) The resistance will probably be quite low: thick copper wires are used.

With a p.d. of about 2.5 V across the rotor terminals the field current (about 1 A) is turned on. What happens to the current in the rotor as it begins to turn and speeds up? What might cause the rotor current to vary in this way? (Remember that we now have a conductor moving in a magnetic field, and think about the effects observed when the rotor was turned by the hand drill in demonstration H9.)

By Lenz's rule (*i.e.* conservation of energy), the induced e.m.f., $\mathscr{E}$, must act in the opposite direction to the p.d. applied to the rotor terminals, V. We can use Kirchhoff's Second Law to describe the circuit: $V - \mathscr{E} = IR$, and from measurement of I, $\mathscr{E}$ can be calculated.

Torque

The torque produced by the motor is proportional to BIl. B is constant, as long as the current to the field coils is held steady. If the load on the motor is increased (the p.d. applied to the rotor being kept the same), the motor slows down. How will $\mathscr{E}$ change as the motor slows down? Use $V - \mathscr{E} = IR$ to predict how I will change, and hence how the torque will change.

Power

The total power transformed by the motor is of course VI. The power which heats the rotor wires is I^2R. The remainder provides the useful mechanical output power and unavoidable magnetic and mechanical losses.

The mechanical output power can be measured using a band brake – figure H46(b). It is

$$2\pi rn(F_2 - F_1)$$

F_2 and F_1 are the tensions on either side of the band, r the radius of the wheel which the brake rubs on, and n the number of rotations per second.

OPTIONAL EXPERIMENT
H11 The efficiency of a small d.c. motor

small d.c. motor with pulley wheel
battery, 12 V
ammeter, 1 A d.c.
voltmeter, 10 V d.c.
rheostat, 10–15 Ω, 5 A

either
2 retort stand bases, rods, bosses, and clamps
2 newton spring balances, 10 N
string
means of measuring rotational frequency, *e.g.*,
photodiode assembly with light source and oscilloscope
(hand stroboscope and stopwatch would do)
or
hanger and slotted masses, 10 g
string
stopwatch
metre rule

leads

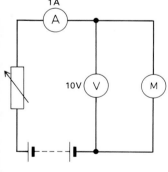

Figure H47
Energy input to a d.c. motor.

In a small d.c. motor the magnetic field is supplied by permanent magnets; the only current supplied to the motor is to the rotor.

To calculate the useful power output of the motor you can measure the steady rate at which the motor raises a load; or you can use a band brake, as in demonstration H10.

Calculate the electrical power supplied to the motor; and compare this with the useful power output. Calculate the efficiency of the motor. You can also calculate the power which goes to heating up the rotor coil (I^2R).

Do not expect to account for all losses. Such small motors are usually quite inefficient. Suggest where some of the other losses might be.

If you have time it is instructive to plot graphs of rate of rotation against load, and of current against load.

DEMONSTRATION
H12 Moving wires and changing flux

H12a Moving wires

demountable transformer kit (use 300-turn coil)
l.t. variable voltage supply
low-voltage smoothing unit
rheostat, 10–15 Ω, 5 A
demonstration meter, 5 A d.c.
sensitive galvanometer
stopclock
leads

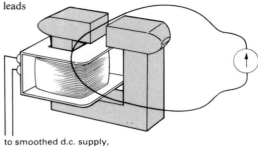

to smoothed d.c. supply,
rheostat, and ammeter

Figure H48
Moving a wire and changing a field.

The 300-turn coil supplied with 3 A produces a magnetic field between the pole pieces.

Record the time taken to move the wire down between the pole pieces of the magnet and into the 'U' of the electromagnet without exceeding a certain reading on the galvanometer. Can the wire be brought back up out of the 'U' in less time, without exceeding the same reading (in the opposite sense)?

Now, with the wire in the 'U', record the time it takes to increase the current in the coil from 0 to 3 A, again without exceeding the previous galvanometer reading. Repeat the time measurement as the current is decreased from 3 A to 0.

It is instructive to repeat these tests with two or three turns of wire and with a folded piece of wire.

H12b Changing flux

Apparatus as for demonstration H12a plus:
set of solenoids
(demountable transformer kit not needed)

This version of the demonstration uses two close-wound solenoids. The outer one carries 3 A d.c.; the inner one is connected to a sensitive galvanometer. The minimum time in which the current in the outer coil can be reduced from 3 A to zero without exceeding a certain galvanometer reading is recorded. It is compared with the least time taken to withdraw the inner solenoid completely while a current of 3 A flows in the outer one, again without exceeding the same reading.

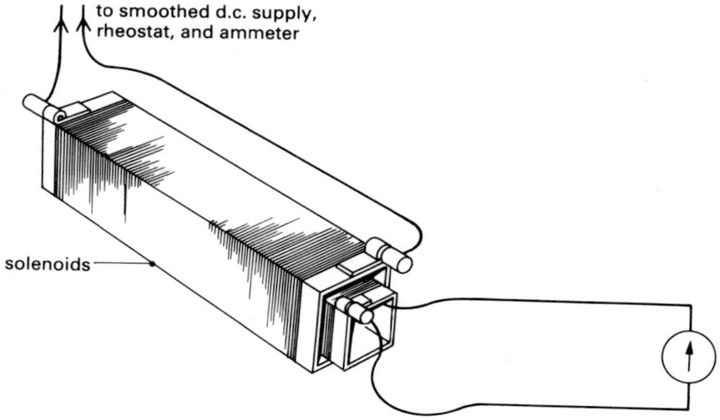
to smoothed d.c. supply, rheostat, and ammeter
solenoids

Figure H49
Changing the flux in a coil in two ways.

DEMONSTRATION
H13 A continually changing field

demountable transformer kit (use 300-turn coil)
signal generator
0.45 mm PVC-covered copper wire
rheostat, 10–15 Ω, 5 A
double-beam oscilloscope
demonstration meter, 1 A a.c.
wire strippers
leads

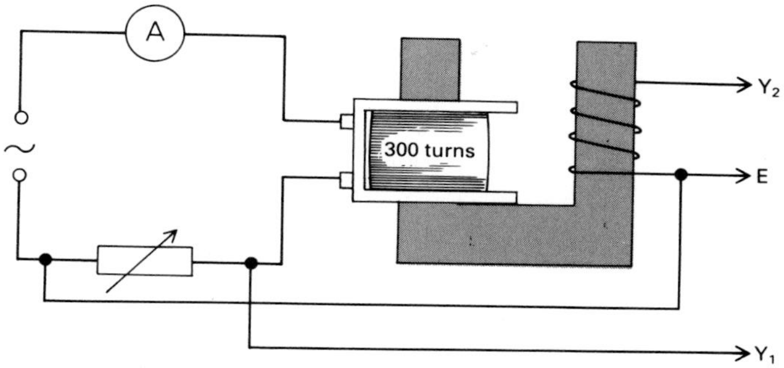
A
300 turns
Y_2
E
Y_1

Figure H50
Induction of a.c.

Alternating current in the 300-turn coil sets up a continually changing field and so the flux through the wire wound round the other limb of the iron core is continually changing.

This demonstration allows an investigation of how various factors affect the alternating e.m.f. induced in the wire:

a the number of times this wire is wound around the iron;

b the size of the current in the 300-turn coil;

c the frequency of this alternating current;

d whether or not the iron transformer core has an iron 'yoke' across the top, making a complete ring of iron.

When, in relation to the alternating current in the 300-turn coil, does the alternating e.m.f. induced in the wire reach its maximum value?

H14 Induction using a.c.

In these demonstrations you can show the effect on induced e.m.f. of:

a   number of turns

b   area

c   field and rate of change

d   orientation

H14a Number of turns

large, close-wound solenoid
signal generator (or transformer)
oscilloscope
0.45 mm diameter PVC-covered copper wire
leads

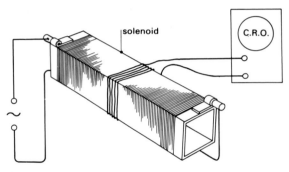

Figure H51
Effect of number of turns on induced e.m.f.

Current to the solenoid comes from the low-impedance output of a signal generator set to 2 kHz, or from a transformer giving about 3 A at 50 Hz. Wrap a long piece of wire around the centre of the solenoid, adding one turn at a time, using an oscilloscope to monitor the e.m.f. induced in the wire.

H14b Area

large and small close-wound solenoids
transformer

either
Hall probe with circuit box and meter
or
search coil

double-beam oscilloscope
0.45 mm PVC-covered copper wire
leads

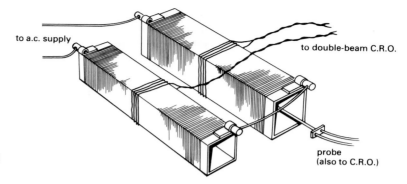

Figure H52
Effect of area on induced e.m.f.

Connect large and small solenoids in series, but keep them well apart. The current is the same in each (*e.g.* from a 12 V, 50 Hz supply).

Use a search coil or Hall probe to compare the magnetic field strengths inside the two solenoids. Use wires wrapped tightly around the outside of the two solenoids and connected to the two inputs of a double-beam oscilloscope to compare the induced e.m.f.s. Since induced e.m.f. depends on rate of change of flux, this will enable you to compare the total fluxes in the two solenoids. What is the ratio of the cross-sectional areas of the two solenoids?

H14c Field and rate of change

large, close-wound solenoid
signal generator
double-beam oscilloscope
resistor, 15 Ω
clip component holder
leads

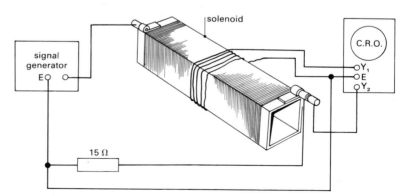

Figure H53
Effect of rate of change
of flux on induced e.m.f.

Use the double-beam oscilloscope to monitor both the current in the solenoid and the e.m.f. induced in ten turns of wire wrapped around it. Note what happens to the peak value of the induced e.m.f., and also to the maximum slope of the current trace on the oscilloscope, as you vary the frequency in the region of 1 kHz. Use the low-impedance output of the signal generator, and adjust its output, if necessary, to make sure that the peak current in the solenoid is the same at each frequency.

Then, working at one fixed frequency, investigate the effect of changing the current in the solenoid. Again look for a relationship between peak induced e.m.f. and maximum rate of change of current.

H14d Orientation

magnetic field board
0.45 mm PVC-covered copper wire
transformer
ammeter, 5 A a.c.
search coil
oscilloscope
leads

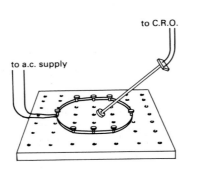

Figure H54
Effect of orientation on induced e.m.f.

Use an oscilloscope to find out how the e.m.f. induced in the search coil depends on its orientation with respect to the coil on the magnetic circuit board, which should have about ten turns. Pass an alternating current of several amperes and use an oscilloscope to find out how the e.m.f. induced in the search coil depends on its orientation with respect to the coil on the board. Keep the search coil in the same position (*e.g.* at the centre of the coil), and tilt it as shown in figure H54. Try to formulate a rule which relates the e.m.f. to the angle between the plane of the board and the plane of the search coil.

DEMONSTRATION
H15 The effect of iron in a solenoid

retort stand rod of mild steel (not stainless)
transformer
double-beam oscilloscope
large close-wound solenoid
0.45 mm PVC-covered copper wire
ammeter, 1 A a.c.
leads

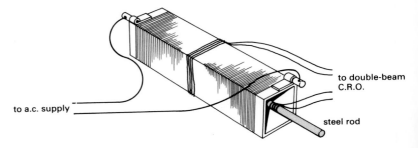

Figure H55
The effect of iron.

A coil of wire is wrapped around the solenoid, and another one with the same number of turns is wrapped around the steel rod (figure H55). A double-beam oscilloscope is used to compare the e.m.f.s induced in these two coils when there is an alternating current in the solenoid. Since e.m.f. depends on rate of change of flux, and since both fluxes change at the same frequency, comparing the e.m.f.s allows us to compare the fluxes in the two coils.

How does the flux in the steel rod compare with the total flux in the solenoid? Does the flux through the small coil change if the steel is removed? How?

EXPERIMENT
H16 Increasing the iron in a magnetic circuit

2 C-cores, preferably matched, with clip
pieces of card and paper
scissors
transformer
0.45 mm PVC-covered copper wire
oscilloscope
ammeter, 1 A a.c.
voltmeter, 5 V a.c.
rheostat, 10–15 Ω, 5 A
micrometer screw gauge
leads

Wind two ten-turn coils round one C-core. Feed one coil with 1 A a.c. from a transformer. Connect the other to an oscilloscope which displays the induced e.m.f., and hence gives a measure of the flux linked with the second coil.

How does the flux linked with this 'pick-up' coil vary with its position on the C-core?

What happens if it is slid off the end of the C-core?

Now try using two C-cores as shown in figure H56. Does the flux linked with the pick-up coil change when the magnetic circuit is completed, *i.e.* when the second C-core is added? Does the flux linked with the coil depend on its position on the C-cores? What is the effect of putting a piece of card between the two C-cores?

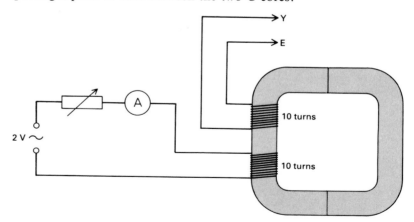

Figure H56
Increasing the iron in a magnetic circuit.

Compare the flux linked with the pick-up coil when the two coils are close together in air (no iron), with the flux when both coils are on the continuous magnetic circuit with no gaps between the two C-cores. Use flux = current − turns/reluctance and the fact that when there is an air gap the two reluctances (air and iron) are in series, to estimate μ_r the relative permeability of iron. (See page 9.)

DEMONSTRATION
H17 Mutual inductance of two coils

The e.m.f. induced in a secondary coil depends on the rate of change of flux, and therefore on the rate of change of current in the primary coil. If the e.m.f. is directly proportional to the rate of change of current ($\mathscr{E} \propto dI/dt$) then a constant dI/dt, i.e. a steadily changing current in the primary, should give a steady output at the secondary. In this case the constant of proportionality, M, the mutual inductance, can be calculated from $M = \mathscr{E}/(dI/dt)$.

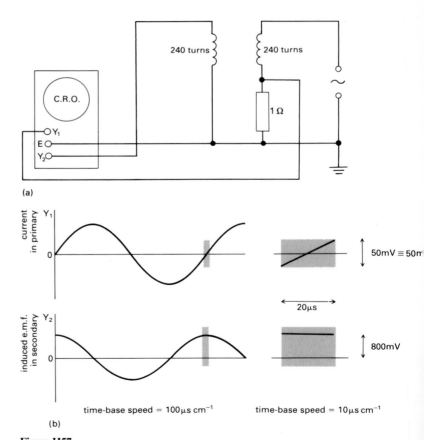

Figure H57
(a) Mutual inductance.
(b) Measuring mutual inductance – oscilloscope display.

It is possible to investigate how M depends on the numbers of turns in the two coils. M also depends on the size of the core, and the properties of any iron. Since the magnetic properties of iron vary with the flux density, M may be found to depend on the current in the primary coil.

DEMONSTRATION
H18   Self induction

high-inductance coil
double C-core with clip
2 m.e.s. lamps, 2.5 V, 0.3 A
m.e.s. neon lamp
3 m.e.s. lampholders
cell holder with two cells
mounted bell push
rheostat, 10–15 Ω, 5 A
leads

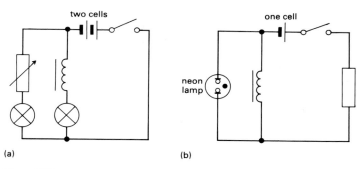

Figure H58
Simple inductor experiments.

The rheostat is adjusted so that, with a steady current flowing, the two lamps – figure H58(a) – are equally bright: the currents in the resistor and inductor are equal.

Observe carefully what happens when the switch is first closed.

Observe also what happens to the neon lamp – figure H58(b) – when the switch is opened.

The explanation of these effects depends on the fact that changing the current in a coil causes a change in flux, which in turn leads to an induced e.m.f. in the coil itself.

DEMONSTRATION
H19   Measurement of self inductance

In this demonstration the oscilloscope is used to monitor both the p.d. across an inductor and the current through it (Y_1 and Y_2, respectively, in figure H59).

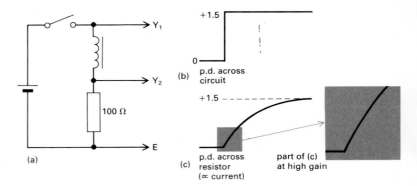

Figure H59
Measurement of self inductance.

Observe carefully what happens when the switch in the circuit of figure H59 is closed. What effect does the inductor have on the current in the circuit? Is it a permanent or a transient effect?

In a d.c. circuit an inductor does not affect the final steady current; it only affects how quickly the current reaches this value.

The inductance of a coil, $L = V/(dI/dt)$, can be found by measuring the p.d. across the coil when the current is changing at a known rate. For this it is convenient to use a 50 Hz supply as shown in figure H60.

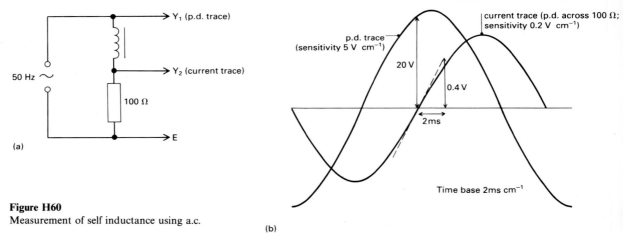

Figure H60
Measurement of self inductance using a.c.

The oscilloscope is used to make measurements of V and dI/dt. Of course the voltage sensitivity of the two traces must be known, and also the time-base speed.

Notice that in figure H60 the Y_1 input of the oscilloscope is connected across the resistor as well as the inductor. How big an error does this introduce into the measurement of V, the p.d. across the inductor? How can this error be kept small?

EXPERIMENT
H20 Investigation of transformer action

transformer to provide 6 and 12 V a.c.
2 coils with 120 + 120 turns
double C-core and clip
2 ammeters, 5 A a.c.
2 s.b.c. lamps, 12 V, 6 W
2 s.b.c. lampholders on bases
retort stand rod, steel
rheostat, 10–15 Ω, 5 A
oscilloscope
leads

H20a What is the effect of iron in the circuit?

In figure H61(a) the coil and lamp are connected in series to a 12 V a.c.
supply. Observe and explain what happens:
i when an iron rod is inserted into the coil, and
ii when there is a complete C-core in the coil – figure H61(b).

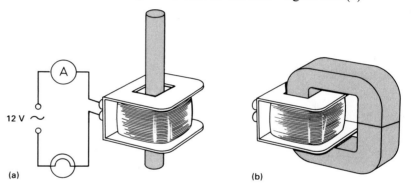

Figure H61   (a)   (b)

H20b What is the effect in a second coil on the same core?

Now add a second coil, with the complete C-core linking both coils. For
a 6 volt input to one coil investigate how the e.m.f. induced in the
secondary coil depends on the ratio of the number of turns in the two
coils. Can you use a 6 volt input to light a 12 V lamp?

H20c How does the current in one coil depend on the current in the other?

Use the rheostat to control the resistance of the secondary circuit (figure
H62). Measure pairs of values of current in the two coils. How does the
current ratio depend on the turns ratio?

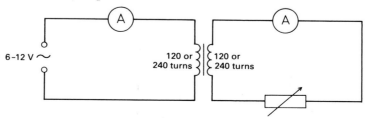

Figure H62

H20d How do the input and output powers compare?

Use the circuit shown in figure H62 to compare the input and output powers of the transformer. Loss of power is due to heating of the wires in the primary and secondary coils (I^2R), and also to heating of the core by eddy currents (and magnetic hysteresis).

DEMONSTRATION
H21 Eddy currents

transformer to provide 12 V a.c.
demountable transformer kit
demonstration meter, 5 A a.c.
mild steel retort stand rod (or even a flat file)
leads

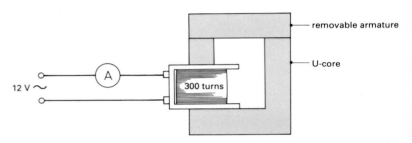

Figure H63
Eddy current heating.

The current in the 300-turn coil is measured with various iron pieces across the top of the laminated U-core (figure H63). The inductance and therefore the current in the coil, depend on the amount and type of iron in the magnetic circuit.

The changing flux in the iron can set up induced currents in the iron itself. One can't put an ammeter inside the iron, so how might such currents be detected? (Think back to demonstration H3, Forces on induced currents.)

These internal currents in the core, called eddy currents, can be reduced by using laminated iron. Look for laminations in this core, in the C-cores used in experiment H20, and also in the iron of any other electrical machinery available – motors, generators, and so on.

Eddy currents become more important at high frequency (why?) High-frequency currents circulate in the coil of a radio tuning circuit (about 1 MHz for the medium wave band). The coil needs a core to increase its inductance. To cut down on losses due to eddy currents, a high-resistivity material is used. Take off the back of a radio if you can and have a look at the coil(s) and the core.

DEMONSTRATION
H22 Power in a resistive circuit

cell holder with three cells
transformer to provide 2 V a.c.
rheostat, 10–15 Ω, 5 A
oscilloscope
2 mounted bell pushes (or s.p.d.t. switch)
m.e.s. lamp, 2.5 V, 0.3 A, in holder
leads

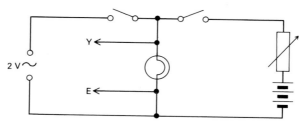

Figure H64
Comparing the brightness of a lamp lit
from a.c. and d.c.

The rheostat is adjusted until the lamp is equally bright when connected to the d.c. or to the a.c. supply. The oscilloscope (set to d.c.) shows the relative values of the steady p.d. across the lamp and the amplitude of the alternating p.d.

What is the *average* value of the alternating p.d.? How does the steady p.d. compare with the maximum value of the alternating p.d.?

When the lamp is equally bright on a.c. or d.c. the rate at which energy is transformed, the power, must be the same for both. For a given resistance does power depend on V, or V^2, or ...?

DEMONSTRATION
H23 Slow a.c. in a circuit containing a capacitor

When a.c. passes through a resistor the p.d. across the resistor always 'keeps up' with the current through it: the two are in phase.

Two meters, or a double-beam oscilloscope, can be used to investigate the phase relationship between p.d. across a capacitor and current in the circuit, using a slowly alternating current (figure H65).

Is there a phase difference in a circuit containing capacitance?

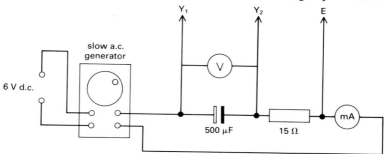

Figure H65

What is the effect of changing the frequency?

You should be able to explain your observations using knowledge of capacitors from Unit B, 'Currents, circuits, and charge'.

DEMONSTRATION
H24 Power in a capacitor

When a lamp or resistor is connected across a joulemeter the joulemeter reading is equal to IV. But when a capacitor is connected across the meter the reading is quite different from IV. What is it?

Use the phase relationship between I and V for a capacitor and power = IV to explain what's going on here.

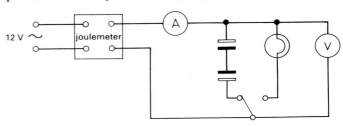

Figure H66

DEMONSTRATION
H25 Alternating currents in a circuit containing capacitance and inductance

For a given p.d. the alternating current through a resistor does not depend on the frequency of the supply: resistance does not depend on frequency.

When the frequency is increased in figure H67(a) the lamp glows more brightly – more current passes for the same p.d. Why is this? (Look back at demonstration H23, Slow a.c. in a circuit containing a capacitor, if necessary.)

Before seeing the effect in the circuit shown in figure H67(b), try to predict what will happen. Would you expect the current in the inductor to depend on the frequency? If so, how? (Remember that $V = L\, dI/dt$.

Another demonstration uses both capacitor and inductor in a parallel circuit – figure H67(c). After you have seen this demonstration try to explain the result, *i.e.* the relationships between the currents in lamps 1, 2, and 3. It may help to replace the lamps by low-value resistors and to display the p.d.s across them (proportional to the currents) on a double-beam oscilloscope.

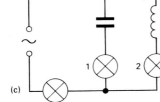

(a)

(b)

(c)

Figure H67

EXPERIMENT
H26 Oscillations in a parallel *LC* circuit

capacitors, 500 μF, 250 μF, 100 μF, 50 μF
high-inductance coil
double C-core and clip
cell holder with four cells
potentiometer, 1 kΩ (100 Ω if available)
oscilloscope
s.p.d.t. switch (if available)
leads

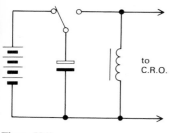

Figure H68
Oscillations in an *LC* circuit.

Use the oscilloscope, with its time-base running slowly, to show the p.d. when the capacitor is discharged through the inductor.

What effect does changing the capacitance, *C*, for example from 500 μF to 100 μF, have on the frequency of oscillation? You can reduce the inductance *L* by slightly separating the C-cores in the inductor. What effect does this have?

Now add extra resistance in series with the inductor. What is the effect on the oscillations you observe? If inductance in an electrical circuit corresponds to mass in a mechanical oscillator, what are the analogues of capacitance and resistance? Why do the electrical oscillations die away even if no resistance is added to the *LC* circuit?

DEMONSTRATION
H27 A simple radio

tuning capacitor, 365 pF to 500 pF maximum
set of solenoids (or other coil)
diode
general-purpose amplifier
loudspeaker (if not in amplifier)
oscilloscope
reel of 0.45 mm PVC-covered wire (for aerial)
leads

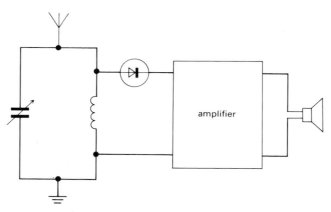

Figure H69
Simple radio circuit.

A long, high aerial and a good earth, such as a water pipe, will improve reception. Use the oscilloscope to display the signal at various stages of the system. Use the tuning capacitor to alter the resonant frequency of the tuned circuit and to pick up broadcasts at different frequencies. A capacitor of the appropriate value can be improvised with two pieces of aluminium cooking foil between the pages of a book: there are two ways to vary its capacitance.

QUESTIONS

Forces on currents, $F = BII$

1(I) On a graph the axes are often labelled x and y.

a If there is also a z-axis, what is its direction?

b List some common objects which have three lines on them, all at right angles to each other.

2(L) Figure H70(a) shows a form of 'current balance' which consists of a pivoted wire frame resting on knife edges through which current enters the frame. The balance is tilted by a vertical force on the wire AB.

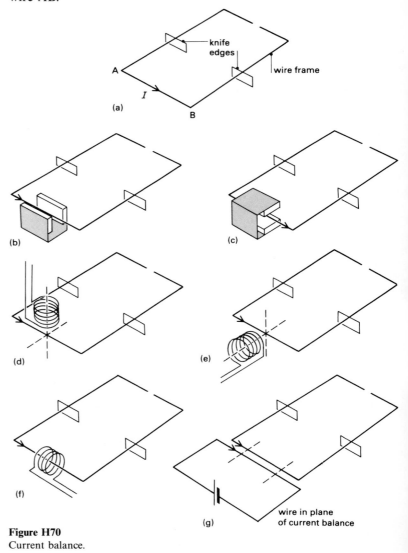

Figure H70
Current balance.

The force on a current is at right angles to the current and to the direction of the *B*-field. Figures H70(b) to (g) show a series of attempts to tilt a current balance using a magnetic force. Which of them will produce a force on the wire which will tilt the balance?

3(P) In these questions you should assume that the magnetic field is perpendicular to the current.

a What magnetic field strength is needed to give a force of 0.01 N (about the weight of 1 gram) on a wire 5 cm long carrying a current of 5 A?

b Calculate the force per centimetre length of wire on a straight wire carrying a current of 2 A in a magnetic field of 0.1 tesla.

c Write down the force per metre on a straight wire carrying a current of one ampere in a magnetic field of T tesla.

4(P)a A 4 cm by 5 cm rectangular coil having 10 turns is situated in a magnetic field of 0.2 tesla in such a way that the 4 cm sides are perpendicular to the field – figure H71(a). What would be the couple, or torque, on the coil if it carried a current of 1 A?

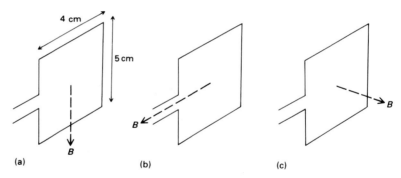

Figure H71
The coil has ten turns.

b What would be the couple if the magnetic field were perpendicular to the 5 cm sides and parallel to the 4 cm sides – figure H71(b)?

c What would be the couple on the coil if the magnetic field were perpendicular to both the 4 cm and the 5 cm sides – figure H71(c)?

5(E)a What current would need to flow in a horizontal copper wire of cross-sectional area 1 mm² to make it self-supporting in the Earth's magnetic field. In Great Britain the Earth's magnetic field has a strength of 1.7×10^{-4} T in a direction about 66° below the horizontal. The density of copper is 8900 kg m⁻³.

b Discuss whether this might be a practical way of supporting power cables.

Force on a moving charge, $F = BQv$

6(I) A satellite is moving in a circular orbit around the Earth.

a Why does the satellite
  i not move in a straight line?
  ii not speed up or slow down?

b If the net force on the satellite is always perpendicular to its motion, can it ever speed up or slow down?

7(L) This question goes from the equation $F = BIl$ to $F = BQv$. It refers to electrons but the same argument can be applied to any charge carriers, for example ions in a mass spectrometer.
  If a current I runs at right angles to a B-field, the force F on length l of the current is given by

$$F = BIl$$

The question is about finding a similar expression for the force on an electron having a charge e and a velocity v. Suppose that, in a time t, N electrons pass any place in the beam, such as Y in figure H72.

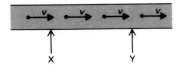

Figure H72

a What is the charge passing Y in time t?

b What is the current I (charge per second) at Y?

c If the speed is v, what length, l, of beam passes Y in time t?
  (*Hint:* Suppose a length XY of the beam will pass Y in time t. How long is XY?)

d Use $F = BIl$ and substitute the value of I from **b** and of l from **c**. What do you get for the force on N electrons?

e What is the force on a single electron?

f What would be the force on a particle with charge Q?

Hall effect

8(I)a A mass of 1 kg which is attached to a slack spring is allowed to fall. When the mass has stopped oscillating, what forces are acting on the mass?

b Why does the mass not fall or rise?

9(L) A result from Unit B, 'Currents, circuits, and charge' is useful. If I is the current when there are n charge carriers per unit volume, each with negative charge Q passing through an area A with a velocity v, then:

$$I = nAQv$$

a When the magnetic field B is switched on, what force will be exerted on one moving charge carrier?

b What is the direction of the force? Mark it on a copy of figure H73(a).

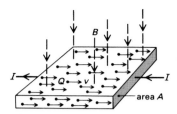

negative charge carriers going from left to right; there are n of them per cubic metre

(a)

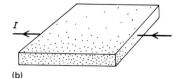

(b)

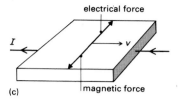

electrical force

magnetic force

(c)

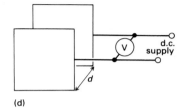

d.c. supply

(d)

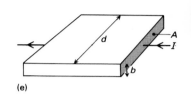

(e)

Figure H73

c After a time there will be higher density of negative charge near the front edge than near the rear edge, as shown in figure H73(b). Why?

d A charge carrier in the middle, figure H73(c), will still experience a force due to the magnetic field, but it will also be repelled by the extra negative charge near the 'front edge'. How big must the electrical force be for there to be no further change in the numbers of negatively charged particles near the edges?

e Which edge of the strip will be positively, and which negatively, charged?

f If, in another experiment, there were two parallel plates separated by a distance, d, and one plate was kept positively charged and the other negatively charged, then there would be an electric field, E, present between the plates, given by $E = V/d$ where V is the p.d. between the plates.

A charge, Q, placed between the plates would experience a force due to this electric field:

force $= EQ$

The electric force acting on a charge moving in the metal strip has been given by your answer to **d**. What is the potential difference which has been produced between the front and rear edges of the strip?

g But $I = nAQv$. What is A if the strip has thickness b?

An equation for the number of charge carriers is wanted which does not contain the velocity of the charge carriers.

h Use $I = nAQv$ to eliminate v from your equation for the potential difference and obtain an equation relating the number of charge carriers per unit volume to the potential difference. (Check that your expression for n has the units metre^{-3}.)

10(R) In a form of flowmeter, a fluid is passed between a pair of electrodes and the poles of a magnet (figure H74).

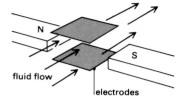

Figure H74

A voltage is induced across the fluid and its equilibrium value is measured by a high resistance voltmeter connected to the two electrodes. Which one of the following statements is *not* correct?

A The voltage is proportional to the rate of flow of the fluid if the field is constant.

B The fluid must be a conductor of electricity.

C The voltage is proportional to the size of the magnetic field if the rate of flow is constant.

D The voltage would be increased by making the fluid flow parallel to the magnetic field.

E There is no resultant force on particles in the fluid in a direction perpendicular to the magnetic field and to the direction of flow.

(Coded answer paper, 1974)

Forces on charged particles

11(L) This question is about the bending of beams of charged particles into curved paths.

a Electrons are emitted from the cathode, in a fine-beam tube. They are accelerated towards an anode by a potential difference between the anode and the cathode. If the charge on an electron is e and the potential difference between cathode and anode is V, how much energy does each electron acquire by the time it reaches the anode?

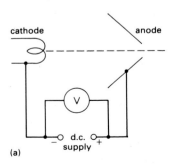

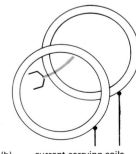

Figure H75   (a)   (b)   current-carrying coils

b How fast will the electrons be moving when they emerge from the hole in the anode?

c The electrons emerge from the anode into a magnetic field, strength B. They then travel at right angles to the B-field. What force is exerted on the electron because it is moving across the field? In what direction is this force?

d What acceleration will the electrons have because this force acts?

e The electrons are accelerating. Does their *speed* increase?

f Derive an expression for the ratio of the electrons' charge, e, to their mass, m, in terms of the measurable quantities V, B, and r. (Acceleration towards the centre of a circular path $= v^2/r$.)

12(L) In a cyclotron, protons are kept moving in a circular path by a uniform B-field at right angles to the plane of the path – figure H76(a). In the first cyclotron, made by E. O. Lawrence, protons were accelerated to an energy of 13 keV.

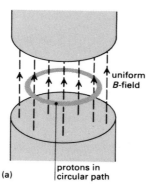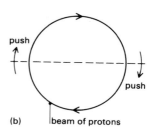

Figure H76

a What velocity has a proton with this kinetic energy?

b The largest possible path had a radius of about 50 mm. What strength of B-field must have been used?

c What radius path would a proton with *half* this maximum energy follow in this field?

d How long must it have taken the 13 keV protons to travel once round their path? How long for those with half this energy?

The cyclotron worked by giving particles of any energy, on their respective paths, a push every time they had completed half an orbit – figure H76(b).

e How was it possible for particles of differing energy all to be accelerated together?

mass of proton $= 1.7 \times 10^{-27}$ kg

charge on proton $= 1.6 \times 10^{-19}$ C

13(P)   Figure H77 shows a cathode-ray tube of the sort used in a television set. The coils around its neck are magnetic deflection coils, used to sweep the electron beam to and fro.

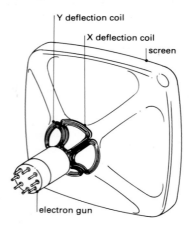

Figure H77
The X and Y deflection coils in a television cathode-ray tube.

The beam has to paint out 625 lines to make a full picture every 1/25 second. Sketch a graph of the variation with time of the current:

a   in the coils which move the beam in a horizontal direction;

b   in the coils which move the beam in a vertical direction.

Your graph should cover the time needed to draw out, say, three complete horizontal lines. Label the graph as necessary to indicate the purpose of the current variations.

14(R)   The photograph, figure H79, shows the path of an electron beam in a bubble chamber when there is a magnetic field at right angles to the plane of the beam. Figure H78 shows the apparatus.

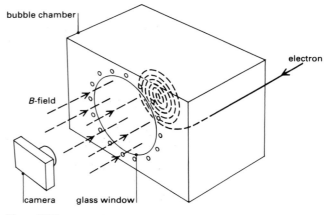

Figure H78

a   The path is a spiral. Consider what could be changing as the electron moves in the bubble chamber, and suggest why the path is not a circle.

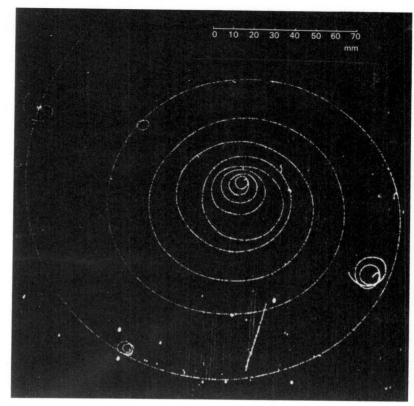

Figure H79
The path of an electron beam in a bubble chamber.
Lawrence Berkeley Laboratory, University of California.

b   The magnetic field was $1.2\,\mathrm{N\,A^{-1}\,m^{-1}}$. Estimate the initial momentum of the electron using the scale shown.

c   *Optional extra.* Plot a graph showing how the momentum of the electron beam changes as the distance covered in the chamber changes.

Note: In fact, the speed of the electron hardly changes, even though its momentum decreases. This is because its speed, v, is near to the speed of light, c. The theory of relativity says that the momentum is not mv but $m_0 v / \sqrt{1 - v^2/c^2}$, where m_0 is the rest mass (the mass measured at low velocities).

15, 16(R) A particle P with charge Q, mass m, and constant speed v crosses line XY into a region where a uniform magnetic field B causes it to move in a circular path of radius r, determined by the equation $BQv = mv^2/r$, so that $r/v = m/BQ$. The particle P takes a time $t = \pi r/v$ to travel in a semicircle from X to Y (figure H80).

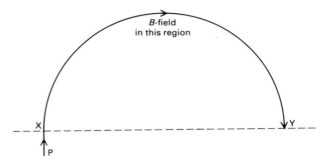

Figure H80

What time will a particle take to go around from X so as to recross the straight line XY if it is identical with P, except that it has:

15 speed $2v$?

16 charge $2Q$?

A $t/4$ **B** $t/2$ **C** t **D** $2t$ **E** $4t$

(Coded answer paper, 1977)

Fields near currents

17(L) It can be shown experimentally that near a long straight wire $B \propto I$ and $B \propto 1/r$. This means that the magnetic field of an infinite straight wire can be expressed as $B = kI/r$ where k is some constant. The ampere is defined as that current which, flowing in two infinitely long wires of negligible diameter, one metre apart, gives a force of $2 \times 10^{-7}\,\text{N}$ per metre length of the wires.

Figure H81 shows two long straight wires, A and B, one metre apart, each carrying a current of one ampere.

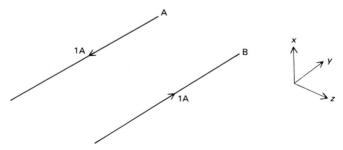

Figure H81

a What is the field due to the current in wire A, 1 metre away, in terms of k?

b Is the field in the direction x, y, or z?

c How big is the force on 1 metre of wire B, in terms of k?

d Is the force in the direction x, y, or z?

e The force is 2×10^{-7} N. What value does this give the constant k?

The field of a straight wire is normally given as $B = \mu_0 I/2\pi r$. (The extra 2π is added so that the denominator is actually the circumference of the circle, distance r from the wire, at which B is calculated. It also ensures that the formula for a uniform field, such as that inside a solenoid, does not include a π.)

f What is the value of μ_0, and what are its units?

In theory the two wires should be in a vacuum. In practice the presence of air makes very little difference. It changes the force between the wires by a very small factor (less than 1.000 001).

18(P) A current of 10 A flows in a long straight wire. What is the B-field:

a *i* 1 cm from the wire?
ii 10 cm from the wire?

b What would be the force on another wire of length 10 cm carrying a current of 5 A if it were placed parallel to the first at distances of 1 cm and 10 cm from the first wire?

c Would these forces be enough to support 1 cm of tickertape with a mass per metre length of 0.62 g?

19(P)a Use the formula $B = \mu_0 NI/l$ for an infinite solenoid to calculate the B-field at the centre of a solenoid of length 30 cm with 360 turns carrying a current of 1 A.

b What is the field at one end of the solenoid? (Remember that $B = \mu_0 NI/l$ assumes that the solenoid extends 'to infinity' in both directions from the point at which B is calculated.)

20(R) A space of about 10 cm × 10 cm × 10 cm with no magnetic field is needed for experiments on small living organisms. To cancel the Earth's magnetic field it is proposed to pass a current through a 20-turn square coil of side 1 m, with the experiment placed at the centre of the coil.

a Using the formula for a straight wire, $B = \mu_0 I/2\pi r$, find an approximate value for the current which would be needed to cancel the Earth's field of 1.7×10^{-4} T.

b The formula does not apply close to short wires. Estimate the actual current which would be needed.

c The direction of the Earth's B-field in the UK is about 7° West of North and about 66° below the horizontal. In what plane would the coil have to be placed?

21(R)   Explain how you would estimate the quantities **a** and **b** below.
Say what would be done at each step of the calculation, giving reasons for each step. Say what numerical information you would need. Indicate where you would make simplifications or approximations.

Your explanation should be such as to enable someone, provided with the numerical information, to perform the calculation.

a   The distance an electron falls under gravity as it travels from the electron gun to the screen of a television set.

b   The magnetic field (B) that you could obtain close to the wire by connecting a thick piece of copper wire direct from terminal to terminal of a car battery.

(Special paper, 1977)

22(R)   The graph in figure H82(a) shows the variation with distance of the magnetic field strength (B) near a long straight wire carrying a current of 10 A. The small circle with a cross in it – figure H82(b) – to the right of the graph, represents the wire carrying the current perpendicularly into the paper.

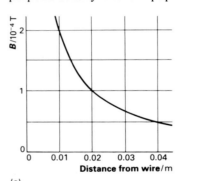

Figure H82   (a)   (b)

a   Show, by drawing on a copy of figure H82(b), the shape and direction of the magnetic field near the wire.

Does your drawing also represent the variation of field strength shown by the graph? Say either how your drawing does this, or how it could be modified to do so.

b   Using information from the graph, determine:
i the strength of the magnetic field at a distance of 0.005 m from the wire when the current is 10 A;
ii the current which, at a distance of 0.02 m from the wire, would give a value of B equal to 2×10^{-5} T. In each case show how you obtain your answer.

c   A second wire of length 0.3 m, which also carries a current of 10 A, is placed parallel to the original wire and at a distance of 0.01 m from it. What is the magnitude of the force on this second wire due to the current in the original wire? Show the steps in your calculation.

(Short answer paper, 1980)

Induction

23(L) This question is about the e.m.f. induced in a conductor moved in a magnetic field.

Figure H83 shows a conducting rod moving at right angles to its length, *l*, across a *B*-field. The rod, and all the charge carriers in it (each with charge *Q*) are carried along at velocity *v*.

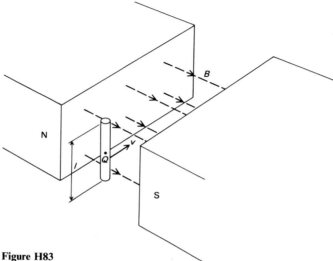

Figure H83

a What magnetic force will be exerted on one carrier? Will the force be parallel to the rod, the *B*-field, or the velocity?

b What will happen if a galvanometer is connected to the ends of the rod? (The galvanometer is stationary.)

c The carriers tend to pile up at one end of the rod, if there is now no external circuit (such as the galvanometer) for them to get through. An induced e.m.f., $\mathscr{E}$, develops in the rod. If $\mathscr{E}$ is steady, no further piling up of charge carriers can be going on. What electric field E then exists across the rod, length *l*?

d What force EQ acts on each charge carrier in the rod?

e When the carriers are no longer piling up more and more, the electric force (from **d**) must counterbalance the magnetic force (from **a**). Write an expression for $\mathscr{E}$ involving only *B*, *l*, and *v*.

f Will the magnitude and sign of the induced e.m.f. depend upon the magnitude and sign of the charge Q on each carrier?

g Suppose now that the moving rod is connected to an external resistor (at rest) so that current *I* flows through resistance *R*. How much energy will be dissipated in *R*, in time *t*, in terms of *I*, *R*, and *t*?

h When the rod moves there is a current *I*, and so there is a force $F = BIl$ on the rod. Could this force be in such a direction as to increase the speed of the rod? Explain.

i   What distance does the rod move in time t?

j   Energy has to be delivered to the rod to keep it moving, since the moving rod is delivering energy to the resistor. Write down the work involved in pushing the rod for a time t, from previous answers for force and distance.

k   Compare the answers to **j** and **g**. Express the induced e.m.f. $\mathscr{E}$ in terms of B, l, and v.

l   Suppose the rod were its own resistor (say a rod of the material used to make radio resistors), its ends being connected together by as short a piece of copper wire as possible. If this combination were pushed through the field, would any current flow?

24(L)   This question is about another – at first sight not very helpful – way of writing down the e.m.f. $\mathscr{E}$ induced in a rod of length l, moving as shown in figure H84, at right angles to the field B, at velocity v. The induced e.m.f. $\mathscr{E}$ is given from question **23** by

$$\mathscr{E} = Blv$$

a   Make up an argument to give a quantitative algebraic expression for the following verbal rule for $\mathscr{E}$: The e.m.f. $\mathscr{E}$ is equal to B multiplied by the rate at which the rod sweeps out area A perpendicular to B.

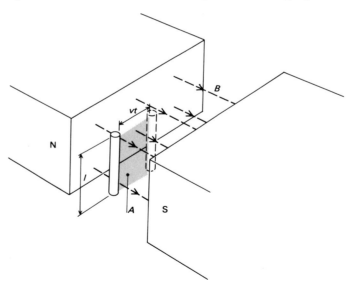

Figure H84

b   (*Harder*) Suppose that the rod were a zig-zag shape, and its length were larger than the distance l between its ends, as shown in figure H85. Would the induced e.m.f. be larger than $\mathscr{E} = Blv$?

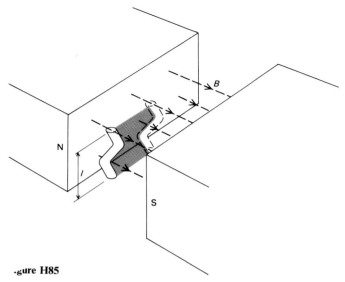

Figure H85

25(R) The Earth's magnetic field over the North Atlantic has a horizontal component B_H pointing North, and a vertical component B_V pointing downwards, as shown in figure H86. When Concorde is flying due East at a fixed height, between which parts of the aircraft will an e.m.f. be induced:
1 between the wing tips?
2 between the nose and the tail?
3 between the top of the tail and the bottom of the fuselage?
A 1 only   **B** 2 only   **C** 1 and 3 only
D 2 and 3 only   **E** 1, 2, and 3.

Figure H86

(Coded answer paper, 1979)

Direct current motors

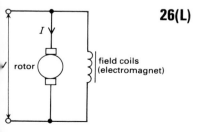

Figure H87

26(L) In many electric motors the magnetic field in which the rotor rotates is provided by an electromagnet. One way of connecting the rotor and field coils (electromagnet) is in parallel, as shown in figure H87. Since the field coils are in parallel with the rotor, the current through them, and hence the magnetic field, stay pretty constant irrespective of what happens to the rotor.

The rotor has resistance R, carries current I, and has a p.d. V across it. In this question, the steady current drawn by the field coils is ignored.

a Write an equation for the current I if the rotor is held still.

b When the rotor turns conductors are being moved in a magnetic field and an e.m.f. $\mathscr{E}$ is induced in the coil. The equation from **a** becomes

$$V - \mathscr{E} = IR$$

If R is constant and $\mathscr{E}$ is proportional to the rate of rotation, sketch a graph of I against rate of rotation.

c The torque produced by the motor depends on the current I. How, if at all, will the torque vary with speed of rotation?

d When a motor is required to drive a larger load, the current its rotor draws increases. By what means does this happen?

27(P) Table H4 gives some results of an experiment using a d.c. motor.

Field coils		Rotor		Load	Rate of rotation
V/V	I/A	V/V	I/A		/s^{-1}
5	0.35	5	1.0	zero	27
5	0.35	5	1.9	light	21
5	0.35	5	3.1	heavy	13

Table H4

Resistance of rotor $= 1\,\Omega$.

The field and rotor windings were supplied independently, from two different sources. Readings of applied p.d. V and current I for both field coils and rotor were taken.

a The ratio V/I for the rotor varies, and is never equal to $1\,\Omega$. Why?

b Why is the rotor current larger when the motor is working against a load?

c How could the motor be made to turn the 'heavy' load at 27 revolutions per second?

Flux

28(P) The magnetic field strength B (flux density) in a long solenoid carrying a current I is given by $B = \mu_0 NI/l$, where there are N turns in length l. Calculate the field strength B, and the flux Φ in the following rectangular solenoids. The current is 0.5 A in each case.

a A 360-turn solenoid, 300 mm long, cross-section 70×70 mm.

b A 360-turn solenoid, 300 mm long, cross-section 50×50 mm.

c A 240-turn solenoid, 200 mm long, cross-section 280×30 mm.

29(P)a What is the flux density at the centre of a solenoid which has a turns density of 1200 turns per metre and carries a current of 1.5 A?

b What will be the flux through a $10 \times 10\,\mathrm{mm}$ Hall probe held at the centre of the solenoid if

    i it is perpendicular to the *B*-field?

    ii its plane makes an angle of 30° to the direction of *B*?

Alternating current

30(I) The p.d. across a $5\,\Omega$ resistor is displayed on an oscilloscope, giving the trace shown in figure H88. The oscilloscope settings were: time-base speed 2 ms per division; voltage sensitivity 5 mV per division.

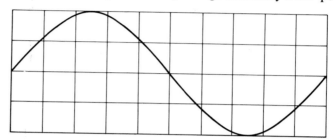

Figure H88

a What is the frequency of the alternating current in the resistor?

b What is the *peak* value of this current?

c What is the *average* value of the p.d. across the resistor, and of the current in it?

Flux and reluctance

31(L) Figure H89 shows an iron ring, in which magnetic flux Φ is set up by N turns of wire wrapped round the ring, carrying current I. The flux Φ is given by

$$NI = \Phi l / \mu_r \mu_0 A$$

where l is the length round the ring, and A is its cross-sectional area. The quantity $\mu_r \mu_0$ is more or less constant, as long as the current is not large.

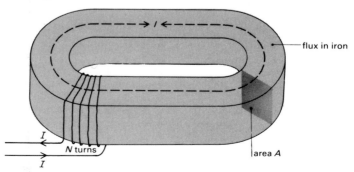

Figure H89

In a copper wire, the steady current flowing depends on the applied p.d. and the resistance. The resistance depends on the length of wire and the cross-sectional area of the wire.

a Write an expression for the resistance of a wire in terms of its length and area.

b Write an equation analogous to that for current-turns, flux, length, and area, but for the p.d. driving current in a wire. Current is to be analogous to flux. What is the p.d. analogous to in the 'magnetic circuit'?

c To what quantity does the combination $\mu_r \mu_0$ compare in the analogy?

d The general form of the relationship is

driving force = rate of flow × length/(conductivity × area)

What corresponds to each term in the case of energy leaking from a hot water tank through its lagging (the fibre-filled jacket over the tank)?

e The magnetic circuit equation is sometimes written

$NI = \Phi \times (\text{reluctance})$

To what electrical quantity does reluctance correspond, in the analogy with current?

32(L) A solenoid is rather like a pipe which carries magnetic flux, and the flux in a solenoid can be calculated just as if one were calculating the flow of electric current along a copper bar, the thermal flow of energy ('heat flow') along a conducting bar, or (neglecting many of the real-life complications) the flow of fluid down a tube.

A calculation of the 'flow' of flux in a straight solenoid, such as that shown in figure H90(b), is complicated by the difficulty of working out what happens at the ends. One way of avoiding the difficulty is to regard the solenoid as part of a very long one whose ends are brought round to meet each other, as in figure H90(a).

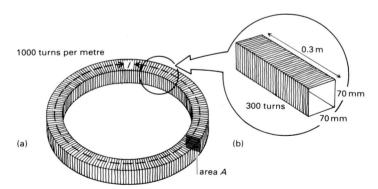

1000 turns per metre

0.3 m

70 mm

300 turns

70 mm

(a)

(b)

area A

Figure H90

a The reluctance of the large, closed solenoid pipe shown in figure H90(a) is given by $l/\mu_0 A$, where l is the length all around the pipe, and A is its cross-sectional area. Calculate the contribution made to this reluctance by the shorter, almost straight section in figure H90(b).

b The flux 'going round' the large closed solenoid is given by

current-turns = flux × reluctance.

Explain why, if the length l is altered, keeping the number of turns per metre and the current the same, the flux is unaltered.

c Calculate the flux 'going through' any section of the solenoid, using the answer to **a**, if the solenoid carries one ampere.

d What is the value of B within the solenoid?

e Suppose that a steel rod having roughly the cross-sectional area of a retort stand rod were put in the middle of the solenoid. You may suppose that the rod is bent round so that the two ends meet. The reluctance of a steel rod is given by the same relationship as that in **a**, but with μ_0 multiplied by a large factor, μ_r, which you may take to be 500. Use a rough estimate of the rod's cross-sectional area to estimate the ratio of the flux going through the rod to the flux going through the rest of the inside of the solenoid.

33, 34(R) In figure H91(a) a potential difference V across a long iron rod produces a current I in the rod, the resistance of the rod being V/I.

In figure H91(b) current-turns NI around the rod produce a flux Φ in the rod, the reluctance of the rod being NI/Φ.

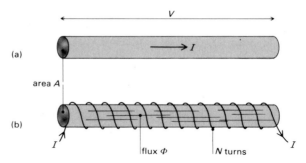

Figure H91

If the area A of cross-section of the rod were doubled (the length staying the same and being large compared to the diameter), by which of the factors **A** to **E** below

33 is the *resistance* of the rod multiplied?

34 is the *reluctance* of the rod multiplied?

A $\frac{1}{4}$ **B** $\frac{1}{2}$ **C** 1   **D** 2   **E** 4

(Coded answer paper 1981)

35(R) This question asks you to say more about four brief statements about magnetic flux.

a The passage below consists of four main statements, numbered *i*, *ii*, *iii*, and *iv*. For each of these statements you are asked to give arguments which explain and support the statement; these might refer to theoretical principles, or to experimental evidence, or both. Your arguments should include explanation of the principles and description of the evidence.

b Statement *iii* could be described in general terms as a statement about practical applications based on an experimental result (the value of μ_r). For each of statements *i*, *ii*, and *iv* give a similar description to say what sort of ideas are in the statement, for example, it is a definition based on previous ideas; or it is a summary of experimental results; or some other description you think appropriate; give a *brief* justification for each description.

Passage
i We can show from experiments with solenoids in air that magnetic flux Φ is related to the current I and number of turns N by an equation of the form

$$NI = \frac{\Phi l}{\mu_0 A}$$

where l is the length and A the cross-sectional area; however, it takes a whole set of careful experiments to sort out the various factors correctly.
ii The equation is very like the equation which relates the flow of electric current in a circuit to the various factors which determine it; we can compare the two equations term by term, so that it seems reasonable to say that magnetic flux is like the flow of something.
iii Useful practical applications nearly always use solenoids filled with iron because when iron is used μ_0 is replaced by $\mu_0\mu_r$, and the value of μ_r can be as much as 1000.
iv The idea of flux as a flow around a magnetic circuit is often helpful. For example, it can easily be shown that if an iron ring electromagnet has a small air gap cut in it there is a large reduction in Φ – just like the effects on the current when a large resistance is inserted in series in an electrical circuit.

(Long answer paper, 1979)

36(L) Mutual inductance; $\mathscr{E} = M\mathrm{d}I/\mathrm{d}t$.

Two coils A and B are wound on an iron core. The current in A increases steadily from 0 to 30 mA in 1 ms. The p.d. across coil B is found to be 1.5 V.

a What is the mutual inductance, M?

Explain, using such terms as flux, flux linkage, and rate of change, the effect of each of the following independent changes.

b The iron core is removed, and the current is increased from 0 to 30 mA in 1 ms as before.

c The number of turns of wire in coil A is doubled.

d The number of turns in coil B is doubled.

e The current is decreased from 30 mA to 0 in 2 ms.

Inductance

37(P) When the switch in figure H92 is closed, the current in the circuit rises to 0.5 A in the first 0.01 s. For this period, the rate of rise of current is very nearly steady. R is 0.1 Ω, and L has negligible resistance.

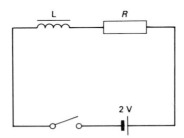

Figure H92

a What, approximately, is the inductance of L?

b How might the rise of current be observed?

c R is increased to 0.2 Ω and the experiment is repeated. Will the rate of rise of current double, halve, or be roughly the same as before?

d R is increased to 2 Ω. At what rate will the current rise initially? When the current is 0.5 A, will the current still be rising at a uniform rate? What will the rate of increase of current be at this stage?

38(R) A coil of inductance L (and zero resistance), and a resistance R are connected via a switch to a battery of voltage V (and no internal resistance). See figure H93.

Which one of the following statements about the circuit is correct?

A Just as the switch is closed, the rate of change of the current is V/R.

B Just as the switch is closed, the current is V/L.

C After the switch is closed, the final steady current does not depend on the value of L.

D After the switch is closed, the final steady current does not depend on the voltage V.

E When the current is finally steady, there is a constant large induced voltage across the inductor.

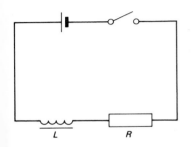

Figure H93

(Coded answer paper, 1979)

39, 40(R)   A coil of inductance 0.1 H is connected, as shown in figure H94, to a resistor of resistance 20 Ω, and to a 10 V battery (of negligible internal resistance). The switch is initially open.

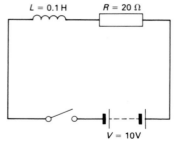

Figure H94

39   Which of **A** to **E** below is a correct calculation of the initial rate dI/dt at which the current I in the circuit changes with time, at the moment when the switch is closed?

A $10/0.1 \, \text{A s}^{-1}$
B $10/20 \, \text{A s}^{-1}$
C $10 \times 0.1 \, \text{A s}^{-1}$
D $20/0.1 \, \text{A s}^{-1}$
E $20 \times 0.1 \, \text{A s}^{-1}$

40   Which of **A** to **E** below is a correct calculation of the *final* value of the current in the circuit, a long time after the switch has been closed?

A $10/0.1 \, \text{A}$
B $10/20 \, \text{A}$
C $10 \times 0.1 \, \text{A}$
D $20/0.1 \, \text{A}$
E $20 \times 0.1 \, \text{A}$

(Coded answer paper, 1978)

41(R)   A solenoid carries a sinusoidal alternating current. A search coil is placed at its centre, with the coil's axis parallel to that of the solenoid.

If the frequency of the current in the solenoid is doubled, but the amplitude of the current is kept the same, which of the following quantities will also be doubled?

1   the maximum rate of change of flux through the search coil
2   the amplitude of the induced voltage in the search coil
3   the frequency of the alternating voltage in the search coil

A 1 only   **B** 2 only   **C** 1 and 3 only
D 2 and 3 only   **E** 1, 2, and 3

(Coded answer paper, 1979)

Transformers

42(P) A transformer for a toy railway set converts the 240 V alternating mains supply to a 12 V alternating voltage.

a What is the turns ratio?

b What do you think determines the actual number of turns?

c Could the transformer be used with a steady d.c. input?

43(P) In figure H95, P is a primary coil of 20 turns, joined to a 1 V alternating supply. S is a secondary of 50 turns joined to a small 2.5 V lamp, L, which lights with what we may call 'normal brightness'. These facts are expressed in the top line of table H5.

Copy and complete the table. For the third column, write 'normal' if the lamp is normally bright, 'dim' for dim or not alight, 'bright' for brighter than normal (including 'burnt-out').

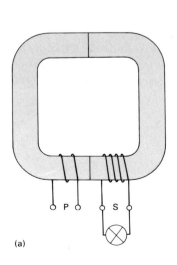

Figure H95

Number of turns on primary P	Number of turns on secondary S	Brightness of lamp L	Alternating p.d. across S/volts
20	50	normal	2.5
50	20		
20	30		
40	100		
20	80		

Table H5

44(P) Figure H96 shows three different arrangements of the same transformer. P is a primary coil of 20 turns, always connected to a one-volt alternating supply. S is a secondary coil of 50 turns, joined to a 2.5 V lamp. In figure H96(c) the secondary is wound on top of the primary. The coils are wound on a double C-core.

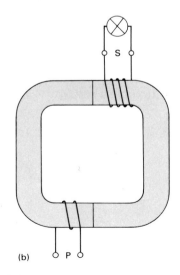
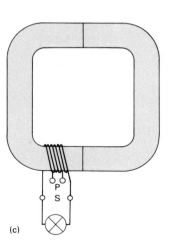

(a) (b) (c)

Figure H96

a There seems to be little difference between the three arrangements: in every case the lamp lights normally although the secondary coil is in different places. How do you explain this?

b Figure H97 shows the arrangement of figure H96(a) with the two C-cores slightly separated. This gives a different result: the lamp lights only very dimly. Why does separating the two iron cores of a transformer cause it to work much less efficiently?

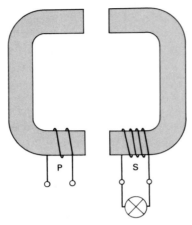

Figure H97

c If the iron C-cores in the arrangement of figure H96(c) are slightly separated, the lamp lights dimly. Why is this?

d Look again at figure H96. Suppose that a transformer is made by winding all three secondary coils and the single primary coil on the same pair of C-cores. Each secondary is joined to a lamp, and all three lamps are found to light normally. How do you explain this result?

e How would you expect the primary current in this case to compare with the primary current when there is one secondary coil with one lamp?

45, 46(R) A 6 volt alternating supply is connected to the 100-turn primary coil of a transformer. The 200-turn secondary coil runs a lamp which is dissipating 24 watts. (Assume that the transformer is a good one, with no flux leakage, low resistances, and an unsaturated core.)
Here are five values of currents:

A 4A **B** 2A **C** 1A **D** $\frac{1}{2}$A **E** $\frac{1}{4}$A

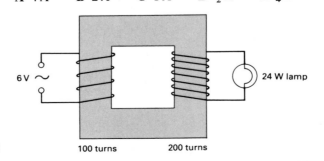

Figure H98

45 Which is the best estimate of the current in the secondary circuit?

46 Which is the best estimate of the current in the primary circuit?

(Coded answer paper, 1979)

47(R) Describe a series of demonstrations you could do to show an A-level Physics class the principles and behaviour of alternating current transformers. Include losses and saturation besides fundamental principles. For each demonstration:

    a say clearly what idea(s) you are showing, and how the demonstration illustrates them.

    b discuss the selection of coils, cores, voltages, currents, and frequency, and the choice of measuring instruments, such that the effect to be shown can in fact be detected easily.

(Special paper, 1983)

Transmission of electric power

48(L) Figure H99 shows a very simplified representation of a transmission line delivering power P from a generator to a load. The potential difference across the load is V. The total resistance of the cables between generator and load is R.

Figure H99

    a What is the current?

    b What is the power loss in the transmission line?

    c For a given value of P, how can this power loss be minimized?

Your answers so far should have shown that it is more economical to transmit power at high voltages.

    d Why is an a.c. rather than a d.c. system used, and why are transformers needed at both ends of the transmission line?

As well as the running costs associated with power dissipation in the cables, it is important to consider the capital costs of a power transmission system. Suppose the same power is to be transmitted by a 132 kV system and by a 400 kV system.

    e What is the ratio of the currents in the two systems?

    f For the same power dissipation what will be the ratio of the resistance per unit length of cable for the two systems?

g How therefore would you expect the amount of metal needed and hence the cost per kilometre length of the two transmission lines to compare?

Figure H100 shows that the cost of the cables is not the only consideration.

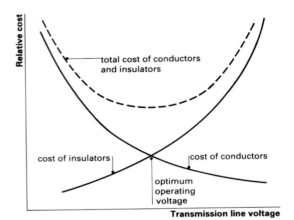

Figure H100
Transmission line capital costs. There exists an optimum operating p.d. for which the installation cost is a minimum.
Based on WRIGHT, J. P. The vital spark. Heinemann, 1974.

h Why does the cost of insulators rise as the transmission voltage is increased?

Power in a resistive circuit

49(L)a What energy is dissipated every second in a resistance R, on average,
i if a steady current I flows?
ii if a current I flows in short bursts, with gaps of no current in between, the gaps and bursts lasting equally long? (During a burst the current is steady.)
iii if current I flows in short bursts, first in one direction and then in the other, taking no time to change direction? (Again, the current is steady during a burst.)

b What steady current would dissipate energy at the same rate as the current I in **a***ii*, which comes in bursts?

c Suggest why the current in **b** is called the root mean square current.

d The alternating current from the a.c. mains varies as $\sin \theta$. Figure H101 is a sketch graph of $\sin^2 \theta$, over one cycle. The two shaded areas are equal. What is the average value of $\sin^2 \theta$ over one cycle?

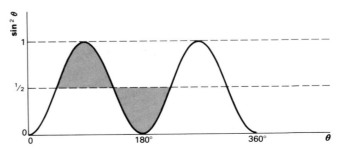

Figure H101

What steady current would dissipate as much energy in a resistor as an alternating current of maximum value I?

Alternating current in circuits containing capacitors

50(L) The curve in figure H102 shows one cycle of a sinusoidal variation of the p.d. V across a $100\,\mu\text{F}$ capacitor.

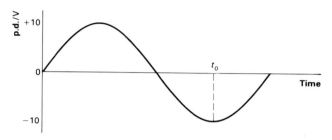

Figure H102

a What is the charge, Q, on the capacitor when $V = +10\,\text{V}$, $0\,\text{V}$, $-10\,\text{V}$? Sketch a graph of Q against t. Is there a charge on the capacitor at time t_0?

b When is the current flowing into or out of the capacitor at a maximum, and when at a minimum? Sketch a graph of current against time. Is there any current at time t_0?

c What other information is needed to give a rough estimate of the maximum current?

51(L) A moving-coil ammeter works because there is a force on a current in a coil placed between the poles of a magnet. The magnitude of the force is proportional to the current, and it reverses direction if the current reverses.

    The magnitude of the force is also proportional to the strength of the magnetic field. A wattmeter can be made by replacing the magnet of an ammeter with a fixed coil which carries a small current proportional to the p.d. across the circuit, because this makes the strength of the magnetic field proportional to the p.d. The force on the coil is now proportional to the product of the current and p.d., that is, to the power.

    Figure H103 shows just half of a cycle of the variation of current and p.d. for a capacitor in an a.c. circuit.

a Will there be a force on the wattmeter coil at time 2? Why?

b Will there be a force on the wattmeter coil at times 0 and 4? Why?

c At times 1 and 3 the magnetic field in the wattmeter will be exactly the same, for V has the same value at these times. How will any forces on the coil compare at these times?

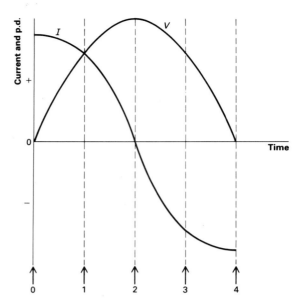

Figure H103

d What does the average wattmeter reading seem likely to be, if it is set to measure the average power delivered to a capacitor by an alternating supply?

e What would be different if a lamp were now placed in series with th capacitor?

52(L) In figure H104 the oscilloscope's Y-sensitivity is set at $1\,\text{V cm}^{-1}$.

a What is the amplitude of the alternating p.d. (the biggest p.d. at any time during the cycle) across the capacitor?

b What is the p.d. across the capacitor when the greatest charge at an time during the cycle is on the capacitor plates?

c When the greatest charge is on the capacitor plates, at what rate is the charge changing?

d What is the current 'through' the capacitor at the instant when the greatest charge is on the capacitor plates?

e What is the rate at which electrical energy is being transformed in the capacitor when the p.d. across the capacitor is 3 volts?

f What is the rate at which electrical energy is being transformed when the p.d. across the capacitor is zero?

g Is the energy stored in the capacitor increasing or decreasing while the p.d. across it is increasing?

h Is the energy stored in the capacitor increasing or decreasing while the p.d. across it is decreasing?

i What is the average rate at which electrical energy is being converted to other forms, taken over many cycles?

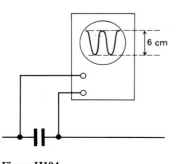

Figure H104

Alternating current in circuits containing inductance

53(L) Suppose that the input to the circuit of figure H105 is an alternating voltage of constant amplitude, but variable frequency.

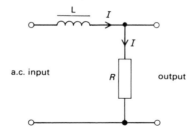

Figure H105

a If the frequency is doubled, what would happen to the maximum rate of change of the current drawn from the supply, if the maximum current stayed the same? (It does not, at constant voltage.)

b If R is small, nearly all the p.d. is across L, equal to the supply p.d. If this is unaltered, the rate of change of current must be the same as before, since V, the p.d. across L, is given by $L\,dI/dt$. How can the rate of change of current be unaltered, though the frequency has doubled?

c If the maximum current has roughly halved, how has the maximum output p.d. changed?

d Why do you think such a circuit is often called a 'low-pass filter'?

54(R) An alternating voltage, V, varying with time sinusoidally as shown in figure H106, is applied across an inductor, which has negligible resistance.

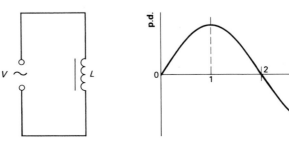

Figure H106

Which of the following statements about what is happening at the times 1, 2, and 3 indicated is/are correct?

1 At time 1 the current in the circuit is a maximum.
2 At time 2 the magnetic flux linking the turns of the inductor is a maximum.
3 At time 3 the rate of change of current in the inductor is a maximum.

A 1 only   **B** 2 only   **C** 1 and 3 only
D 2 and 3 only   **E** 1, 2, and 3

(Coded answer paper, 1983)

55(R)   Figure H107 shows how the alternating potential difference *V* applied to the ends of a coil made from thick copper wire, and the current *I* through the coil, vary with time *t*.

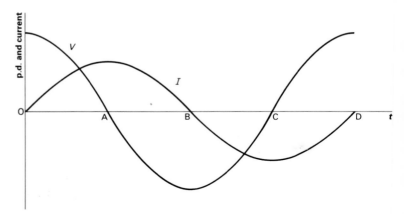

Figure H107

a   Why is the applied potential difference zero when the current *I* has maximum value?

b   During which of the periods of time OA, AB, BC, and CD would th source of power be *i* supplying energy, *ii* receiving energy?
   How did you decide on these answers?

When the source of power *receives* energy, where does the energy come from?

(Short answer paper, 197

Electrical oscillations

56(L)a   Figure H108(a) shows a trolley tethered between springs fixed to rigid walls. The trolley is pulled to one side, stretching and compressing the springs. The system has gained energy. Where is th energy?

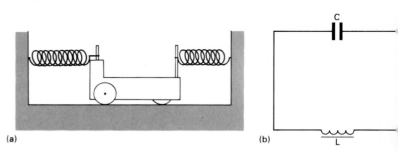

Figure H108

b   Figure H108(b) shows a capacitor about to be connected across an inductor. The capacitor has been connected to a battery, giving it a charge. The system has gained energy. Where is this energy?

c   The trolley is released. What determines its initial acceleration?

d The switch is closed. What determines the initial rate of rise of current?

e In the middle position, is the velocity of the trolley constant, zero, or changing?

f When the capacitor has no charge is there a steady, a zero, or a changing current in the circuit?

g Because the trolley is still moving when the springs are not displaced, it soon does displace them. What effect does this have on the trolley's velocity?

h Because there is a current when the capacitor is uncharged, the capacitor soon becomes charged again. What effect does this have on the current?

i There comes a time when the trolley is at rest again, displaced from the centre by as far as it was to begin with, if there was negligible friction. How much energy has the system and where is this energy?

j There comes a time when the current is zero again, with the capacitor charged by as much as it was to begin with, if there was negligible resistance in the circuit. How much energy has the system, and where is it?

57(R) When the switch in the circuit of figure H109 is closed, the current in the circuit oscillates for a while. After some time, the oscillations stop. When the oscillations have stopped, which of the following correctly describe(s) the potential differences across the resistor R, the inductor L, and the capacitor C?

1 There is then *no* potential difference across R.

2 There is then *no* potential difference across L.

3 There *is* then a potential difference across C, equal to the voltage of the battery.

A 1 only   **B** 2 only   **C** 1 and 3 only
D 2 and 3 only   **E** 1, 2, and 3

(Coded answer paper, 1979)

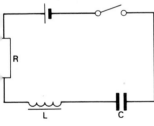

Figure H109

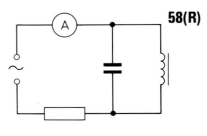

Figure H110

58(R) The ammeter records the alternating current I drawn by the inductor and capacitor in parallel, as shown in figure H110, from an alternating source of constant voltage, with a resistor in series with it. Which of the graphs in figure H111 correctly represents the variation of the current I as the frequency f is varied?

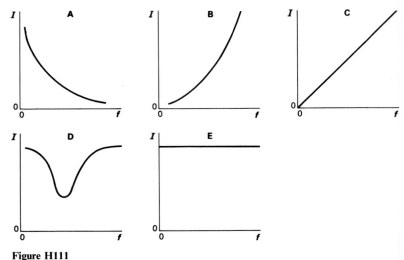

Figure H111

(Coded answer paper, 1980

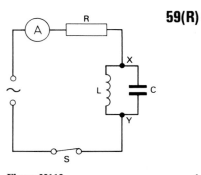

Figure H112

59(R) This question is about the explanation of resonance in an *LC* circuit
  A student is shown the circuit illustrated in figure H112, with the a.c. generator set at the resonant frequency of the circuit. He notices that the current indicated on the ammeter A is quite small.
  He is told to study the notes **1, 2, 3** below but he has not studied much a.c. theory before and he finds that he cannot understand them.
  You are asked to write out a full explanation for each of the notes **1, 2,** and **3** in order to help the student. (About half the marks for this question will be available for the explanation of note **1**.)

Notes
1 The currents between X and Y, through L and through C, are in opposite directions at all times even though they have the same potential difference across them.
2 Because the frequency is just right, these currents will be about equal so that there will be little or no current in R even though there is a large current flowing in both the L and the C arms. However, if the frequency were altered (increased or decreased), there would be a current in R.
3 Just as with a trolley oscillating on the end of a spring, the energy is continually changing between potential (in the spring) and kinetic (in the trolley), so in this circuit energy changes continually between being stored in the field associated with L and being stored in the field associated with C.

(Long answer paper, 1978

Unit I
LINEAR ELECTRONICS, FEEDBACK AND CONTROL

Wilf Mace
King Edward VII School, Sheffield

I

SUMMARY OF THE UNIT

SUMMARY OF THE UNIT

INTRODUCTION

Unit C of this course was about digital electronics – devices like gates and multivibrators whose output is either high or low, 0 or 1. This Unit is concerned with linear electronics – devices and circuits whose output can vary continuously between minimum and maximum levels. The output of course depends on the input, and may be proportional to it.

Figure I1
Digital and continuously variable signals.

As well as the details of some particularly useful circuits, this Unit is concerned with some more general and powerful ideas related to feedback and control. Feedback, usually negative feedback, is a feature of many electronic circuits, and many control systems use electronics. But the ideas of feedback and control can be applied in many other fields as well, including mechanics, biology, economics, and perhaps even psychology.

As in Unit C, 'Digital electronic systems', we are not concerned with the details of how a particular electronic component works, or what there is inside it. What we *are* interested in is what the output is for various inputs, and how the component can be used to do a wide range of jobs. The work of the Unit involves much experimental work, and the solving of practical problems. It also makes use of many basic ideas about electric circuits: current, resistance, p.d., capacitance, and so on.

DEMONSTRATION I1
Introduction to linear electronics and control

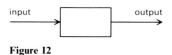

Figure I2

QUESTIONS 1 to 7

Section I1

BASIC OPERATIONAL AMPLIFIER CIRCUITS

The operational amplifier

One of the most useful devices available to electronic engineers today is the operational amplifier. The operational amplifier is an integrated circuit, or 'chip', a product of the microelectronics revolution. That revolution, which started in the 1960s when lighter and more reliable electronic components were demanded by the space race, shows no sign of slowing down. It has been called a second Industrial Revolution, and it may well affect our lives, and those of coming generations, in just as profound a way as the mechanical inventions of the eighteenth and nineteenth centuries changed the lives of our ancestors.

Figure I4 shows the internal circuit of one common operational amplifier: a single integrated circuit on a silicon chip, less than 2 mm square and about 0.2 mm thick, may contain the equivalent of tens of individual transistors, resistors, and capacitors.

Figure I3
A 'chip'.

An operational amplifier can be used to amplify and to do mathematical operations (add, integrate, etc.)

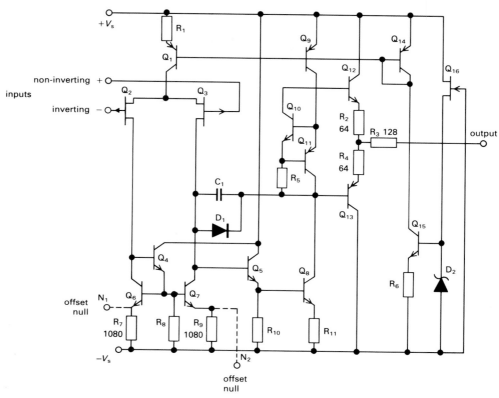

Figure I4

Schematic diagram of the TL081 operational amplifier.
From The BIFET Design manual, *Texas Instruments Ltd.*

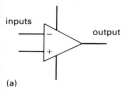

(a)

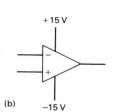

(b)

Figure I5

The operational amplifier is conventionally represented by a triangle. Its two inputs, inverting and non-inverting, are shown by a − and + respectively. A useful circuit will consist of one or more operational amplifiers with various resistors and capacitors (and perhaps transducers such as thermistors, light-dependent resistors, and so on) connected around them. For greater clarity the power supply is often omitted from simplified circuit diagrams – but the operational amplifier won't work without it. A typical operational amplifier is designed to operate from a power supply that gives + 15, 0, and − 15 V, but many will operate from as little as + 3, 0, and − 3 V.

The operational amplifier has one output terminal – shown at the right of the conventional symbol. The output voltage can be positive or negative with respect to the 0 V line of the power supply. But it cannot be more than the positive or less than the negative supply voltage, in fact if the supply voltage is, say, ± 15 V, the output voltage range will be a little less, perhaps ± 13 V. Within this range the output voltage can have any value; in other words, it can vary continuously.

Operational amplifier fundamentals

$$V_{\text{out}} = A(V_+ - V_-)$$

An operational amplifier gives an output voltage (V_{out}) which depends on the difference between the two input voltages, V_+ and V_-. The voltage gain of the device itself, A, is very large – typically 10^5. The input resistance of an operational amplifier is very high – perhaps 2 MΩ. This and other useful data are summarized in table I1.

It is important to remember that the voltage gain and input resistance quoted here refer to the operational amplifier on its own.

Type	741	081
Supply voltage	± 3 to ± 18 V	± 3 to ± 18 V
Maximum differential input voltage	30 V	± 30 V
Maximum input voltage (either input to earth)	15 V	$\pm V_s$ (supply voltage)
Open-loop voltage gain	2×10^5 (106 dB)	2×10^5 (106 dB)
Input resistance	2 MΩ	$10^{12}\,\Omega$
Output voltage swing	± 13 V	± 13.5 V

Table I1
Partial specification for two operational amplifiers.

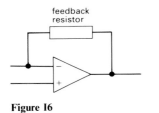

feedback resistor

Figure I6

In fact an operational amplifier is never used on its own. Its very high gain makes its behaviour unstable. By putting it in a circuit in which there is some negative feedback – some of the output voltage is fed back and subtracted from the input – stability is greatly increased. The gain of the circuit with feedback will certainly be less than the 'open-loop gain', the gain of the operational amplifier alone; and its high input resistance may be reduced too. In spite of these apparent drawbacks, almost all useful operational amplifier circuits have some negative feedback.

OPTIONAL DEMONSTRATION I5
Current and voltage in an operational amplifier

Two important simplifications follow from the high gain and high input resistance of the operational amplifier. We can assume that:
a the two inputs are at the same potential;
b there is no current into either input.
These two assumptions (which are valid as long as the output voltage doesn't reach its upper or lower limit), together with straightforward application of basic ideas about electrical circuits, are enough to explain or predict the behaviour of many operational amplifier circuits.

QUESTIONS 12, 13, 14

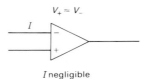

$V_+ \approx V_-$

Figure I7   *I* negligible

QUESTION 44

It turns out, surprisingly enough, that the behaviour of the circuit does not depend on the gain or input resistance of the operational amplifier itself. As long as they are high enough for us to make the above simplifying assumptions, the properties of the circuit depend only on the values of the resistors, capacitors, etc., around the operational amplifier. So any changes in the operational amplifier's behaviour, such as variation of A with temperature, or at different frequencies, are unimportant.

Some basic operational amplifier circuits

EXPERIMENTS I2, I3, I4
Operational amplifiers

As well as feedback from output to input, which may be through a feedback resistor, R_f, most operational amplifier circuits also have an input resistor, R_{in}.

$$V_{out}/V_{in} = -R_f/R_{in}$$

QUESTIONS 8 to 18

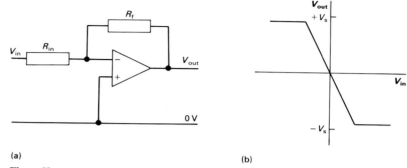

(a)   (b)

Figure I8
(a) Inverting amplifier circuit; (b) its voltage characteristic.

EXPERIMENT I6a
Summing amplifier

An important application is in digital-to-analogue conversion

QUESTIONS 19 to 23

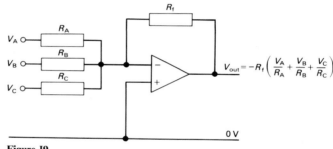

$$V_{out} = -R_f\left(\frac{V_A}{R_A} + \frac{V_B}{R_B} + \frac{V_C}{R_C}\right)$$

Figure I9
Summing amplifier.

EXPERIMENT I6c
Integration

QUESTIONS 24 to 27

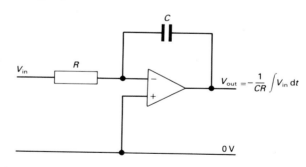

$$V_{out} = -\frac{1}{CR}\int V_{in}\,dt$$

(a)

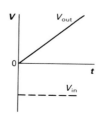

Figure I10
(a) Integrator circuit.
(b) Behaviour of integrator circuit.

(b)

Circuits using the non-inverting input

QUESTIONS 28 to 31

EXPERIMENT I7a
Follower circuit with variable gain

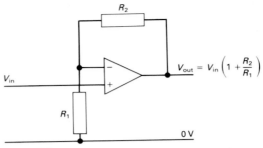

R_2
$V_{out} = V_{in}\left(1 + \frac{R_2}{R_1}\right)$
V_{in}
R_1
0 V

Figure I11
Non-inverting feedback amplifier.

unity gain

EXPERIMENT I7b
Input and output currents of voltage follower

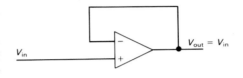

$V_{out} = V_{in}$
V_{in}
0 V

Figure I12
Follower circuit with unity gain.

QUESTIONS 32 to 34

EXPERIMENT I7c
Use of voltage follower circuit

These circuits (figures I11 and I12) have extremely high input resistance. An operational amplifier's output resistance is low, and with negative feedback it is very much lower still, so circuits like those in figures I11 and I12 can supply much bigger currents – perhaps to a moving-coil meter or chart recorder – than they draw from the input source.

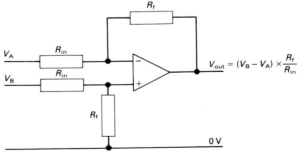

R_f
V_A
R_{in}
V_B
R_{in}
$V_{out} = (V_B - V_A) \times \frac{R_f}{R_{in}}$
R_f
0 V

Figure I13
Differential amplifier.

QUESTIONS 35 to 38

The differential amplifier is useful in many control applications. Its sensitivity obviously depends on the ratio R_f/R_{in}.

Section I2 MORE FEEDBACK; CONTROL

EXPERIMENT I8
Integrator with feedback

In most of the circuits shown so far, the feedback from output to input has been via a resistor or capacitor. Such feedback tends to reduce the difference in potential between the input and output. Feedback by a simple wire means that the two potentials must be equal, as in the unity-gain follower (figure I12).

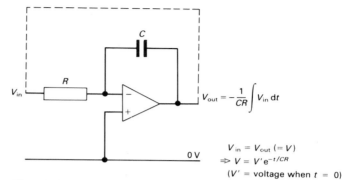

$$V_{out} = -\frac{1}{CR}\int V_{in}\, dt$$

$$V_{in} = V_{out}\ (= V)$$
$$\Rightarrow V = V' e^{-t/CR}$$
$$(V' = \text{voltage when } t = 0)$$

Figure I14
Integrator with feedback.

'Electromechanical similarities' in the Reader *Physics in engineering and technology*

QUESTIONS 39, 40

Systems like that shown in figure I14 are the basis of analogue computing: a process in which circuits are used to produce voltages which are analogous (similar in some respect) to time-varying quantities such as displacement, speed, acceleration, or perhaps population size. The circuit shown in figure I14 gives a voltage which decays exponentially as in the graph in figure I15.

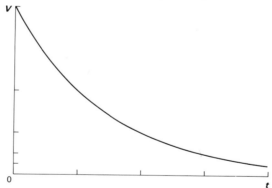

Figure I15

DEMONSTRATION I9
A circuit to produce oscillation

Other circuits can be built to model exponential growth, or to produce oscillations. The time constants or frequencies of these circuits depend on the values of the resistors and capacitors in them.

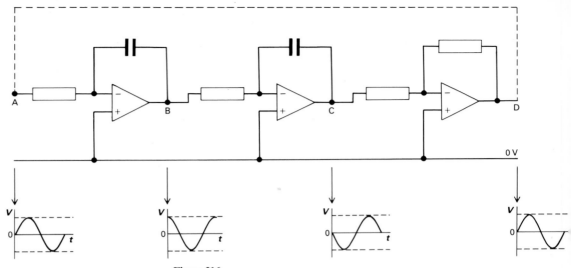

Figure I16
An oscillator circuit, showing the voltages at various points.

QUESTIONS 41 to 43

DEMONSTRATION I10
Feedback in public address systems

OPTIONAL DEMONSTRATION I11
Oscillation in a feedback system

In the circuit of figure I16 each of the integrators introduces a phase lag of 90° ($\pi/2$); the inverter introduces another 180° phase lag. The total delay around the circuit is thus $90° + 90° + 180° = 360°$. So the signal feedback to point A is in phase with the signal there.

This positive feedback causes oscillations in other systems as well. The annoying howl sometimes produced by a public address system is an example. Here the time taken for the sound to travel from loudspeaker to microphone introduces the extra phase change.

Control systems

Feedback is an essential component of any efficient control system. In a system without feedback the output is subject to variations caused by changes in the ambient conditions, disturbance to the system, increase in load, and so on.

To try to keep the output at a constant level it is monitored and information about the output is fed back to a comparator or error detector. Here the output is compared with the reference signal or preset level. Any difference between the two gives rise to an error signal. Since the feedback signal is subtracted from the reference signal, this is a case of negative feedback. The error signal is used to control power to the 'plant', that is the lamp, motor, or whatever is producing the output. If there is no error signal then the output is already at the required level and there is no change to power.

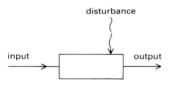

Figure I17
Open-loop system.

Figure I18

Figure I19

An *on–off* system is one in which power to the plant is switched on if the error signal rises above a certain level, and goes off if the error signal is below another, slightly lower level. In a *continuous* system the power varies steadily with the size of the error signal. In principle, at least, a continuous system can settle down to produce an output which is exactly the preset value – figure I20(b). But the output of an on–off system will be continually rising and falling a little above and a little below the required level – figure I20(a).

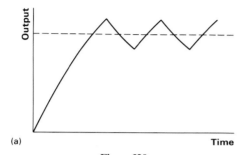
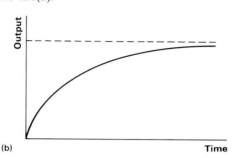

Figure I20
(a) On–off, and (b) continuous control.

Most practical systems require some kind of amplification between the error detector and the power unit, or 'plant'. For example, the error detector might be a bridge circuit or an operational amplifier used as a comparator: neither of these could supply enough power to light a lamp or drive a motor, so a power amplifier or relay of some sort is necessary (control unit in figure I21).

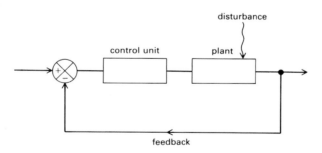

Figure I21

Positive feedback, oscillations, and damping

A control system is designed to have negative feedback. But if there is any delay in the system – perhaps due to inertia – the feedback may become positive. Then the feedback signal will be added to the reference signal. If a disturbance causes the output to increase, the error signal will now cause it to increase further. Under these conditions the system is likely to go into oscillation. If it is an electrical system the period of oscillation will depend on the resistance, capacitance, and inductance of the circuit; in a mechanical system the masses of moving parts and the forces between them are the important factors.

In a simple mechanical oscillator, like a pendulum, more friction reduces the amplitude and – unless the oscillator is driven – causes the oscillations to die away more quickly. Similarly, oscillations in a feedback control system are reduced by damping, that is dissipation of energy in some part of the system.

Figure I22
Damped oscillation.

General ideas with very wide applications

The subject is called cybernetics

homeostasis

*J. M. Keynes,
English economist
(1872–1945)*

QUESTION 50

It is important to realize that the ideas about control systems, which are described in an entirely qualitative way here, have in fact been developed very fully mathematically, and they can be applied in many fields. In biology there are many systems which function to maintain an organism in the same state. The functioning of a (capitalist) economic system is thought to be explicable in terms of feedback – the interaction of supply and demand, and so on. And, at least according to one school of thought, the economic system can be controlled – that is, its output (goods, services) brought to a desired level by adjustments to the feedback and input (investment, taxation, and so on).

The same basic ideas have been applied to all these, and many more apparently diverse systems.

Section I3

QUESTIONS 47, 49

EXPERIMENT I16
Putting electronics to use

PUTTING ELECTRONICS TO USE

Electronics is such an essential part of technology today, that it would be as difficult to make a classified list of applications as it would to try to list applications of mechanical devices. The power of electronics lies in the way in which essentially simple building blocks can be assembled into systems. Basic devices such as transistors lead to integrated circuits. These lead to specific units such as amplifiers and signal generators, and these in turn are assembled, for example, into radio and television transmitters and receivers, radar systems, radio telescope receivers, and recorders. Devices can be constructed for monitoring electrically a wide variety of variables (position, velocity, acceleration, flow rate, strain, pressure, temperature, humidity, illumination, noise level, vibration), and these can be linked at a simple level to warning systems for human operators, or to automatic control systems which need no human intervention.

The field of control engineering embraces manufacturing systems, navigation (radar, automatic pilot), electrical power generation and distribution, air traffic control, medicine (pacemakers, life support systems), transport (road traffic control, railway signalling, automated railway sidings), high-energy physics (particle accelerators and detectors), and a host of other essential activities and services. The 'mini-projects' suggested in the Laboratory notes are a selection of real-world problems from the fields of instrumentation, communications, computing, and automatic control.

READING

MAKING MEASUREMENTS IN HOSTILE ENVIRONMENTS

(This passage is adapted from NOLTINGK, B. E., *Physics in technology*, Vol. **10**, 1979.)

Instrumentation is sometimes needed operationally, to provide data for controlling plant: this may be minute-by-minute adjustments or perhaps occasional checks against malfunctioning. It is sometimes needed for research purposes, to study behaviour that is not completely understood.

In conventional boilers it is desirable, but very difficult, to know the heat flux (that is, flow) from the flames on different parts of the tubes which form the walls. The principle of a heat-flux meter can be simple enough: measuring with a pair of thermocouples the temperature drop across a known thermal resistance gives the 'heat' flowing through it. The difficulty comes in translating that into practice. The thermocouple leads must follow a route where they will not be too vulnerable. Implicit assumptions about the direction of heat flow must not cause invalidities in the calculations or in the deductions from any calibration.

Some materials in generating plant are used near their limits of strength. It is not surprising, therefore, that there is a call to study behaviour in service. Structural engineers are accustomed to using bonded resistance strain gauges in surveys, but conventional gauges exhibit too much drift to be effective for measuring static strains at temperatures above 300 °C or 400 °C. Accordingly, a new type of strain gauge has been developed in which the strain to be measured changes an electrical capacitance instead of a resistance. This has the advantage of escaping from critical dependence on a material property – resistivity – that has proved very difficult to hold constant and consistent in severe environments. Capacitance can be made to depend almost exclusively on shape and size, allowing dimensional stability to be the one quality asked of the materials from which the gauge is made.

Figure I23 gives an exploded view of the device. The feet of the two arches are welded together and then welded on the structure to be examined. Strain in that structure differentially alters the height of the arches, thus changing the separation of the electrodes mounted between them and so changing their capacitance.

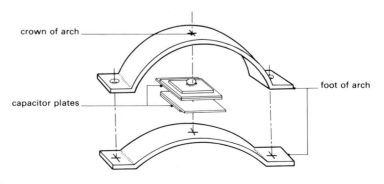

crown of arch

foot of arch

capacitor plates

Figure I23
Exploded view of a capacitor strain gauge
for use at high temperatures.

By taking great care over materials and construction techniques it has been found possible for the gauge to retain its dimensions and hence the strain it indicates, even over long periods at temperatures up to 600 °C. It has thus opened up new possibilities for studying creep and thermal strains and the cracking they may cause.

Measurements of small movements are often desirable at the phase of investigating questionable performance. One method uses a novel configuration that allows a gap to be measured using the fringing capacitance between two electrodes that are both placed on the same side of the gap.

Questions

a Give an example of data being needed
  i 'to control plant',
  ii to provide 'occasional checks against malfunctioning'.

b *i* Explain in simple descriptive terms why 'heat flux' can be deduced from two thermocouple readings.
  ii In what units is thermal resistance measured?

c One place where assumptions have to be made about the 'direction of heat flow' through a wall would be near to a corner. Draw a sketch to illustrate this, and explain how different assumptions would lead to different conclusions about the flux.

d What is meant by 'drift'?

e Explain in a simple case how capacitance is related to 'shape and size'.

f 'Dimensional stability' is 'the one quality asked of the materials'. Explain this statement in simple language.

g Draw 'before' and 'after' diagrams showing the changes that occur in this type of strain gauge when the structure it is welded to is strained.

h How can 'thermal strains' (or 'creep and thermal strains') result in cracking?

i Explain in principle how you think a gap width could be monitored using 'fringing capacitance'.

LABORATORY NOTES

NOTE ON APPARATUS LISTS IN UNIT I

For each experiment you are told in the list what values of *potentiometers*, *resistors*, or *capacitors* are needed. You may find that these are already fitted where you want them on the operational amplifier units. If they are not, then use separate components and clip component holders.

DEMONSTRATION
I1 Introduction to linear electronics and control

I1a Manual control of illumination

I1b Automatic control of illumination

I1c Light follower

Essential parts of any control system include a sensor or transducer, a feedback path, and some means of comparing two signals. Try to identify these components in each of the demonstrations you see.

Why is a power amplifier necessary in many control systems? If the system includes an operational amplifier, what is its function?

A control system may start to oscillate in certain circumstances. What factor or factors may cause this?

The demonstrations will be repeated later, and details are given under demonstrations I13 and I15.

EXPERIMENT
I2 Introduction to operational amplifiers

operational amplifier unit with power supply and resistors, $10\,\mathrm{k\Omega}$, $100\,\mathrm{k\Omega}$
potentiometer, *e.g.* $1\,\mathrm{k\Omega}$ linear
leads

Figure I25 (page 100) shows the basic circuit for many operational amplifier experiments. The diagram does not show the power supply, but you must make sure that the power supply is correctly connected to the three terminals marked $+$, 0 (or earth), and $-$. If you have a special power supply it will have sockets marked appropriately. If you are using dry cells then connect them as in figure I24.

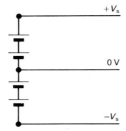

Figure I24

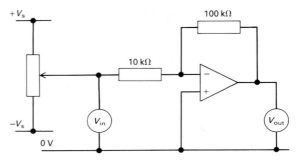

Figure I25
Circuit for experiment I2a (power supply connections not shown).

In each experiment (I2a to I2e) answer the questions, concerning th
output voltage V_{out} and the input voltage V_{in} (these voltages are alway
measured with respect to the 0 V power line).

I2a Input and output voltages

Apparatus as for experiment I2 with:
either
2 voltmeters, 1 V, 10 V d.c.
or
oscilloscope
voltmeter

Use the potential divider to vary the input voltage (figure I25). Tr
positive and negative values, up to the + and − power supply voltage
Use a voltmeter or oscilloscope to measure V_{in}, V_{out}. What is th
maximum value of V_{out}? What is the minimum value? When is V_o
positive? When is it negative?

I2b Response to a.c.

Apparatus as for experiment I2 with:
either
signal generator
or
transformer

oscilloscope

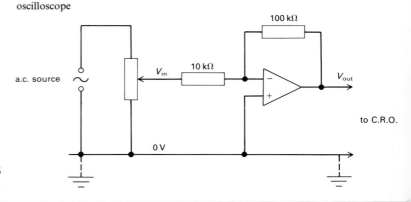

Figure I26
Operational amplifier with a.c. input.

Use the circuit of figure I26. Note that the a.c. source and potential divider are now connected to the 0 V line, not to $+V_s$ and $-V_s$. If your source is a signal generator with one side earthed, this side must be connected to the 0 V line, and so must the earthed terminal of the oscilloscope (see dashed lines in figure I26). If your source is a transformer, use its 2 V output.

Use the potential divider to increase the input steadily from zero, and observe what happens to the output signal on the oscilloscope. Does its behaviour confirm or add anything to your observations in experiment I2a?

I2c   Effect of changing input resistance

Apparatus as for experiment I2 with:
either
resistance substitution box
or
additional resistors

Use the circuit shown in figure I25. What difference does it make to the behaviour of the circuit when the value of the input resistance (the $10\,k\Omega$ resistor in figure I25) is: *i* halved; *ii* doubled; *iii* multiplied by 10?

I2d   Effect of changing feedback resistance

Apparatus as for experiment I2 with:
either
resistance substitution box
or
additional resistors

Use the circuit of figure I25. What difference does it make to the behaviour of the circuit when the value of the feedback resistance (the $100\,k\Omega$ resistor in figure I25) is: *i* doubled; *ii* halved; *iii* divided by 10?

I2e   Amplifier circuit with two inputs (optional)

Apparatus as for experiment I2 with:
potentiometer, *e.g.* $1\,k\Omega$ linear

either
resistor, $10\,k\Omega$
or
resistance substitution box

either
voltmeter
or
oscilloscope

Use the circuit of figure I27 (page 102), in which each input resistance is $10\,k\Omega$. How does the output voltage depend on the input voltages, separately and together?

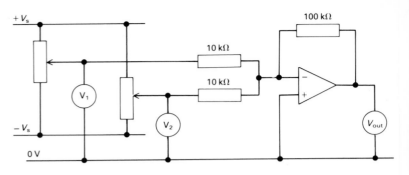

Figure I27
Operational amplifier circuit with
two inputs.

DEMONSTRATION

I3 Behaviour of a feedback amplifier circuit

operational amplifier unit with power supply and resistors, $10\,k\Omega$, $100\,k\Omega$
signal generator
double-beam oscilloscope
leads

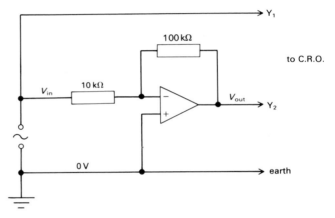

Figure I28
Measurement of input and output
voltages on double-beam oscilloscope.

Note that the earthed side of the signal generator and also that of the
oscilloscope must be connected to 0 V.

It is helpful to have the oscilloscope's time-base switched off for
parts of this demonstration.

Set up a demonstration to show (visually, not by detailed graph
plotting) that $V_{out} \propto - V_{in}$; that there is an upper (and lower) limit to the
value of V_{out}; that a small sinusoidal signal is faithfully amplified, but a
bigger one is not.

If there is time, show the effect of changing the value of either of the
resistors. What is the amplification factor when the resistors are equal?

EXPERIMENT

I4 Input–output characteristic of a feedback amplifier circuit

operational amplifier unit with power supply and resistors, $10\,k\Omega$, $100\,k\Omega$
potentiometer, *e.g.* $1\,k\Omega$ linear
voltmeter, 1 V d.c.
voltmeter, 10 V d.c.
leads

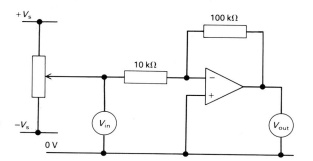

Figure 129
Measurement of input–output
characteristics.

Use the potential divider connected across the operational amplifier power supply to provide a variable input voltage, V_{in}. Plot a graph of V_{out} against V_{in} for the whole range of possible input voltages.

What is the slope of the graph (where it is a straight line)?

If you have time, repeat the experiment with other resistors.

OPTIONAL DEMONSTRATION

I5 Investigation of currents and voltages in an operational amplifier

operational amplifier unit with power supply and resistors, $10\,k\Omega$, $100\,k\Omega$
potentiometer, *e.g.* $1\,k\Omega$ linear
leads

I5a Currents

Apparatus as for demonstration I5 with:
2 microammeters, $100\,\mu A$

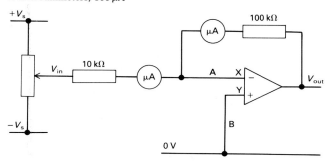

Figure I30
Measurement of currents.

Connect the circuit of figure I30.

According to an operational amplifier's specification the input resistance is very high, and in analysing operational amplifier circuits we usually assume that no current enters or leaves the device itself.

Use the microammeter readings to show that the current through the $100\,k\Omega$ resistor is the same as that through the $10\,k\Omega$ resistor. (How small a difference between these currents could you detect?)

If the connections to the unit allow, move one of your meters to the point A and verify that no detectable current is present.

You may also want to check for any current in the lead to the non-inverting input, by inserting a meter at B.

I5b Voltages

Apparatus as for experiment I5 with:
2 voltmeters

Another assumption made in predicting the behaviour of operational amplifier circuits is that the potential difference between the inverting and non-inverting inputs is negligibly small. In your circuit the + terminal, Y, is connected to 0 V, so the inverting input, X, should also be virtually at 0 V.

Connect your voltmeters so as to measure V_{in} and V_{out} simultaneously. Use the voltmeter readings and the values of the input and feedback resistances to calculate the potential at A.

Why would it not be sensible simply to connect a voltmeter between A and the 0 V line? (Think about the input resistance of the operational amplifier.)

Assumptions and limits

Parts **a** and **b** of this demonstration were to check some assumptions which are *usually* true of operational amplifiers.

Try to find out (by varying the input voltage) when these approximations are valid and when they are not.

EXPERIMENT
I6 More uses of the feedback amplifier

This group of experiments deals with slightly more complicated operational amplifier circuits. Whichever experiment you do, *first* use what you know about the operational amplifier to predict the circuit's behaviour; *then* set up the circuit and check your predictions.

operational amplifier unit with power supply and resistors, 10 kΩ, 100 kΩ
potentiometer, *e.g.* 1 kΩ linear
2 voltmeters
leads

I6a Summing amplifier

Apparatus as for experiment I6 with:
potentiometer, *e.g.* 1 kΩ linear

either
2 resistance substitution boxes
or
additional resistors

either
voltmeter
or
oscilloscope

The two input voltages (V_A and V_B) can be varied independently.

Suppose all the resistors in the circuit (figure I31) have the same value

$(R_A = R_B = R_f = R)$. Derive an expression for V_{out} in terms of V_A and V_B. Then check it experimentally.

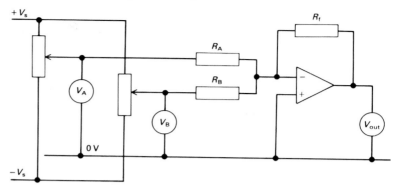

Suppose the values of the resistors are not equal. What is V_{out} in terms of V_A, V_B, R_A, R_B, and R_f? Use your result to set up a circuit for which $V_{out} = -10(V_A + V_B)$, and another one for which $V_{out} = -(10V_A + V_B)$.

I6b   Subtractor

Apparatus as for experiment I6 with:
operational amplifier unit with resistors, 100 kΩ, 100 kΩ, 100 kΩ, 100 kΩ, 100 kΩ
potentiometer, *e.g.* 1 kΩ linear

either
voltmeter
or
oscilloscope

A feedback amplifier can be used to multiply an input voltage by a constant (negative) factor: $V_{out} = -kV_{in}$. If the input and feedback resistors are equal then $V_{out} = -V_{in}$.
    Use this as a starting point to design a circuit using two operational amplifiers and five equal resistors to subtract two voltages.

I6c   Integration

Apparatus as for experiment I6 with:
capacitor, 1 μF

either
switch
or
mounted bell push

stopwatch

With the switch open make sure that the capacitor is discharged. (See figure I32, page 106.) Then make the input voltage a few volts negative and observe what happens to V_{out} when the switch is closed.
    You should be able to explain what you have observed using what you know about the operational amplifier and capacitors.

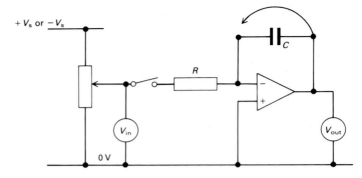

Figure I32
Integrator.

Check your explanation by trying other values of V_{in}, R, or C, and use the stopwatch to verify the exactness of the circuit's behaviour.

As an extension, change the component values to give a very rapid rate of change of output voltage (say 100 volts per second) and for input V_{in} use a signal generator set to square-wave output. Think out how you expect V_{out} to behave. Check your conclusions by using an oscilloscope.

I6d Differentiation

Apparatus as for experiment I6 with:
capacitance substitution box
oscilloscope
signal generator

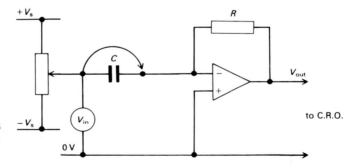

Figure I33
Operational amplifier circuit for
differentiation.

Use the oscilloscope to observe the output voltage. Start with $C = 1\,\mu F$ and $R = 1\,M\Omega$. Initially the capacitor should be discharged. What happens to V_{out} if V_{in} is changed to a new value quickly, or slowly? What effect do the values of R and C have on the behaviour of this circuit?

Use a signal generator to provide 'square-wave' or 'saw-tooth' input signals, and observe the output on the oscilloscope. Explain how the circuit acts to differentiate the input signal.

EXPERIMENT
I7 Using the non-inverting input

operational amplifier unit with power supply and resistors, 100 kΩ, 100 kΩ
voltmeter, 10 V d.c.
leads

In this series of experiments the input signal goes to the non-inverting input of the operational amplifier (marked + in the symbol for an operational amplifier), which is not connected to 0 V as in the previous experiments. There is feedback from the output to the inverting input, which may be connected to 0 V through a resistor. Figure I34 shows a typical circuit.

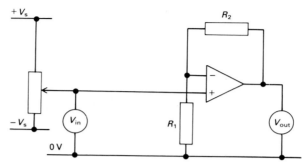

Figure I34
Using the non-inverting input.

I7a   Follower circuit with variable gain

Apparatus as for experiment I7 with:
potentiometer, *e.g.* 1 kΩ linear
voltmeter

either
2 resistance substitution boxes
or
additional resistors

Start with $R_1 = R_2 = 100\,\text{k}\Omega$.

Use a potentiometer to vary the input voltage V_{in}; try positive and negative values.

What is the relationship between V_{out} and V_{in} for this circuit?

Is the term 'non-inverting' appropriate for this input?

You should be able to explain why the circuit behaves as it does, and predict the ratio V_{out}/V_{in} for other values of R_1 and R_2. (Questions **28** and **29** might help.)

Test your predictions.

What would happen if $R_2 = 0$ or R_1 is infinite?

Set up this circuit and test your prediction.

Why is 'voltage follower' an appropriate name for this circuit?

I7b   Input and output currents of voltage follower

Apparatus as for experiment I7 plus:
potentiometer, 5 kΩ or 10 kΩ linear
milliammeter, 10 mA d.c.
microammeter, 100 μA d.c.

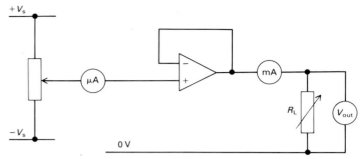

Figure 135
Input and output currents of voltage follower.

Use one potentiometer as a potential divider to vary the input. The other, used as a variable load resistance R_L, is connected between the output terminal and 0 V.

For a fixed value of R_L, how does the output current depend on the input current?

For a fixed value of input voltage, how does the output current depend on R_L?

How large an output current can we take, if the output voltage is not to drop by more than 1 %? 20 %?

If output current is much greater than input current, where does the extra current come from?

Suggest a use for this circuit.

I7c   Use of voltage follower circuit

Apparatus as for experiment I7 plus:
capacitor, 50 μF
cell holder with one cell

Charge the capacitor to 1.5 V and then connect the voltmeter across its terminals. What happens to the voltmeter reading? Why?

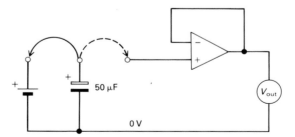

Figure 136
Unity-gain voltage follower.

Now try again using the unity-gain voltage follower circuit as a buffer between the capacitor and voltmeter (figure I36). Charge the capacitor, then connect it to the input of the circuit.

What happens to the voltmeter reading this time? You should be able to explain the effect of the buffer circuit, and suggest other uses for it. At least one piece of equipment you are familiar with incorporates a buffer circuit.

EXPERIMENT

I8 Integrator with feedback

operational amplifier unit with power supply and resistor, 1 MΩ, capacitor, 1 μF
oscilloscope
leads

I8a Negative feedback: solving $dV/dt = -V/RC$

Apparatus as for experiment I8 plus:
cell holder with four cells

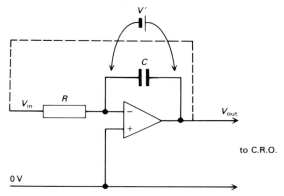

Figure I37
Integrator with feedback.

Without the feedback wire (shown dashed in figure I37) the output of
the integrator circuit is

$$V_{out} = -\frac{1}{RC} \int V_{in} \, dt + \text{constant}$$

(see experiment I6c). Or we can write

$$dV_{out}/dt = -V_{in}/RC.$$

The rate of change of the output depends on the size of the input.

If the output is connected to the input by a feedback wire then
$V_{out} = V_{in} (= V$, say). So $dV/dt = -V/RC$. This should be a familiar
equation and you should know its solution (*i.e.*, how V varies with t).

Set up the circuit and display V against t on the oscilloscope. You
will need to have a starting value of V: the capacitor must be charged at
the start of the experiment using the cell (V').

What would be the effect of increasing R and/or C? Or of decreasing
either?

If possible, check your prediction.

I8b Positive feedback: solving $dV/dt = V/RC$

Apparatus as for experiment I8 plus:
operational amplifier with resistors, 100 kΩ, 100 kΩ

The circuit shown in figure I37 solves $dV/dt = -V/RC$. A feedback
amplifier circuit can be used to multiply an input by -1. Use these two

ideas to build a circuit using two operational amplifiers with feedback to solve $dV/dt = + V/RC$. You will need a lead to discharge the capacitor first.

This is the rate-of-change equation for exponential growth. A quantity which is growing exponentially continues to grow indefinitely, and at an ever-increasing rate. Does your circuit model this behaviour accurately? Can you explain any differences?

DEMONSTRATION
I9 A circuit to produce oscillation

3 operational amplifier units with power supply and resistors, 1 MΩ, 1 MΩ, 1 MΩ, 1 MΩ, and capacitors 1 μF, 1 μF
cell holder with one cell
double-beam oscilloscope
2 resistance substitution boxes
2 capacitance substitution boxes
leads

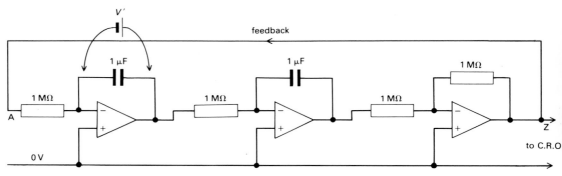

Figure I38
Circuit to produce oscillation.

This circuit should produce oscillation when a feedback connection is made by a piece of wire between Z and A. (If it does not start to oscillate try applying 1.5 V momentarily across one of the capacitors.)

Measure the frequency of the oscillation. The circuit consists of three sub-circuits you are familiar with. What does each unit do? Imagine that a sinusoidal signal is fed into the circuit at A. How will it be changed by each of the units?

How will the signal at Z compare with the signal at A? What is the effect of feedback from Z to A?

Use the double-beam oscilloscope to compare the output of each unit with its input to check your answers to the questions above.

How could you change the frequency of the oscillation? Try it! What change(s) or addition(s) would you need to make to produce a 'square-wave' output?

DEMONSTRATION

I10 Feedback in public address systems

operational amplifier unit with power supply

either
potentiometer, 1 MΩ
or
resistance substitution box

microphone
small loudspeaker (not earpiece)
leads

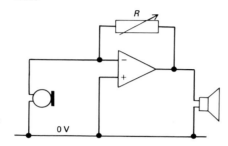

Figure I39
Howl produced by positive feedback.

0 V

Figure I39 shows the circuit; the loudspeaker and microphone should initially be about 1 m apart. You may have to cover the microphone with your hand to prevent the system from oscillating.

Show that the circuit is acting as an amplifier, by scratching the microphone.

Investigate the oscillation behaviour by:

a changing the gain by adjusting R, and

b putting loudspeaker and microphone close together and then moving them slowly apart.

OPTIONAL DEMONSTRATION

I11 Oscillation in a feedback system

3 operational amplifier units with power supply and resistors, 100 kΩ, 100 kΩ or 1 MΩ, 1 MΩ
potentiometer
4 resistance substitution boxes
2 capacitance substitution boxes
signal generator
oscilloscope
cell holder with one cell
leads

To the circuit of demonstration I9 two things are added: an extra input from the signal generator, and an extra feedback loop from the output of the first operational amplifier to the input resistor S_2 (see figure I40, page 112). In terms of a mechanical system, this is equivalent to adding an extra force to a moving object, proportional to its velocity and in the opposite direction, that is, frictional damping.

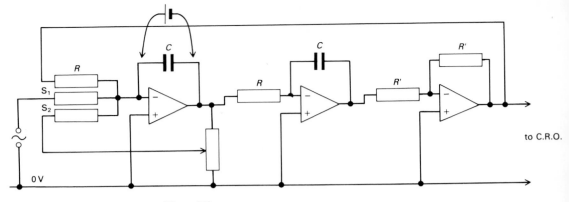

Figure I40
Oscillation in a feedback system.

Resistances R' should be equal: 1 MΩ or 100 kΩ. Choose values of C and R to give a frequency of around 150 Hz (*e.g.* 0.001 μF and 1 MΩ). S_1 and S_2 should have the same resistance as R. Switch off the signal generator and adjust the feedback potentiometer for zero feedback. Touch the leads from the 1.5 V cell briefly across the capacitor as indicated in figure I40: this should start the oscillation. This needs to be made to die away within about 10 seconds, and to achieve this you may have to adjust the feedback potentiometer or change the value of S_2.

Now switch on the signal generator and set it to about 150 Hz. Vary the frequency around this value, and observe on the oscilloscope how the circuit behaves. Try increasing or decreasing the damping. Try disconnecting the signal generator and connecting 1.5 V d.c. in its place.

DEMONSTRATION
I12 On–off control of illumination

operational amplifier unit with power supply not more than + 6, 0, − 6 V (see below)
light-dependent resistor
potentiometer, 1 kΩ linear
2 general-purpose diodes
relay
lamp (12 V, 24 W) and holder

either
l.t. variable voltage supply
or
transformer

leads

Note that the power supply to the operational amplifier needs here to be + 6, 0, − 6 V, in order to operate the relay.

In this demonstration the operational amplifier is functioning simply as a (digital) logic gate. What kind of gate is it?

When the input to the relay is low the contacts are open; when it goes high they close and the lamp goes on. (Why is a relay needed – why not use the gate to control the lamp directly?)

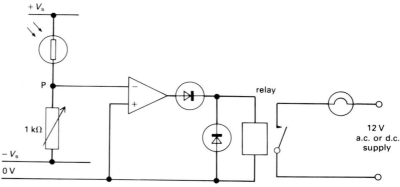

Figure I41
On–off control of illumination.

Why should this circuit make the lamp come on in the dark, that is if little or no light falls on the light-dependent resistor? Try it.

What happens if light from the lamp itself falls on the transducer? Try this, and explain what you observe.

What controls the level of darkness at which the light comes on?

Why can't this system be used to provide a controlled level of illumination?

DEMONSTRATION
I13 Continuous control of illumination

operational amplifier with power supply and resistors, 1 kΩ, 1 kΩ, 10 kΩ, 10 kΩ, 100 kΩ, 100 kΩ, 100 kΩ
potentiometer, *e.g.* 1 kΩ linear
2 lamps, 12 V, 24 W
2 light-dependent resistors (L.D.R.s)

either
ohmmeter
or
cell holder with one cell and milliammeter

power amplifier
2 variable power supplies, 0–25 V d.c.
leads
retort stand base, rod, 2 bosses, 2 clamps

A fairly dark room is needed to make the best of this demonstration. The circuit is shown in figure I42 (page 114). The operational amplifier supply voltage could be any value down to $+3, 0, -3$ V. R_A will need to be 1 kΩ, 10 kΩ, and 100 kΩ in turn (see below). R_B should be 100 kΩ throughout, to avoid making the 'set level' control too sensitive. (In the unlikely event of the set level range being insufficient, R_B can be changed to 10 kΩ.) Long leads will be needed to L.D.R.$_1$ and to the controlled lamp L_C.

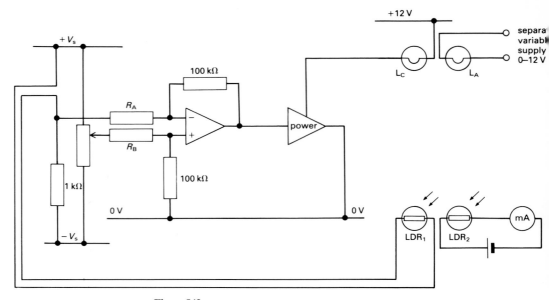

Figure I42
Automatic control of illumination.

Arrangement
The two lamps should be fixed as close together as possible about 50 cm
above bench level, with the L.D.R.s close together on the bench below
them, facing upwards. The meter for L.D.R.$_2$ should also be where light
will fall on it.

Adjustment
Set R_A at 1 kΩ. Turn up the lamp L_A to full brightness. Turn up the
voltage of the power amplifier supply to 12 V. Turn the potentiometer
to maximum positive potential, so that L_C is bright. Further raise the
power amplifier supply voltage as necessary until L_C is as bright as L_A.
Finally, adjust the potentiometer again until L_C is only just visible,
glowing dull red.

Demonstration
Gradually turn down the brightness of L_A. L_C should brighten, and the
meter reading should change very little, if at all. Show by covering
L.D.R.$_1$ that it is controlling the brightness of L_C. Show by making
rapid changes in the light from L_A (including interposing the hand or
even switching off and on) that the system corrects instantly and
precisely – much better than a human operator.

It might be worth increasing R_A to 10 kΩ and then 100 kΩ, to see
how a reduction in gain produces less than total compensation for
changes in ambient illumination.

Questions

What is the purpose of L.D.R.$_2$?

Suppose L$_A$ is made brighter. What effect will this have on L.D.R.$_1$? On the potential applied to R$_A$? On the output potential of the operational amplifier? On the brightness of L$_C$? Why does the change in brightness eventually stop? How long do you think it takes for all this to happen?

DEMONSTRATION

I14 Temperature control with thermal inertia

operational amplifier with power supply and resistors, 1 kΩ, 100 kΩ, 100 kΩ, 100 kΩ
potentiometer, *e.g.* 1 kΩ linear

either
capacitor, *e.g.* 0.001 μF
or
capacitance substitution box

resistance substitution box
bead thermistor, *e.g.* GL23, 2 kΩ–115 Ω
aluminium foil
dull black paint (Aquadag)
lamp, holder, and stand
voltmeter, 12 V d.c.
power amplifier
l.t. variable voltage supply
leads

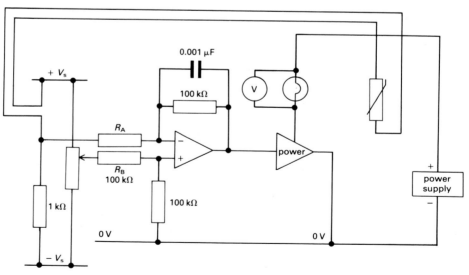

Figure I43
Temperature control with thermal inertia.

gure I44
hermistor mounting.

Preparation

Cut a piece of cooking foil about 2 cm × 1 cm, fold it in half and press it tightly round the thermistor as shown in figure I44. Paint one side dull black. Mount the thermistor level with the 24 W lamp, with the black surface facing the lamp and about 1 cm away from it.

Notes

i The behaviour of this circuit will inevitably depend on such loca factors as the degree of thermal contact between thermistor and for and on the precise characteristics of the power amplifier, so som modifications may have to be imposed on the notes given below.

ii A possible variation is to cover the thermistor and lamp with a inverted beaker, representing a miniature 'room' being heated. Th transfer of energy from lamp to thermistor will then probably depen more on convection than on radiation.

The circuit is shown in figure I43 (page 115). The operational amplifie supply voltage can be any value down to $+3, 0, -3$ V. R_A should be th resistance substitution box, set initially at $100\,k\Omega$. R_B remains at $100\,k\Omega$. The 'set level' adjustment of the potentiometer is very sensitive and ca be disturbed by capacitive effects due to a hand nearby: the feedbac capacitor serves to eliminate this disturbance, and its value is no critical. Long leads will be needed to the thermistor and to the lamp

Adjustment

Set the power amplifier supply to $0\,V$. Turn the potentiometer t maximum positive potential, then raise the power amplifier suppl voltage until the voltmeter shows 8 V. Carefully adjust the poten tiometer until the voltmeter reading falls to 5 V, and continue adjustin as necessary until the radiation feedback to the thermistor holds th reading at this value (response will be sluggish).

Now step up the power amplifier supply voltage by a few volts. Th voltmeter reading should rise, then be corrected within a few second back almost to 5 V. Further upward steps of power amplifier suppl voltage can now be made up to 25 V, and the feedback should continu to return the voltmeter reading fairly closely to 5 V.

The sequence should now be repeated with R_A at $47\,k\Omega$, $22\,k\Omega$, an $10\,k\Omega$, and this time the system should show damped oscillation at eac change of power voltage, and also if the set level is changed from 5 V t an adjacent value.

If the gain is raised to about 100 ($R_A = 1\,k\Omega$), the system shoul simply switch on and off indefinitely – it has become 'on–off' instead o 'continuous'.

Questions

Suppose the voltage of the power supply increases, brightening the lamp. What effect will this have on the thermistor? Will it be instantaneous? What will happen to the thermistor's resistance? To the potential applied to R_A? To the output of the operational amplifier? To the brightness of the lamp?

Why does increased gain lead to oscillation?

DEMONSTRATION
I15 Light follower

For first circuit (figure 145)
power amplifier
2 variable power supplies, 0–25 V d.c.
potentiometer, 1 kΩ linear
2 light-dependent resistors (L.D.R.s)

either
lamp 12 V, 24 W
or
other source of illumination, *e.g.* reading lamp

turntable and motor
insulating tape
leads

Additional for second circuit (figure 146)
operational amplifier with power supply and resistors, 10 kΩ, 10 kΩ, 100 kΩ, 100 kΩ, 100 kΩ

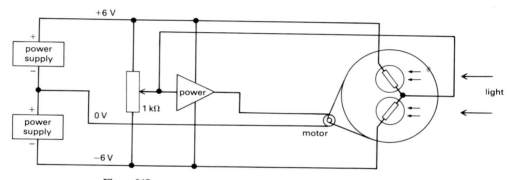

Figure I45
Light follower: first circuit.

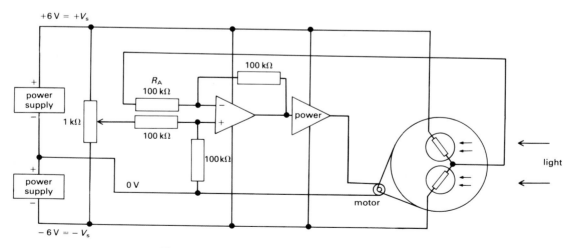

Figure I46
Light follower: second circuit.

Preparation

The two L.D.R.s should be taped firmly to a block of wood so that they face horizontally and are at 90° to one another. The three leads from them should be as light and as flexible as possible, and about 2 m long; 0.45 mm insulated copper wire is suitable. The block should not at first be put on the turntable.

Important note

The motor for the turntable can ordinarily be driven using dry cells since it needs little current. However, some simple power amplifier units provided for schools may draw very much more current than this (typically 3 A between + and − leads when supplying zero output current). Consequently, the 6 V supplies must be provided from two mains-operated power units, not from dry cells.

The circuits

A simple version is shown in figure I45, in which no operational amplifier is required. The zero setting is achieved by means of the potentiometer which biases the potential divider provided by the L.D.R.s. This circuit will respond to a 24 W lamp at distances up to 0.5–1 m away. For better sensitivity the circuit of figure I46 can be used, and in this circuit the operational amplifier requires + 6, 0, − 6 V, and can be powered from the same supplies as the power amplifier.

Adjustment

With the L.D.R.s on the bench and fairly equally illuminated, switch on both power supplies simultaneously (each at 6 V) and adjust the potentiometer until the turntable is stationary. Next place the block with the L.D.R.s on the centre of the turntable, and place a 24 W lamp or reading lamp facing it and about 0.5 m away. If the assembly rotates away from the light, reverse the motor leads. Make a fine adjustment of the potentiometer so that the L.D.R.s settle symmetrically facing the light, which they should then follow when it is moved.

There will probably be some 'overshoot' and even oscillation each time the lamp is moved to a new position. Possibly by exchanging the potentiometer in the first circuit for one of 10 kΩ or 100 kΩ, and certainly with the second circuit, oscillation will be more pronounced and the sensitivity will be greater. If the lamp is switched off, the turntable may hunt around and turn to face other sources of light, such as windows.

If the lamp is swung from side to side at different frequencies, the unit will attempt to follow, but at its resonant frequency it will be very obviously out of phase with the lamp movements.

If, in the second circuit, the gain is increased (by reducing the value of R_A), it is likely that the oscillation will start spontaneously and increase uncontrollably.

Questions

Suppose a light-dependent resistor is set facing a lamp. If it is now turned partly away from the lamp, what change will there be in the amount of light which it intercepts? What effect will this have on its resistance?

If the two L.D.R.s in this apparatus are equally inclined to the incoming light, their resistances will be equal. If the direction of the light changes, what will happen to the resistance of each? Explain why the potential at their common junction will change. Assuming the motor is connected the right way round, what effect will this have on the motor output, the orientation of the L.D.R.s, the light intercepted by each, and the resistance of each?

The turntable tends to overshoot when it moves. Why? Why does high gain increase this?

Information

Communications satellites need to keep their receiving and transmitting equipment accurately aligned on the Earth, *i.e.* to maintain the correct 'attitude'. This is achieved by having pairs of infra-red detectors which react to the thermal radiation from the Earth and provide a feedback signal to their attitude control systems.

INDIVIDUAL TASKS

I16 Putting electronics to use

Explanatory note

Most of your time so far in this Unit has been spent in getting to know how operational amplifiers behave and why, and in learning about the range of operations they can be made to perform: amplification, addition, integration, etc. – that is, pure electronics. At the same time you have seen that these operations have obvious potential for use in the world of applied science: they can be used to make things work.

We now look at this applied aspect, moving rather more into the field of the electrical engineer, whose job it is not only to know the theory, but to be able to put it to practical use as well.

The following selection of practical problems gives you the chance to make something work. Each of the problems listed below gives you an objective, and each can be solved using the knowledge of electronics which you should now have. How you solve the problem is up to you – often several equally good solutions are possible.

One important point: the worst possible engineering practice is to act first and think afterwards. The first thing an engineer reaches for is pencil and paper, and you must do the same. Think first, plan your solution, and sketch it on paper, so that you are as sure as you can be that it will actually work. Only when you have done that is it the time to build and test your system.

List A: easier

A1 Make a 4-digit digital-to-analogue converter with four input switches to represent the binary numbers and the analogue output registering on a meter (see question **21**, page 133).

A2 Make a light meter, assuming that the resistance of a light-dependent resistor is inversely proportional to light intensity (which it very nearly is). The meter should have two ranges, one for dim lighting and one for brighter conditions.

A3 Make an ohmmeter which gives directly the value of a resistance as a linear reading on a meter scale. Provide two ranges.

A4 Make a high-impedance voltmeter in one or more of the ways listed

a a simple follower;
b an inverting amplifier (provide ranges 0.1 V, 1 V, and 10 V);
c use a non-inverting circuit and use an ammeter in the feedback loop as your measure of voltage.

You could use your meter to measure the e.m.f. generated by a photovoltaic cell, and you could verify the circuit's high input impedance by trying to measure the p.d. across a charged capacitor.

A5 Set up a comparator (see question **37**, page 141) as a switch for one of the purposes below. For a warning signal use a lamp, a light-emitting diode, a bell, a buzzer, or an 'audible warning device'. Suggestions for applications:

a to switch on traffic bollard lights as daylight fades;
b to warn if temperature gets too high, or too low (and possibly to switch on a heater);
c to warn if water level becomes too high;
d to warn when a kettle emits steam.

A6 Make an intercom between two stations, in which each has an earpiece or small loudspeaker which also acts as a microphone, and can be switched from 'speak' to 'receive'. The amplifier is situated at one of the two stations. Special points:

a When an amplifier is used for a.c. it may be desirable to feed into it and out of it via capacitors; try 0.1 µF.
b You may need to provide a second stage of amplification, since neither earpiece nor loudspeaker are likely to be very efficient as microphones.

A7 Make an a.c. signal mixer with fade-in facility, *i.e.* two inputs with variable gains down to zero, giving mixed output in any proportion. *Note:* when an amplifier is used for a.c. it may be desirable to feed into it and out of it via capacitors; try 0.1 µF.

A8 Make a short-interval timer to measure times of a few thousandths of a second. Use it to measure the contact time in some bouncing process. An integrator is recommended, and a reset button will be required. Adapt your circuit to measure human reaction time.

List B: harder

B1 Make a direct reading fluxmeter. When a coil of N turns is moved into a magnetic field so that a flux change of Φ becomes linked with it, the e.m.f. induced in the coil is $\mathscr{E} = Nd\Phi/dt$. Try a 5000-turn lateral search coil and a strong magnet at first.

Extension

When a piece of iron is placed in an increasingly strong magnetic field, B_0, the flux density in the iron, B, increases until magnetic saturation is reached, and will then increase no further. If the applied field is reduced to zero, B will decrease but not to zero – there will be 'residual magnetization' which can only be removed using a reverse field. The total behaviour of a magnetic material can be studied by putting it in an alternating field and monitoring the changes in B.

Figure I47 shows a typical result, which is called a magnetization cycle. Try various combinations of 240- and 1100-turn coils side by side (co-axially) with a short iron rod (say 5 cm long) inside them. Feed a.c. (maximum 4 V, from a mains transformer) into one coil and use the other as a search coil. Use Ext X on an oscilloscope to plot B_0, with B as Y deflection.

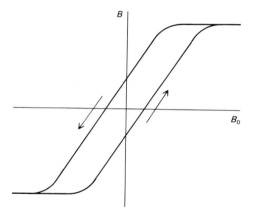

Figure I47
Magnetization cycle.

B2 Use a comparator (see question **37**, page 141) as a bridge balance detector in a Wheatstone bridge circuit. The power supply for the bridge could be the + and − supply to the operational amplifier, *but* the resistances must be large enough to prevent current drain on the supply being more than 100 mA. If this is not possible, extra resistors must be included between the bridge and the supply.

The output of the comparator will flick from one saturated state to the other on either side of the balance point (and you might consider how the meter could be replaced by a pair of light-emitting diodes, one for each direction of the output, thus saving weight, space, and cost). In order to *measure* changes in resistance you will need to have a standard resistance box as one of the arms of the bridge, and adjust it for balance each time the resistance changes. Alternatively, you could use a differential amplifier (see question **35**, page 140) in place of the comparator, so that small changes in resistance show as changes in the output meter reading, which can then be calibrated to read ohms or fractions of an ohm.

Suggested uses are:

a Measure the change in resistance as a wire is strained.

b Set up a resistance thermometer. (Note that resistance wire such as constantan is no use, being designed to have negligible temperature coefficient: a pure metal is needed. As an alternative there is always the thermistor, though obviously this would be unsuitable for high temperatures.)

c Make a hot-wire anemometer: one of the arms of the bridge is a thin wire made warm by the current through it. It cools in a current of air, changing its resistance.

B3   Make up an analogue computing circuit for one of the following:

a vertical motion under gravity, with means of starting the motion with any chosen values of height and of initial velocity;

b radioactive decay: A decays into B which decays into stable C;

c radioactive decay: A is being produced at a virtually steady rate from a substance with enormously long half-life. A decays into B which is also radioactive. Start from the point where all of A and B have been extracted from the mixture, and will begin to appear again.

B4   Make an oscillator in which the frequency is determined by an *LC* resonant circuit.

B5   Make a timing device for a photographic enlarger which will start when the lamp is switched on and will switch it off after a pre-determined time (normally a few seconds).

B6   Make a capacitance meter which gives a direct reading on a meter scale.

B7   Make a system to control the temperature of something by controlling a heater.

B8   Make a system to control the temperature of a heated object by means of a fan which cools it.

B9   Make a linear variable transformer to display the position of its core as a reading on a d.c. meter, and possibly to control or measure something.

Two coils are set side by side, with the movable iron core (any suitable short rod) inside them, as shown in figure I48. Alternating current is supplied to one coil, and the position of the core determines the amplitude of the alternating e.m.f. induced in the other coil.

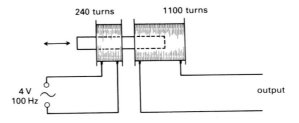

240 turns   1100 turns

4 V
100 Hz

output

Figure I48
Linear variable transformer.

B10 Make a variable-reluctance transducer, in which very small movements of a piece of iron change an a.c. voltage. This in turn is made to change a d.c. current which is used to measure or control something.

B11 Use an operational amplifier to make an astable multivibrator (see question **38**, page 142) whose frequency depends upon one of the following:

a temperature
b illumination
c water level.

B12 Make a system to maintain a constant current in spite of variations in supply voltage.

QUESTIONS

Potential difference, current, and resistance

1(I)a Two resistors (R_1, R_2) are connected across a power supply giving a p.d. of V (figure I49). What is the potential at A (*i.e.* the potential difference between point A and 0 V)? (Assume no current through the voltmeter.)

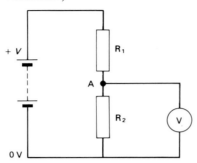

Figure I49

b Suppose $V = 10$ V, $R_1 = 5$ kΩ, $R_2 = 10$ kΩ. What is the potential at A?

c Using the same values as in part **b**, calculate the current in the resistors.

d Suppose that R_1 is changed to 50 kΩ and R_2 to 100 kΩ. What is the potential at A now? What is the current in the resistors?

2(I) What is the potential difference between the two ends of the resistor shown in figure I50?

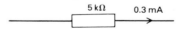

Figure I50

3(I) In figure I51 the current in each resistor is the same.

a What is the total p.d. across both resistors?

b What is the ratio of the p.d.s across the two (V_1/V_2)?

c Suppose the current is doubled. Will the values of **a** or **b** change?

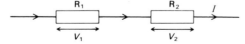

Figure I51

4(I) An operational amplifier with negative feedback has the remarkable property of holding the potential at a point in a circuit fixed at very nearly 0 V (earth), but *without any current flowing to or from earth* at that point. So in figure I52 point X is held at 0 V, although there is no current to earth at this point, and hence the current in the two resistors is the same.

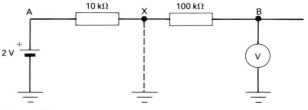

Figure I52

The potential at A is $+2$ V, *i.e.* there is a p.d. of 2 V between A and earth.

a   What is the current in the 10 kΩ resistor?

b   What is the current in the 100 kΩ resistor?

c   What is the p.d. across the 100 kΩ resistor?

d   Which end of the 100 kΩ resistor is at the higher potential, X or B?

e   Is the potential at B positive or negative, *i.e.* is it above or below 0 V?

This circuit is sometimes compared to a see-saw. Point X is fixed, and if the potential at one end goes up the potential at the other goes down, and vice versa.

f   Suggest resistor values that would make the changes at the two ends of the see-saw equal in magnitude, *i.e.* if A goes down by 2 V, B goes up by 2 V.

Capacitors

5(I)   How much charge is stored on a 10 μF capacitor when the p.d. across it is

a   2 V?

b   10 V?

6(I)   A steady current of 0.1 mA is used to charge a capacitor.

a   How much charge goes on to the capacitor in 5 seconds?

b   The p.d. across the capacitor is now found to be 0.75 V. What is the capacitance of the capacitor?

c   Suggest how this p.d. might be measured. (Why would it not be a good idea to use a voltmeter?)

7(I)   Figure I53 represents a typical graph of charge against time for a capacitor being charged.

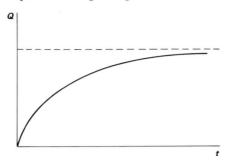

Figure I53

a   Sketch a graph showing how the current varies with time as the capacitor charges up.

b   What is the relationship between the two graphs?

Suppose the charging current is instead somehow maintained at a constant level.

c   How will the charge on the capacitor and the p.d. across it vary with time?

Operational amplifier circuit characteristic

8(P)   Say what you understand by the terms *inverting* and *limiting value* applied to an operational amplifier circuit.

9(P)   Figure I54(a) shows a graph of V_{out} against V_{in} for the operational amplifier circuit shown in figure I54(b).

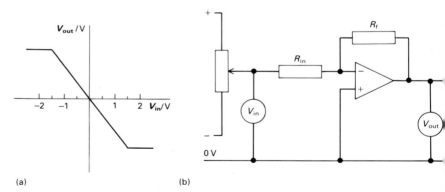

(a)   (b)

Figure I54

a   The sloping part of the graph is straight, downwards to the right, and goes through the origin. What important facts does this indicate about the amplifier?

b   The graph flattens at the ends. Describe accurately in words what this means about the way the output changes as the input is changed. (One sentence should suffice; two at the most.)

c What change(s) would occur in the graph if

  i R_f were unchanged but R_{in} halved in value;

  ii R_{in} were unchanged but R_f reduced to one third of its value;

  iii The supply voltage to the operational amplifier were increased?

10(P) An a.c. signal is applied to the input of the amplifier circuit whose voltage characteristic is sketched in figure I54(a). Sketch the output signal you would expect if the input had a peak-to-peak voltage of

a 1 V

b 4 V

11(E) A student is confused about *amplifiers* and *transformers*. Both seem to do the same thing – turn small voltages into big ones. Explain what the differences are.

The operational amplifier

12(P) The very high gain of an operational amplifier and its very high input resistance allow two simplifications to be made about its behaviour. What are they?

13(L) *Optional* The gain of an operational amplifier is often quoted in dB (decibels). The arithmetical gain A (ratio of output to input voltage) is related to the gain in dB by

$$\text{gain (dB)} = 20 \log_{10} A$$

a Calculate the gain in dB for $A = 10, 20, 40, 80$. You should see that the decibel gain increases by the same amount every time A is multiplied by a constant factor.

b What is A if the gain is 100 dB?

c What is A if the gain is 106 dB? (Use your answer to part **a** – there is no need to use logarithms.)

14(P) An operational amplifier has a voltage gain of 10^5, and an input resistance of 1 MΩ. When the output voltage is $+5$ V

a What is the differential input voltage, the p.d. between non-inverting and inverting terminals $V_+ - V_-$?

b What will the input current be?

15(L) Question **14** showed that for output voltages V_{out} of a few volts, the p.d. between X and Y (figure I55, page 128) is a small number of microvolts, and the current taken by the operational amplifier is a small number of picoamperes. For a large range of uses to which the operational amplifier is put, these are regarded as negligible. In this question you are to assume that both are *zero*.

a In figure I55, Y is connected to 0 V. What is the p.d. between X and 0 V?

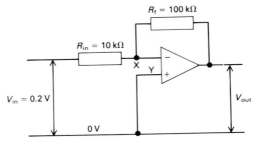

Figure I55

b What then is the p.d. across the $10\,\mathrm{k}\Omega$ input resistor?

c What will be the current through this resistor?

d Since no current enters or leaves the operational amplifier at X, what is the current through the $100\,\mathrm{k}\Omega$ feedback resistor?

e What then will be the p.d. across this resistor?

f V_{in} is $+0.2\,\mathrm{V}$, that is, positive with respect to $0\,\mathrm{V}$. What is the sign of the actual potential V_{out}?

g If instead of the values given, R_{in} and R_f were $100\,\mathrm{k}\Omega$ and $1\,\mathrm{M}\Omega$ respectively, and the input voltage V_{in} were still $0.2\,\mathrm{V}$, what would be the current through these resistors?

h What would the output voltage V_{out} be?

16(L) In this question you are to make the assumptions explained in the paragraph at the beginning of question **15**. The circuit concerned here is that of figure I56 in which the potentials marked are all with respect to $0\,\mathrm{V}$.

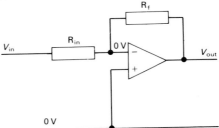

Figure I56

a In terms of the quantities given on the diagram, what is the *fall* in potential (left to right) across R_{in}?

b What then is the current (from left to right) in R_{in}?

c In terms of the quantities given on the diagram, what is the *fall* in potential (from left to right) across R_f?

d What therefore (in terms of these same quantities) is the current (from left to right) in R_f?

e Since no current enters or leaves the input of the operational amplifier, the two currents you have calculated are equal. Write this fact as an equation, using your answers to **b** and **d**, and rearrange the equation to give: $V_{out}/V_{in} = \ldots$

This question and the next two may help you to understand how certain operational amplifier circuits work. The key is to realize that the resistors connected around the operational amplifier can be seen as potential dividers. Question **17** is a preliminary one about potential dividers alone.

17(P)   Resistances of 10 kΩ and 5 kΩ are connected to form a potential divider as shown in figure I57. A current of 0.2 mA flows through the resistors to earth.

a   What are the potentials at A, B, and C?

A helpful semi-graphical way of portraying the above potential-dividing process is illustrated in figure I58, which might be called a 'potential ladder diagram'. Horizontal distances represent the size of the resistances, and potential is plotted vertically.

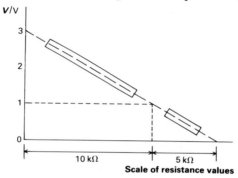

Figure I57

Figure I58

b   Why must both 'resistances' be drawn with the same gradient on this diagram?

c   *i* Draw a diagram of this sort to represent the potential divider of figure I59(a), and show on your diagram the values of the potentials at A and B.
ii Draw a diagram to represent the potential divider of figure I59(b).

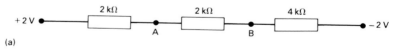

(a)

Figure I59   (b)

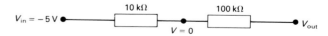

d   On the same axes, illustrate what happens to the potentials in *ii* above, if the value of V_{in} is changed from -5 V to $+3$ V.

e Draw potential ladder diagrams to represent (using two diagrams on the same axes) the changes in potentials in the operational amplifier circuit of figure I60, under the following conditions:

i $V_{in} = +2\,V$, changing to $V_{in} = -1\,V$
ii $V_{in} = +2\,V$, and R_f is changed from $20\,k\Omega$ to $15\,k\Omega$
iii $V_{in} = +2\,V$, and both resistances are doubled.

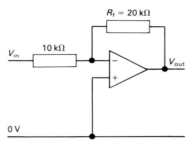

Figure I60

18(L) *Optional* This question will help you understand how the feedback in an operational amplifier circuit functions to maintain a constant overall gain, which is very nearly independent of the gain of the amplifier itself.

To keep numbers as clear as possible, we imagine an operational amplifier with an open-loop gain, A, of only 1000. $V_{out} = A(V_+ - V_-)$. Its input resistance is so high that we can assume that it draws zero current at its inputs, and it is connected as shown in figure I61.

To keep clear the magnitude of the quantities involved, express all your answers in millivolts.

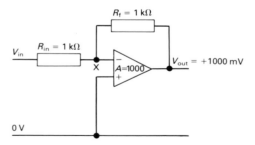

Figure I61

a Since V_{out} is $+1000\,mV$ and A is 1000, what is the potential (V_-) of X?

b What is the p.d. across R_f?

c What must be the p.d. across R_{in}?

d What then is the input potential V_{in}?

Now suppose some disturbance (perhaps a change in temperature) causes A to increase to 2000.

e If no other changes occurred in the circuit, so that V_- remained fixed at $-1\,mV$ by the feedback current, what would the value of V_{out} now be?

f If V_{out} *did* rise from $+1000\,mV$ to $+2000\,mV$, this in turn would raise the potential at X because of the feedback (V_{in} being fixed). By how much would this make V_- change? What would the new value of V_- be?

g Would this change in V_- be increasing the effect of the disturbance (*i.e.* raising the value of V_{out} even further), or would it be in the opposite direction?

h Would this change due to feedback be sufficiently large to compensate for the disturbance (*i.e.* bring the output back to $+1000\,mV$), or much too small, or much too large?

At this point you should have found that a $1000\,mV$ rise in V_{out} would cause a rise in V_- of $500\,mV$, which is in the right direction to compensate for the disturbance (*i.e.* to bring V_{out} down again), but is much too big!

The result of all this is that V_{out} *starts* to rise, but can only rise very little, to the point where the effect of the disturbance is nullified by feedback. We can see roughly how this works as follows.

i Suppose V_{out} has risen by only $1\,mV$. What change will this have caused in V_-? Which way?

j What will now be the value of V_-?

k Since the gain is 2000, what value of V_{out} ought this to produce? Is it the same as the value $+1001\,mV$ we assumed it to have?

This calculation should now have shown that a rise of $1\,mV$ in V_{out} would almost exactly compensate for the disturbance by raising V_-, the input, by $0.5\,mV$. (This gives the correct value for an output of $1000\,mV$, though it is not quite negative enough for an output of $1001\,mV$.) In fact, careful calculation shows that input and output will match the gain *and* compensate for the disturbance if V_- changes to $-0.500\,499\,5\,mV$ and V_{out} changes to $+1000.999\,mV$ (to 7 significant figures). The precise values are not important. The important thing is that a disturbance which without feedback would cause a 100 % change in output can, with negative feedback, result in a change of only 0.1 %, which is 1000 times smaller. This was with a gain only of the order of 1000. If, as with most operational amplifiers, the gain were more like 10^5, we should have found the change to be 10^5 times smaller than without feedback (*e.g.* $1000\,mV$ would change to $1000.01\,mV$ as a result of doubling the gain).

Negative feedback, then, provides an automatic self-correcting mechanism, so that the circuit is *stabilized* against disturbances. And from the point of view of the circuit as a whole, the *overall gain* is stabilized at a value depending virtually entirely on the values of R_f and R_{in}. If the input and feedback resistors are equal, then $V_{out} = -V_{in}$.

More uses of the operational amplifier

19(L) In the circuit shown in figure I62 (page 132) there are two input points, which are held at the potentials shown.

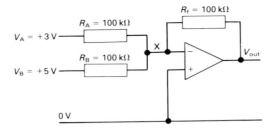

Figure 162

a What is the potential at X?

b What is the drop in potential (left to right) across R_A?

c What is the current (left to right) in R_A?

d What is the current in R_B?

e What is the value of the current leaving X?

f What must be the p.d. across R_f?

g What is the potential V_{out}?

h How is the output potential, therefore, related to the input potentials?

Suppose now that R_A is changed to $50\,k\Omega$, all the other values shown in the diagram remaining the same.

i Repeat the calculations above, and state how the output is now related to the inputs.

j What is now the output, if $V_A = 2\,V$, $V_B = 3\,V$?

Write down the relationship between output and input voltages in the following cases, and in each find the value of V_{out}, if $V_A = 0.3\,V$, $V_B = 0.5\,V$.

k $R_A = 50\,k\Omega$, $R_B = 50\,k\Omega$, $R_f = 100\,k\Omega$.

l $R_A = 100\,k\Omega$, $R_B = 100\,k\Omega$, $R_f = 1\,M\Omega$.

20(L) Consider the circuit in figure 163.

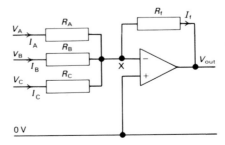

Figure 163
Summing amplifier.

a What is the potential at X?

b What is I_A (in terms of V_A, R_A)? Obtain similar expressions for I_B and I_C.

c Write down an expression relating I_f to I_A, I_B, and I_C.

d Express I_f in terms of R_f and V_{out}, and use this expression together with your answer to **c** to express the output potential in terms of the input potentials and the resistances in the circuit (be careful to get the sign right).

e What can you say about the values of R_A, R_B, R_C, and R_f if the circuit is to be used to add three potentials?

21(L) *Optional* This question is about one form of digital-to-analogue converter, that is, a circuit which will convert information in binary code (*e.g.* five is represented by 101, six by 110, etc.) into a voltage proportional to the number. Modern computers handle data in digital form, so if the computer output is to be displayed on a meter it will need to be converted to an analogue signal. For the reverse process, analogue-to-digital conversion, see question **22**.

Digital-to-analogue conversion can be accomplished using the summing amplifier as discussed in questions **19** and **20**. In the circuit shown in figure I64, each input can only be either 'high' or 'low'; typically, 'high' means $+5\,V$, 'low' means $0\,V$. Binary numbers are represented by the state (high or low) of the inputs, for example as follows: for binary 101, V_A is high, V_B is low, and V_C is high.

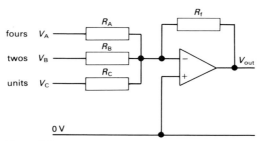

Figure I64

If only V_C is high $(+5\,V)$, this is required to give an output of $-1\,V$.

a Express R_C in terms of R_f.

If only V_B is high, this is required to give an output of $-2\,V$.

b Express R_B in terms of R_f.

If only V_A is high, this is required to give an output of $-4\,V$.

c Express R_A in terms of R_f.

d Suggest suitable numerical values for the four resistances if this system is to work.

e You need to extend the circuit to cope with *six* binary digits. However, 111111 is denary 63, and your operational amplifier saturates at about $-13\,V$. You therefore need to arrange that one unit is represented in the output as $-0.1\,V$. Suggest suitable values for all the resistances.

22(R) *Optional*   Digital-to-analogue conversion is easily done using an operational amplifier, as in question **21**. The opposite, analogue-to-digital conversion, is needed for example in digital display meters, and in interface units for feeding the values of real voltages into a computer. There are several systems, and one, voltage-to-time conversion, works as follows. A ramp generator provides a voltage which rises steadily from zero, repeatedly. This is compared with the potential of the negative terminal of the analogue input, and then with the potential of its positive terminal.

In each case a pulse is sent out when the compared voltages are equal. One pulse starts a binary counter driven from a 1 MHz clock, the other stops it. The resulting reading is held until the next cycle of the ramp generator.

a Use the units described in figure I65 to make a block diagram of this system.

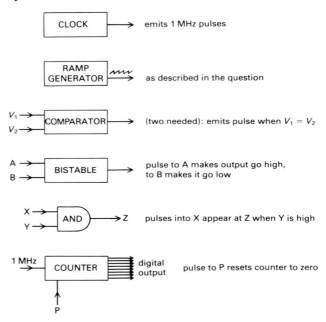

Figure I65

b If this system were used for a digital display meter, how would the display actually behave? What modification or specification would be needed to ensure that it was easily readable?

23(R)a Design a circuit using operational amplifiers to give an output voltage $V_{out} = +(V_A + 10V_B)$, where V_A and V_B are two input voltages.

b Design a circuit using operational amplifiers whose output $V_{out} = 10V_A - 3V_B$.

24(L)   Consider the circuit shown in figure I66.

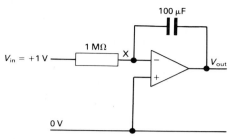

Figure I66

a   What is the p.d. across the 1 MΩ resistor?

b   What current will flow in it?

c   The $+1$ V input is kept constant by the input source, and the potential at X is kept at zero by the properties of the operational amplifier. The current must therefore remain constant. Where must it flow to?

d   Will there be any current on the righthand side of the capacitor?

e   How much charge will there be on the capacitor plates after 10 s? After 20 s?

f   What will be the p.d. across the capacitor after 10 s? After 20 s?

g   Which plate of the capacitor has positive charge, and which negative charge?

h   What is happening to the output potential V_{out}?

i   What is the change of V_{out} per second?

j   Suppose that V_{in} had been $+2$ V instead of $+1$ V. How would V_{out} now behave?

k   Sketch a graph showing how V_{out} would change if V_{in} were $+1$ V for 2 s, then $+3$ V for 5 s, then -2 V for 1 s.

l   If in the circuit the capacitor had been 10 μF instead of 100 μF, what difference would this have made to the behaviour of V_{out}?

25(L)   This question is about the circuit shown in figure I67 whose output voltage is the integral of the input voltage multiplied by a constant.

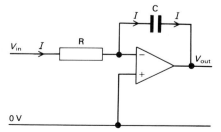

Figure I67
Integrating circuit.

a Write down expressions in terms of V_{in} and R for:
  i the current, I, through the resistor, R;
  ii the rate at which the capacitor, C, is charged.

b Write down another expression for the rate at which C is charged, this time in terms of C and V_{out}. (Remember that the capacitor plate with the positive charge will be at the higher potential.)

c From your answers to **a** and **b** relate V_{out} to V_{in}, C, and R. Use this relationship to show that V_{out} depends on the time integral of V_{in}.

26(R) The circuit of figure I67 (page 135) performs the operation:

$$V_{out} = -\frac{1}{CR} \int V_{in}\, dt + \text{constant}$$

You may sometimes find it easier to use the alternative statement:

$$\frac{d V_{out}}{dt} = -\frac{1}{CR} V_{in}$$

If $R = 1\,M\Omega$ and $C = 1\,\mu F$, sketch how the output varies with time for each of the following inputs. Assume V_{out} at the start is $0\,V$ in each case.

a V_{in} is constant $= 0.5\,V$.

b V_{in} is a 'square wave' between $+2\,V$ and $-2\,V$, of frequency $20\,Hz$. See figure I68(a).

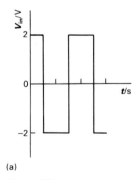 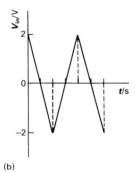

(a)   (b)

Figure I68

c V_{in} is a 'triangular wave' between $+2\,V$ and $-2\,V$, of frequency $0.5\,Hz$. See figure I68(b).

(Be as precise as you can about the shape of the graph of V_{out}.)

27(L) The circuit shown in figure I69 is a differentiating circuit; the output voltage is proportional to the rate of change of the input voltage:

$$V_{out} \propto - d V_{in}/dt$$

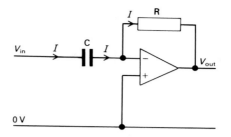

Figure I69
Differentiating circuit.

0 V

a Give the argument, in terms of the current, I, showing why V_{out} and V_{in} are related in this way.

b Various *output* waveforms of a differentiating circuit are shown in figure I70. For each of them pick the appropriate 'ideal' input from figure I71.

c Why is the word 'ideal' used in **b**?

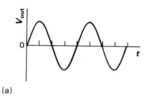

(a)

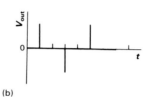

(b)

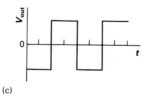

(c)

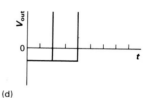

(d)

Figure I70
Output waveforms from differentiating circuit.

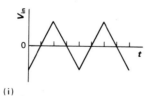

(i)

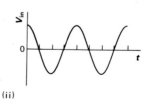

(ii)

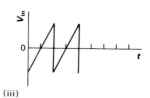

(iii)

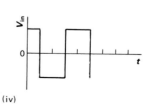

(iv)

Figure I71
Possible input waveforms.

The non-inverting input

28(L) In the circuit shown in figure I72, the 10 kΩ resistor connects the inverting input to 0 V.

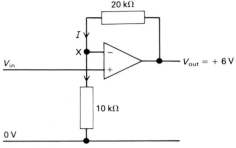

Figure I72

a What is the value of the current I?

b What is the p.d. across the 10 kΩ resistor?

c What is the potential at X?

d What is the value of V_{in}?

e In general, in this circuit, how is V_{out} related to V_{in}?

f Suggest values for the resistances which would give an overall gain (V_{out}/V_{in}) of $+10$.

This circuit is known as the non-inverting amplifier.

g Set up axes of resistance and potential as in question **17**, and draw a 'potential ladder' for the circuit of figure I72. Mark on it the point representing X in the diagram.

h On the same axes show the situation if V_{in} is reduced to half its original value.

29(L)a For the circuit shown in figure I73 obtain two independent expressions for the potential V_X at X:
i using the fact that resistors R_1 and R_2 form a potential divider;
ii from what you know about the input potentials of an operational amplifier (note that the non-inverting input is not connected directly to 0 V).

b What is the voltage gain, V_{out}/V_{in}, of this circuit?

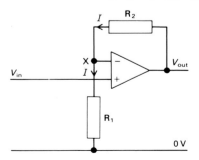

Figure I73

30(L) In the circuit shown in figure I73, R_1 is $100\,\text{k}\Omega$.

    a Calculate the voltage gain for the following values of R_2:

        $1\,\text{M}\Omega$, $500\,\text{k}\Omega$, $100\,\text{k}\Omega$, $50\,\text{k}\Omega$, $10\,\text{k}\Omega$, $1\,\text{k}\Omega$.

    b Looking at your answers to **a**, what value of R_2 (or of R_1) would, theoretically at least, give a gain of precisely 1?

31(P) Suppose in the circuit shown in figure I73 that $V_{in} = 1.5\,\text{V}$ and $R_1 = R_2$.

    a Calculate V_{out}.

    b Calculate I, if $R_1 = R_2 = 100\,\text{k}\Omega$.

    (*Note:* in the circuits you studied before this one, the non-inverting input was connected to 0 V. You learned that the input resistance is very high, so the input current to the operational amplifier is very small. This input current actually flows inside the amplifier between the two inputs: the 'equivalent circuit' for a $2\,\text{M}\Omega$ input resistance would be as in figure I74(a), and in the case of the above circuit figure I73 would be as in figure I74(b).)

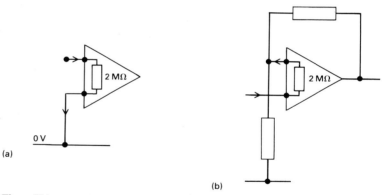

Figure I74

    c Assume that the value for V_{out} which you calculated in **a** is very close to the true value. If the open loop gain of the operational amplifier is about 2×10^5, what is the approximate p.d. between the input terminals?

32(P) Consider the circuit shown in figure I75.

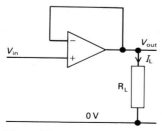

Figure I75
Unity-gain voltage follower.

a How are V_{out} and V_{in} related in this circuit?

b Obtain a relationship between the input voltage, V_{in}, and the current I_L delivered to the load resistor R_L.

c Explain, without calculation, why the input current to the amplifier is very much less than this.

33(P) Draw an operational amplifier circuit whose output is a (measured) current which is proportional to an input voltage. The input *voltage* is in the range -1 to $+1\,V$, but the source cannot supply more than $1\,\mu A$. The output current should be in the range -1 to $+1\,mA$.

34(P) Design an operational amplifier circuit which gives a measured voltage output which is proportional to the current drawn from a source. The input current can vary between -10 and $+10\,mA$; the output voltage should be in the range -1 to $+1\,V$. Suggest suitable values for components in the circuit.

35(L) Figure I76 shows how an operational amplifier can be used in a differential amplifier circuit. To see how it comes about that the output voltage V_{out} is proportional to the difference between the two input voltages $(V_B - V_A)$, consider the following two paths in the circuit: AXC and BYD.

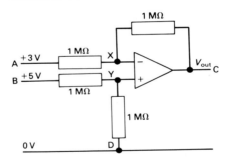

Figure I76

a *i* Using the path AXC, express the potential at X (V_X) in terms of V_{out}.
   ii Using the path BYD, write down the value of the potential at Y (V_Y).

b Write an expression stating that V_X and V_Y must be the same, and rearrange it in the form $V_{out} = \ldots$

c Repeat steps **a** and **b**, using V_A and V_B in place of $+3\,V$ and $+5\,V$.

d Copy the diagram of figure I77 and on it sketch the 'potential ladder' (as in questions **17** and **28**) to represent the potentials at A, B, C, D, X, and Y in the circuit of figure I76.

e Sketch a similar diagram in which the two input resistors AX and BY have had their values changed to $0.5\,M\Omega$ each, and the potentials at A and B are $1\,V$ and $3\,V$ respectively. Deduce from your diagram the value of V_{out}.

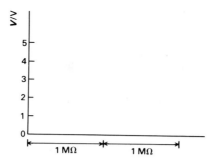

Figure I77

f *Optional* Use the generalized values shown in figure I78 (in which two resistors have the value R_{in} and two have the value R_f) to show algebraically that

$$V_{out} = -\frac{R_f}{R_{in}}(V_A - V_B).$$

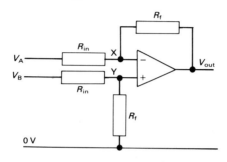

Figure I78

36(R)a Design circuits using an operational amplifier to give output voltages which are
i equal to
ii ten times
iii one-fifth of
the difference between two voltages.

b Suggest a situation in which *ii* would be more useful than *i*.

37(L) The circuit of figure I79 is known as a comparator. What is the output V_{out}:

a if V_+ is greater than V_-?

b if V_+ is less than V_-?

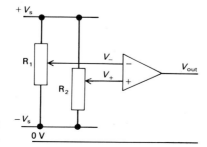

Figure I79
The comparator.

c Sketch how R_1 could be replaced by a fixed resistor and a thermistor, so that V_{out} would go positive for high temperatures and negative for low temperatures.

d What would now be the effect of adjusting the setting of R_2?

e If the output V_{out} were connected to a relay which would switch on a lamp when energized, what would happen as the temperature changed from low to high (be careful!)?

f What component could you add to the circuit (and where) so that the lamp was on for high temperatures and off for low temperatures?

38(L) *Optional*   In the circuit of figure I80, R_1 and R_2 are equal resistors. Suppose the output of the operational amplifier is at $+6$ V, the limiting value due to the power supply.

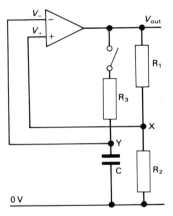

Figure I80

a What is the potential at X (and therefore V_+)?

Suppose C is not charged.

b What is the potential at Y (and therefore V_-)?

c Are these potentials V_+ and V_- such as to keep the output at the limiting value?

Now suppose the switch is closed.

d What will happen to the potential at Y? What will happen to V_-?

e When V_- reaches (and passes) $+3$ V, what will happen to the output?

f What will therefore happen to the potential at X and therefore to V_+?

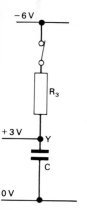

−6 V

R_3

+3 V   Y

C

0 V

Figure I81

The potentials across R_3 and C will now be as shown in figure I81.

g What will now happen to the potential at Y?

h What will happen to the output V_{out} when this potential reaches − 3 V?

i What will happen next? Sketch the way in which the potential of Y has changed so far, and what will happen from this point onwards.

j On the same axes, sketch the way in which V_{out} varies.

k What difference would it make if R_2 were decreased, so that X were set at ± 1 V instead of ± 3 V? Sketch another graph to illustrate this.

This circuit is an *astable multivibrator*, and its frequency can be changed by changing the value of any of the resistors.

Integrators with feedback

39(L) The output and input voltages of the circuit (figure I82) are related by $V_{out} = -\dfrac{1}{CR} \displaystyle\int V_{in}\, dt + \text{constant}$, or, alternatively $V_{in} = -CR\, dV_{out}/dt$.

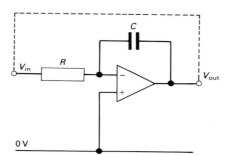

Figure I82   0 V

Suppose the output and input are connected by a piece of wire.

a What is the relationship between V_{out} and V_{in} now?

b What differential equation will the circuit now solve, and what is the solution?

Suppose $R = 1\,\text{M}\Omega$, $C = 10\,\mu\text{F}$, and the capacitor is initially charged to 5 V. What is the output voltage after

c 10 s?

d 20 s?

e 100 s?

40(P) In the circuit of figure I83 the potential of B is initially $+0.1$ V. At this instant,

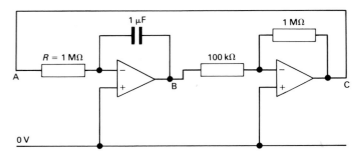

Figure I83

a what is the potential at C?

b what is the potential at A?

c what current will flow in R, and which way?

d what effect will this have on the capacitor, and what will therefore happen to the potential at B? (Numerical answers required.)

Assuming the same values as in the diagram, suppose that (at some time t) the potential at B is V.

e Because of the righthand operational amplifier, what must be the potential at C?

f Because of the lefthand operational amplifier, what must be the potential at A?

g Write the differential equation which this system solves, and the solution of the equation assuming that the value of V at $t = 0$ is 0.1 V.

h Without calculation, sketch a graph showing in general terms how you would expect V to change with time.

i How long will it take for V to reach 3 V?

41(R) In a single operational amplifier integrating circuit with resistance R and capacitance C, the output potential V_{out} is related to the input potential V_{in} by: $dV_{out}/dt = -(1/RC)V_{in}$.

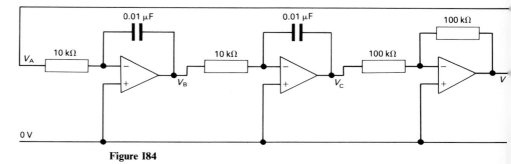

Figure I84

a What differential equation is represented by the circuit of figure I84?

b At what frequency will it oscillate?

42(I) The graph of figure I85 illustrates two oscillations, each with amplitude 2 cm and frequency 10 Hz, with a time lag between one and the other of 0.01 s, representing a phase difference of 1/10 cycle, or 0.2π.

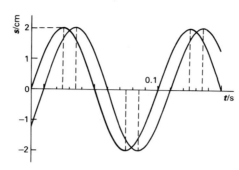

Figure I85

Sketch similar pairs of oscillations as follows, and in each case state the values not given in table I2.

Amplitude /cm	Frequency /Hz	Periodic time /s	Time lag /s	Phase difference
1	0.1	–	2.5	–
1	–	0.5	–	$\pi/2$ ($\frac{1}{4}$ cycle)
10	100	–	0.005	–

Table I2

43(R) A signal generator is connected to a circuit which produces a delay of 0.01 s, *i.e.* its output is identical in amplitude to its input but occurs 0.01 s later (figure I86).

Figure I86

What will be the phase difference between the input and output of the delay circuit if the frequency provided by the signal generator is

a 100 Hz?

b 50 Hz?

c 25 Hz?

d 200 Hz?

Suppose the input signal (at A in figure I86) and the delayed signal (at B) both have an amplitude (peak value) of 1 V. The points A and B are then connected to a summing amplifier as shown in figure I87.

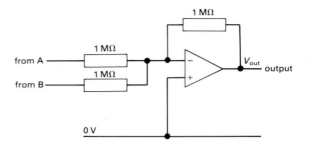

Figure 187

e For each of the cases **a** to **d** (page 145) say whether the output of the amplifier would have an amplitude of 0 V, 2 V, or something in between.

44(L) *Optional* This question is about feedback systems in general. The results it leads to can be applied to many kinds of system. It shows how feedback makes the behaviour of the system insensitive to changes in the characteristics of an amplifier. ('Amplifier' need not necessarily mean an electronic amplifier: a car engine with an accelerator is equally an amplifier, since the small human input force controls the large output force of the engine.)

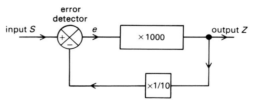

Figure 188

In the closed loop system of figure 188, one-tenth of the output of the amplifier is fed back to the error detector. This is subtracted from the input, S, giving the error, e, as input to the amplifier.

a Write down two expressions for the value of e
i in terms of Z and the gain of the amplifier, and
ii in terms of S and the feedback from Z.

b Combine these two expressions to obtain a relation between S and Z, so as to get a value for Z/S, the overall gain of the system.

c Repeat the calculation, changing the amplifier gain to 10 000.

Figure 189 shows the same system in general terms, with amplification, A, and feedback fraction, β. (β is a number *less* than 1, and the output is *multiplied* by β to give the feedback.)

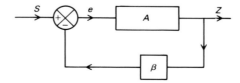

Figure 189

d Using the same method as above, obtain an expression for the overall gain, G, of the system ($G = Z/S$).

e Use the assumption that A is very much bigger than $1/\beta$ (or $1/A$ is very much less than β, or $A\beta$ is very much bigger than 1) to show that your expression can be written to a close approximation without A in it. What does it say about the overall gain?

Control systems

45(P) A lavatory cistern, or the cold water tank to be found in the loft of most houses, are examples of control systems. Which of the terms feedback, reference signal, error signal, input, output, and disturbance apply, and how?

46(R) *Optional* A system for keeping model trains to a constant speed under conditions of changed loads or changing gradients works as follows. The motors are of permanent magnet type, and can therefore be thought of as simply a fixed resistance, R, in series with an e.m.f., $\mathscr{E}$, which is induced in the rotor as it turns in the magnetic field. As the field is constant, $\mathscr{E}$ is proportional to the rate of rotation.

a Show that in the circuit of figure I90 the p.d. between A and B is $\mathscr{E}/2$.

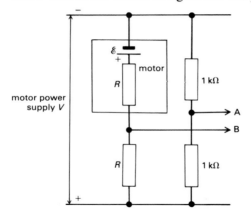

Figure I90

b Devise a way, using one or more operational amplifiers (one can be assumed to be capable of powering the motor), of using the result of **a** to maintain a steady speed.

47(P)a A 'robot' traffic light system controlled by sensors in the road which are activated by approaching cars is an example of a system in which the feedback needs some 'processing' before it is used. Explain, with some detail.

b Describe (or invent) some other system involving the processing of feedback.

48(P) Here are two problems about possible feedback in driving a car.

a If after travelling straight, a car veers sideways due to road irregularities or a gust of wind, the driver's body tends to move sideways relative to the car. Why?

b This movement may be transmitted to the steering wheel through the driver's arms. Consider two possibilities:
i the driver is holding the wheel at points above the axis of the wheel ('2 o'clock and 10 o'clock'), and
ii he is holding it below the axis.
For each, consider what might be the effect on the path of the car.

c Will the effects be the same or opposite, if the car is reversing?

d If a car accelerates or decelerates, the driver's body, including his accelerator foot, tends to move forwards or backwards relative to the car. Explain how this might account for the fact that a learner driver, when reversing, may cause the car to move in jerks ('kangaroo-hopping'). What might determine the frequency of the jerks?

49(P) In a factory, jars on a conveyor belt are each supposed to be filled with 100 g of powder. Each jar passes over a sensor (figure I91). If the mass is, for example, 1 g low, a correction is immediately made to the valve of the hopper causing it to deliver 1 g more; other corrections are proportional.

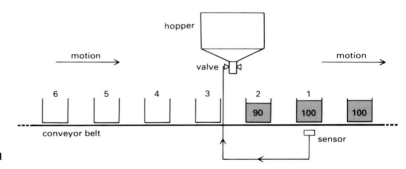

Figure I91

In the diagram it will be seen that starting with jar number 2, the hopper is delivering only 90 g.

a What amounts will be delivered to jars 3 to 11?

b How might the system be modified to improve its performance?

50(E) The term 'self-fulfilling prophecy' is used to describe the idea that the very fact that people believe a certain event is likely and act accordingly makes the event itself more likely to happen. For example, a completely unfounded rumour that sugar is in short supply can cause a shortage of sugar in the shops; if nervous investors think that a particular bank is likely to crash, their actions may help this happen. Describe how these effects happen, in these and other examples you can think of. Is the concept of feedback relevant? Of course there are many situations in which human belief and behaviour will not affect the course of events. Give examples. What distinguishes these from the examples of 'self-fulfilling prophecy'?

Unit J
ELECTROMAGNETIC WAVES

Stephen Borthwick
Marlborough College

Peter Bullett
Rugby School

J

SUMMARY OF THE UNIT

SUMMARY OF THE UNIT

INTRODUCTION

Much of our information about the outside world comes to us in the form of waves: sound, light, and radio waves are particularly important. However we detect them, the waves are inevitably restricted by some sort of aperture, such as the ear, the pupil of the eye, or the dish aerial of a radio telescope. Whenever waves pass through an aperture, they are diffracted and spread out. The effect depends on the size of the aperture in relation to the wavelength. This is why radio telescopes, which use radiation with wavelengths about a million times greater than the wavelength of visible light, have to be much bigger than optical telescopes. Diffraction patterns can be predicted using the principle of superposition (see Unit D, 'Oscillations and waves').

Diffraction limits the amount of information we can obtain, and leads to the limited resolving power of the eye and instruments such as the telescope. But diffraction effects are useful too. For example, we use diffraction gratings to gain knowledge about the waves themselves, and hence about the sources emitting them, as in the study of spectra (taken up again in Unit L, 'Waves, particles, and atoms'). Or, if we know the wavelength of the radiation, we can learn about the structure of the object causing the diffraction, as in X-ray crystallography.

Holography is an application of the principle of superposition which has increasing importance as a means of information storage.

This Unit is specifically concerned with electromagnetic waves. All parts of the electromagnetic spectrum, from the longest radio waves through visible light, to gamma rays, have properties in common. In the last section of this Unit ideas about electric and magnetic fields developed earlier in the course are brought together to suggest an explanation of the nature of electromagnetic radiation itself.

Section J1

WAVES THROUGH AN APERTURE

Single aperture experiments

QUESTIONS 1, 2

EXPERIMENT J1
Looking through a slit and
through a pin-hole

The two most obvious features of diffraction at a single aperture (figure J1) are that the waves spread into the region normally expected to be in shadow, and that within this region there are maxima and minima of intensity.

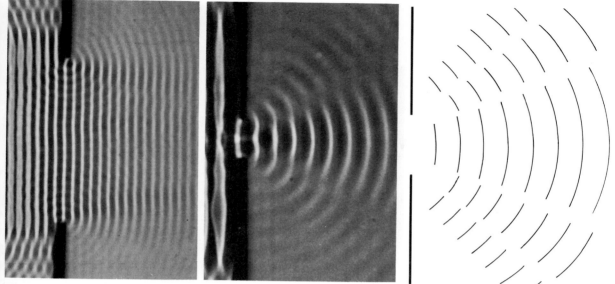

Figure J1
Photographs showing the diffraction of plane waves at a wide and a narrow gap. The sketch on the right is a diagrammatic representation of the photograph next to it. Note the phase differences between the fan-like portions.
PSSC Physics. *2nd edition, 1965; D.C. Heath and Company with Educational Development Centre Inc., Newton, Mass.*

CIRCUS OF EXPERIMENTS J2
Diffraction

HOME EXPERIMENT JH1
A homemade slit

The amount of spreading depends on the ratio of the slit width, b, to the wavelength, λ. If b is large compared with λ then there is little spreading; but if b is small compared with λ then there is much more spreading.

In a single-slit diffraction pattern, the first minimum of intensity is at an angle θ from the central maximum where $\sin \theta = \lambda/b$; so $\theta \approx \lambda/b$ is a good approximation for small values of θ.

There are further minima at angles 2θ, 3θ, etc. on both sides of the central maximum, thus

$$\sin \theta = n\frac{\lambda}{b}$$

where n is 1, 2, 3, ... The central fringe of the diffraction pattern is twice as wide as the equally-spaced fringes on either side. The fringes become less intense with increasing θ (see figure J2).

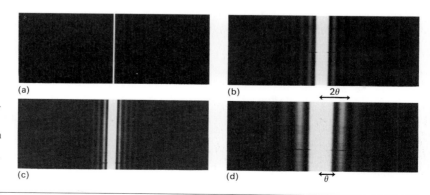

(a)   (b) $\overset{\longleftrightarrow}{2\theta}$

(c)   (d) $\overset{\longleftrightarrow}{\theta}$

Figure J2
Single-slit diffraction patterns for light of one wavelength using slits of width $b \gg \lambda$ in (a); width $b \approx 5\lambda$ in (b); width $b \approx 3\lambda$ in (c); and width $b \approx \lambda$ in (d).
G. R. Graham, Cambridgeshire College of Arts and Technology

If the aperture is circular, the pattern is a set of concentric ring whose spacing is about 20 per cent bigger than the single-slit pattern fo the same b and λ (figure J3).

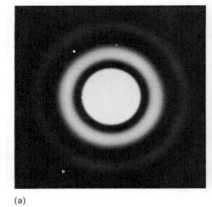 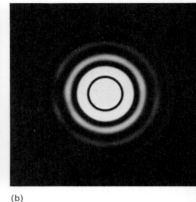

(a)   (b)

Figure J3
Diffraction patterns from a circular aperture with diameter in (a) half that in (b).
Professor C. A. Taylor

The production of fringes and the relationship between apertur size, wavelength of radiation, and the intensity pattern of the sprea wave can be explained in terms of the superposition of waves. First however, it is necessary to show that a single aperture acts as a multipl source of waves.

Huygens's construction

EXPERIMENT J3
Huygens's construction

QUESTIONS 3, 4

The Dutch scientist Christiaan Huygens (1629–1695) suggested tha every point on a wavefront behaves as a point source of waves sendin out energy in the direction of the wave's propagation. To find the new wavefront he used the principle of superposition to add the contri butions from these sources on the original wavefront (figure J4). Thi hypothesis can be used to predict the spreading of waves in a rippl tank. Huygens's construction helps us to understand many aspects o wave behaviour, including the laws of reflection and refraction fo waves in any medium, the single-slit diffraction pattern, the diffractio grating, X-ray diffraction, and holography. It is an excellent example o a simple model which can increase our understanding of a wide range o related phenomena.

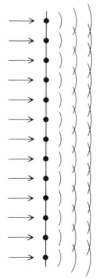

Figure J4
Huygens's secondary wavelets.

Wave amplitude and energy

QUESTION 5

DEMONSTRATION J4
Wave amplitude and energy
Intensity $\propto$ (amplitude)^2

Energy of harmonic oscillator $\propto$
(amplitude)^2
(Unit D, 'Oscillations and waves')

When waves superpose energy is usually redistributed into a pattern of maxima and minima. To find the maxima and minima the *amplitudes* are added together – *not* the energies of the two waves. *Intensity* is defined as the rate at which wave *energy* arrives per unit area. It is proportional to (amplitude)^2. Most wave detectors measure intensity rather than amplitude.

Explaining the single-slit diffraction pattern

QUESTION 6

QUESTIONS 7, 8

DEMONSTRATION J5
Measuring a diffraction pattern

Huygens's construction is applied to a wave passing through an aperture by superposing the secondary wavelets from sources on the plane wavefront at the aperture. The resulting variation in intensity has a central maximum with minima on either side at angles θ, where $\sin \theta = n\lambda/b$ and n is an integer (1, 2, 3, etc.).

The construction shows that incident wave energy has been redistributed into a diffraction pattern. Most of the energy of the wave lies within the central maximum (figure J5).

It is not possible to predict the position or intensity of maxima (which do *not* occur midway between minima) using the simple theory. However, a phasor treatment, in which the amplitude and relative phase of the secondary wavelets are represented by rotating vectors, can be used to predict the intensity pattern shown quantitatively in figure J5.

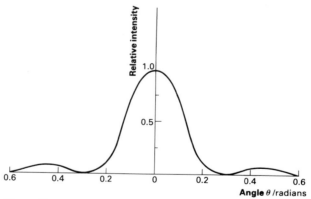

Figure J5
Single-slit diffraction pattern drawn for the case where $b \approx 3\lambda$.

Diffraction at an aperture and image recombination

DEMONSTRATION J6
Diffraction and image recombination

QUESTIONS 9, 10

The diffraction pattern produced by an aperture contains all the information necessary for the aperture's shape to be reconstructed. If this diffraction pattern is itself treated as an aperture then a new diffraction pattern can be produced. This second diffraction pattern is the recombined image of the original aperture.

aperture $\longrightarrow$ diffraction pattern $\longrightarrow$ image of aperture

If the more widely spread parts of the diffraction pattern (the 'higher orders') are removed, then the recombined image lacks definition.

Sharp corners and other fine details vanish progressively as less of the pattern is allowed to contribute to the image (figure J6).

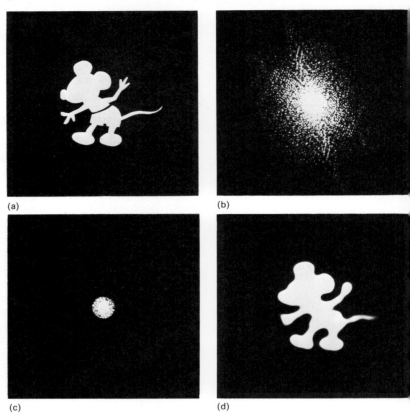

(a)

(b)

(c)

(d)

Figure J6
Image recombination. (a) Irregular object aperture. (b) Its diffraction pattern. (c) A restricted portion of the diffraction pattern, recombined to give an image, (d).
Professor C. A. Taylor

This form of image degradation is very important in the design of optical systems. The object in view scatters light in many directions. The fine detail in the image becomes poorer as the more widely scattered light is excluded by the restricted aperture.

In diffraction imaging, radiation from *each point* of the diffraction pattern contributes to *every point* on the eventual image. If part of the beam is removed, then although the image loses detail, its general outline is preserved. This is in contrast to a conventionally produced image as, for example, that produced by a slide projector, where removing part of the beam removes an entire section of the image.

Resolution

QUESTION 11

EXPERIMENT J7
Resolution

It is not possible to resolve (detect as separate) two small objects if their angular separation is too small. Diffraction at the entrance aperture to the system (for example by a telescope or microscope) is one important factor which limits resolution (figure J7).

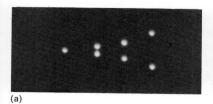
(a)

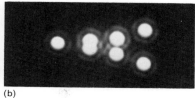
(b)

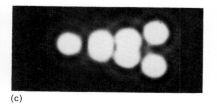
(c)

Figure J7
A constellation of seven close point sources photographed using a telescope with a
progressively smaller aperture.
G. R. Graham, Cambridgeshire College of Arts and Technology

Rayleigh (1842–1919) suggested that if the centre of the diffraction
pattern due to one object coincides with the first minimum of that due
to the other, then the objects can just be distinguished as separate
(figure J8). So, adopting Rayleigh's criterion, λ/b is a good guide to the
limit of angular resolution for a system with slit width b. For a circular
aperture of diameter b, $\theta \approx 1.2\lambda/b$.

J

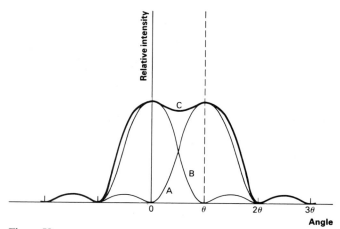

Figure J8
Overlapping diffraction patterns of two images which are just resolved. Curve C,
which the eye responds to, is the sum of the intensities of curves A and B.

QUESTIONS 12 to 16

Lenses, to one degree or another, all possess defects which distort
the image and thus limit the quality of any optical instrument. Our
ability to see fine detail is also determined in part by the closeness of the
retinal receptors, rods, and cones, whose density varies across the
retina. Since the sensation of light is achieved by the eye operating in
tandem with the brain, there are clearly psychological and neurological
factors which affect visual perception as well as the physiological and
physical limitations.

Radio astronomy

Radio telescopes have become increasingly important instruments for
astronomical study, in particular for observing radio galaxies and in
leading to the discovery of quasars and pulsars. Since such sources
typically emit wavelengths about 10^6 times longer than light, a radio

QUESTIONS 17 to 19

DEMONSTRATION J8
Model of radio interferometer

telescope needs to be hundreds of kilometres in diameter to achieve a resolution equivalent to that of the human eye. The interferometer type of radio telescope achieves the benefits of a large aperture by using aerials some distance apart and superposing the signals. The received intensity is, of course, much less than for a continuous detector of equivalent width.

Figure J9
Jodrell Bank, the Mark 1A radio telescope.
The Guardian

Section J2   WAVES THROUGH GRATINGS

The form of the diffraction pattern produced by a grating (an arrangement of regularly spaced scattering centres) is determined by the wavelength of the radiation and the structure of the grating. If the structure of the grating is known then the wavelength of the radiation can be calculated from the diffraction pattern. Since most of our information about the structure of atoms and molecules comes from spectral analysis, the accurate measurement of wavelength over a wide range of the electromagnetic spectrum is of great importance.

If, on the other hand, we know the wavelength, the diffraction pattern can yield information about the structure of the grating. Reconstruction of this information can take place either directly, by diffraction imaging (as in holography) or indirectly, as in X-ray diffraction.

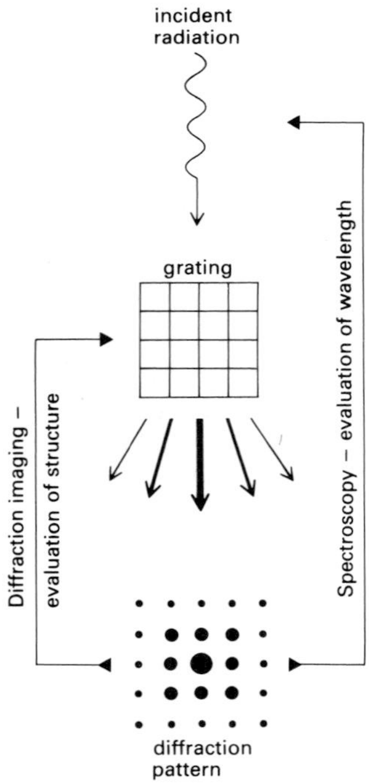

incident
radiation

grating

Diffraction imaging –
evaluation of structure

Spectroscopy – evaluation of wavelength

diffraction
pattern

Figure J10
Waves through gratings.

Grating experiments

An optical grating has many slits, usually parallel grooves on a piece of plastic or glass (figure J11). Looking at a line filament light source through such a grating reveals a diffraction pattern with lines of maximum intensity in each of the colours or wavelengths present. Longer wavelengths are diffracted through larger angles than shorter ones.

If the light source emits only one wavelength, then the diffraction pattern consists of a series of equally spaced bright lines (figure J12).

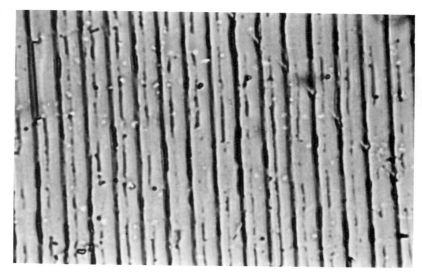

Figure J11
Diffraction grating with 1000 lines per cm (× 700).

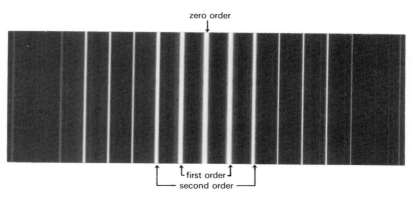

Figure J12
Diffraction pattern with monochromatic light.
G. R. Graham, Cambridgeshire College of Arts and Technology

Grating formula

Huygens's construction can be used to model the scattering action of a grating. Figure J13 shows the path differences for consecutive waves which produce the various maxima or orders.

Zero Order ($n = 0$)
Path difference between waves from adjacent slits $= 0$
1st Order ($n = 1$)
Path difference between waves from adjacent slits $= s \sin \theta_1 = \lambda$
2nd Order ($n = 2$)
Path difference between waves from adjacent slits $= s \sin \theta_2 = 2\lambda$

The general formula for a superposition maximum is:

$$n\lambda = s \sin \theta_n$$

where n is the diffraction order and s is the grating spacing. (There is a limit to the value n can take since $\sin \theta$ must be $\leqslant 1$, thus the maximum number of orders will depend on the particular values of s and λ.)

A simple analysis predicts that the intensity of all maxima would be the same (figure J14).

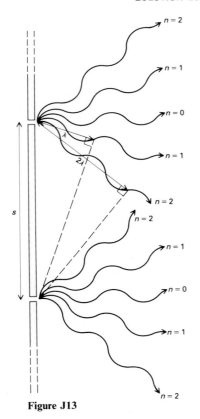

Figure J13

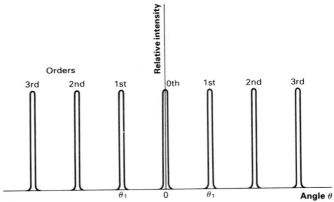

Figure J14
Grating pattern (assuming minute slit width), $\sin \theta_1 = \lambda/s$.

But light does not leave a single slit of width b equally in all directions – there are directions of zero intensity at angles given by $\sin \theta = n\lambda/b$ (figure J15).

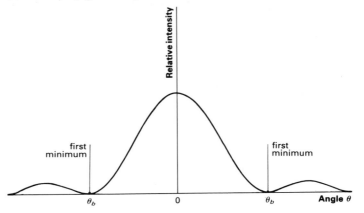

Figure J15
Single-slit pattern, $\sin \theta_b = \lambda/b$.

If no light leaves any slit at one of these angles, for example θ_b in figure J15, then even if the grating condition $n\lambda = s\sin\theta_n$ is obeyed, there will be no maximum at this angle. The effect is to combine the two patterns; the single-slit pattern being the 'envelope' which contains the grating pattern (figure J16).

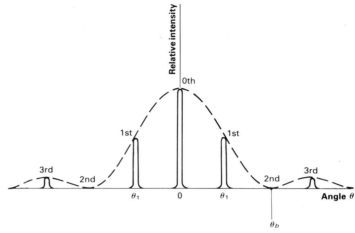

Figure J16
Overall pattern.

QUESTIONS 21 to 24, 32, 34

Notice that the maxima due to the grating are equally spaced (for small values of θ) and that the single-slit 'envelope' which determines the intensity of each maximum, has, by contrast, a central maximum twice as wide as the others. In the example shown the second orders have almost vanished and would not be seen on the screen.

Effect of number of slits on grating pattern

DEMONSTRATION J12
Sharpness of maxima and number of slits

Increasing the number of equally spaced slits has two effects. It increases the brightness of each line, since more light passes through the grating; it also makes the lines sharper (figure J17).

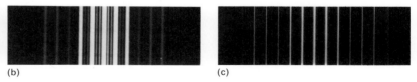

(b)   (c)

Figure J17
Grating pattern produced by (a) 2 slits, (b) 4 slits, (c) 50 slits. (The exposure times of the photographs vary to accommodate the very different intensities in the three cases.)
G. R. Graham, Cambridgeshire College of Arts and Technology

QUESTION 25

EXPERIMENT J13a
Measuring the wavelength of light
using a grating

These two effects are crucial in the study of spectra (figure J18). The individual maxima (corresponding to the various wavelengths) are bright, and also very sharp, thus making it easier to distinguish two close wavelengths. Such a grating is said 'to have good resolution'. A typical grating used in optical spectroscopy might have 15 000 slits each 2×10^{-3} mm apart.

Young's double-slit experiment

EXPERIMENT J13b
Measuring the wavelength of light
using Young's double slits

The experiment performed by Thomas Young at the beginning of the nineteenth century was of considerable importance in showing the wave-like properties of light. Although the path differences are too small to be measured directly, a superposition pattern is produced (figure J19) and the wavelength can be calculated.

Figure J19
Young's double-slit pattern.
G. R. Graham, Cambridgeshire College of Arts and Technology

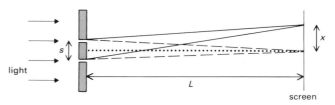

Figure J20
Young's double-slit experiment.

The relationship between the wavelength, λ, the slit spacing, s, the fringe separation, x, and the distance between the slits and the screen, L (see figure J20) is known as the Young's fringes or the double-slit equation:

$$\lambda/x \approx s/L$$

This relationship is just a special case of the general grating formula. It provides quite an easy method for measuring or comparing different wavelengths of light, though it is less precise than using a grating with many slits. If the source used is not monochromatic then a number of overlapping, coloured fringes is produced.

As with a grating, the *positions* of the maxima in the pattern depend on the slit *separation*. The *intensity* of the various maxima in the pattern depends on the slit *width* (figure J21).

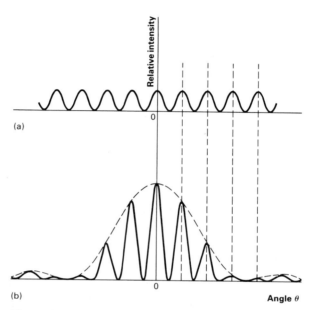

Figure J21
Relative intensity of Young's fringes for (a) infinitely narrow slits (b) slits of finite width.

Reflection gratings

DEMONSTRATION J14
A spectrum using a concave reflection grating

DEMONSTRATION J15
Reflection grating at glancing incidence

Reflection gratings can be made by scratching lines on a suitably reflective surface. The areas between the lines act like the slits in a transmission grating, that is, as Huygens's sources of secondary wavelets. If the line spacing is fairly large compared with the wavelength of the radiation, then the grating must be used at a glancing incidence, which greatly increases the path difference between waves leaving consecutive lines. It is just possible to measure the wavelength of X-rays by this method using the finest optical gratings available.

Complex gratings

DEMONSTRATION J16
Diffraction at complex gratings

The diffraction pattern of a simple multiple-slit grating contains information both about the slit spacing and the slit width (figure J16). Similarly, the diffraction pattern of a complex grating (one which consists of a regularly repeated array of apertures) contains information about the way the apertures are arranged in the grating, and also about

the shape and size of the apertures themselves (figures J22, J23, and J24)
If the grating has no regularity of structure then the resulting diffraction
pattern is as shown in figure J25 – it has no regular fine structure.

READING
Measurement of red blood cell
diameters using a laser (page 171)

Huygens's construction suggests that both a point and a pin-hole
scatter waves in much the same way: so an array of scattering obstacles
behaves just like an array of scattering apertures.

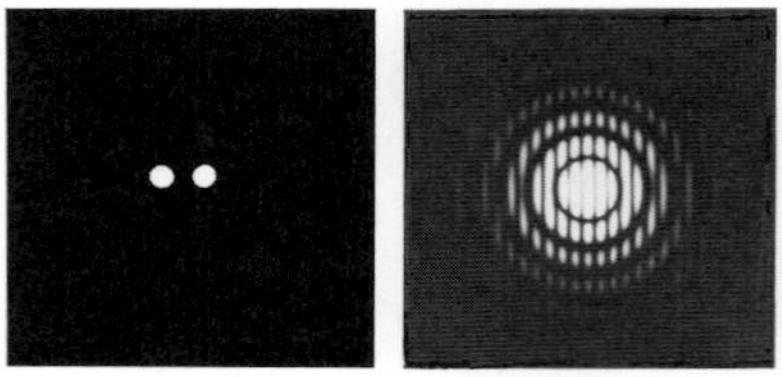

Figure J22
Two holes and their diffraction pattern.
Professor C. A. Taylor

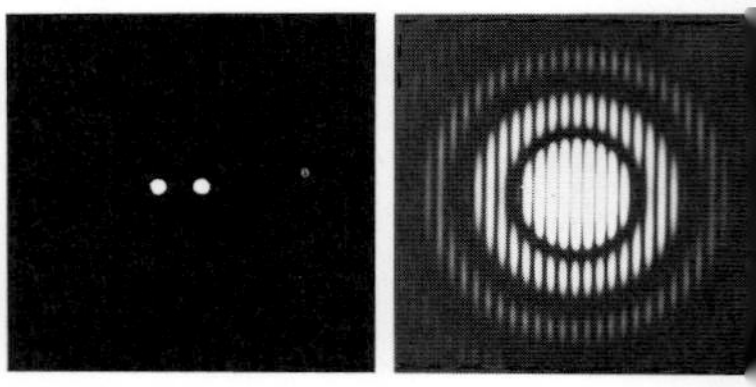

Figure J23
Two smaller holes but with same spacing
as figure J22 and their diffraction pattern
Professor C. A. Taylor

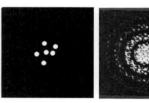

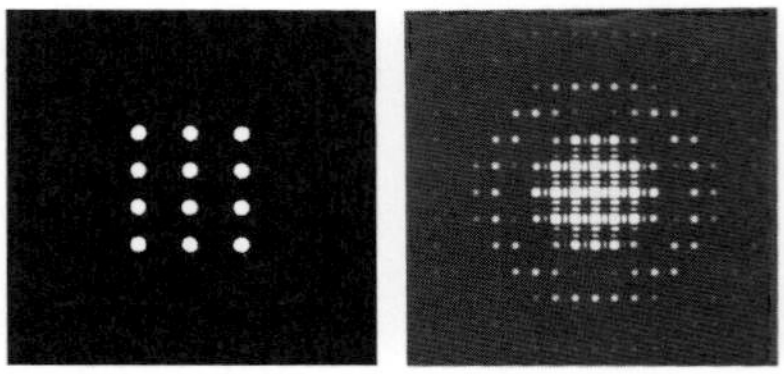

Figure J24
Twelve holes and their diffraction pattern.
Professor C. A. Taylor

Figure J25
Random array of holes and their
diffraction pattern.
Professor C. A. Taylor

X-ray diffraction

QUESTION 29

An array of atoms in a crystal can act as a complex grating for radiation
of a small enough wavelength. X-rays have a wavelength roughly equal
to the size of an atom. Since X-rays cannot be focused, the diffraction
pattern cannot be recombined, so decoding the information in the
diffraction pattern is not straightforward. Furthermore, the scattering
array is three-dimensional, and the diffraction pattern is highly dependent on the orientation of the X-ray beam relative to the crystal. One way
to decode the information in the diffraction pattern is to start from a
'ball-and-stick' model of the structure previously constructed from
other physical and chemical data and to make an optical grating
corresponding to the material in the X-ray beam (see figure J120
page 232). If the optical diffraction pattern of this grating compares
favourably with that from the X-ray experiment, then the model is clearly
valuable. An additional benefit of this method is that it is possible to find
out about the shape and size of atoms, or groups of atoms, from the
intensity distribution within the pattern.

High-speed computers are often used by crystallographers to
predict the diffraction pattern produced by a suggested structure.
Again, if this pattern compares well with that obtained in the X-ray
diffraction experiment then there is a close fit between the suggested
and the actual structures.

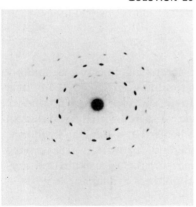

Figure J26
Early X-ray diffraction photograph of
zinc sulphide.
FRIEDRICH, KNIPPING, and *LAUE.*
Sitzungsberichte der Königlich Bayerischen
Academie der Wissenschaften,
Munich, 1912.
By courtesy of The British Library

Holography

QUESTION 30 In holography light illuminates an object and produces a particular set of superposition patterns called a hologram, which can be recorded on a photographic plate. This plate carries all the amplitude and phase information needed to create a true, three-dimensional image of the original object when correctly illuminated.

Figure J27
Perspective obtained by viewing a hologram from different angles.
K. Bazargan

In the production of a hologram a coherent beam of light (one having a constant phase relationship between all the waves, for example a laser beam) is split into two. One beam strikes the object and the other, called the reference beam, travels directly to the plate. The light which is scattered from each point on the object sets up a superposition pattern with the reference beam at the plate. The plate thus records a pattern from every illuminated part of the object – the result is an immensely complex set of diffraction patterns. Since each point on the object scatters waves in very many directions, each part of the hologram contains some contribution from *every* part of the object in the form of the superposition pattern. Thus each piece of the hologram (providing it is not too small) is able to reconstruct a complete image of the object.

DEMONSTRATION J17
Reconstructing the image
from a hologram

In the reconstruction stage, the developed plate is illuminated by the reference beam from its original direction. The image reconstructed from each of the patterns on the plate is actually the image of a point on the original object and the observer thus sees a complete set of images corresponding to one particular view of the object.

'maging' in the Reader *Particles, imaging,
and nuclei*

From a different viewpoint, the observer sees a new set of recombined images corresponding to a different view of the original object. The overall image is thus three-dimensional.

READING
Some applications of holography
(page 174)

Holography is becoming increasingly important as a technique for detecting and measuring minute movements, and in the storage and retrieval of three-dimensional images.

Section J3 ELECTROMAGNETIC WAVES

Radio waves, microwaves, light, X-rays, and gamma rays all belong t
the family of electromagnetic waves called the *electromagnetic spectrum*
(figure J28). The discovery, generation, and application of these wave
have formed an important thread in the development of science an
engineering.

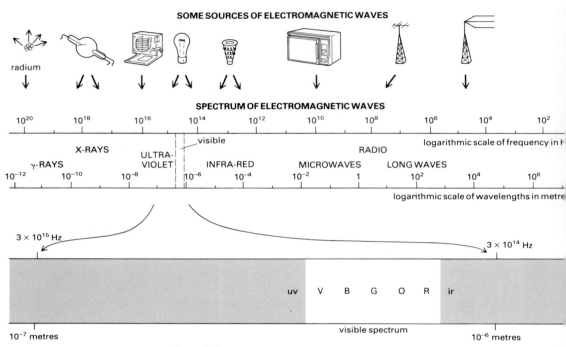

Figure J28
Schematic representation of the electromagnetic spectrum.

Waves that are 'tied' to a 'guide'

An electromagnetic wave which moves along a pair of long paralle
plates or rods is directly associated with the charges in the plates. It i
said to be *tied* to the plates, which form a *waveguide*. An oscillato
connected across the ends of the plates produces an alternating p.d. at
very high frequency, and alternating regions of excess positive an
negative charge are set up on the plates. These charged regions have a
electric or *E*-field associated with them.

Because they are moving they constitute a current, so there is also
magnetic or *B*-field. The patches of moving charge and the associate
pattern of *E*- and *B*-fields (which we call the electromagnetic wave
move along the guide at a very high, though finite speed. (Th
individual charges, for instance electrons, move at a very much lowe
speed.) The plates do not continue indefinitely and the wave is reflecte
at the far end. As the reflected and incident waves have the sam
frequency and speed but move in opposite directions, a standing wave i
produced.

DEMONSTRATION J18a
Guided or 'tied' waves

QUESTION 35

The antinodes of the standing wave can be located using a pair of conducting rods forming a dipole aerial (figure J29). The changing concentrations of positive and negative charge on the plates set up an alternating e.m.f. between the ends of the dipole. This is rectified using a diode.

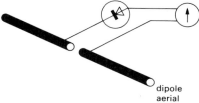

Figure J29
Dipole aerial.

Unit D 'Oscillations and waves'

DEMONSTRATION J19
The speed of a pulse along a coaxial cable

QUESTIONS 36, 37

Since the antinodes in a standing wave pattern are $\lambda/2$ apart, we can calculate the speed of the wave if we know, or can estimate, the frequency of the oscillator.

The speed of the wave can be calculated more directly if the time taken for a pulse to travel down a long coaxial cable is measured. The value is close to $3 \times 10^8 \, \text{m s}^{-1}$, but less, since the wave is travelling partly in plastic. Figure J30 is a representation of the E- and B-fields for an electromagnetic wave pulse in a coaxial cable.

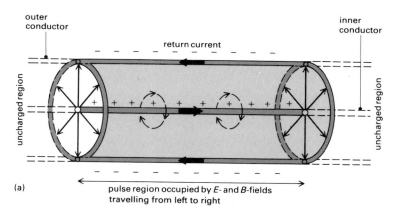

(a)

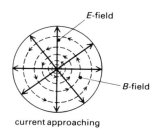

(b)   current approaching

Figure J30
E- and B-fields in a coaxial cable. (a) Side view; (b) end view.

When the pulse reaches an open end it is reflected (with some loss of energy). The direction of the E-field in the reflected pulse is the same as that of the incoming pulse, while the direction of the B-field is reversed. If the conductors are short-circuited at the end, the B-field is unchanged but the E-field is reversed. This results in a reflected pulse of opposite sign when viewed on an oscilloscope (figure J31). With a suitable resistance joining the two conductors it is possible to absorb the pulse: no energy is reflected and the guide behaves as if it were infinitely long.

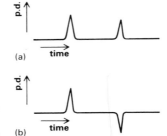

Figure J31
Oscilloscope traces of incident and reflected pulses. (a) Open circuit; (b) short circuit.

QUESTIONS 38, 39

'Systems' in the Reader *Physics in engineering and technology*

Avoiding such reflections, which generate spurious signals, is very important in all systems where waveguides or cables are used to join aerials, receivers, and transmitters. This is an example of the important process called *impedance matching*.

Some suggestions for the geometry of the travelling wave

Figure J32(a) shows how an electromagnetic wave pulse might travel along a waveguide consisting of two long, flat plates, as in demonstration J18a. The moving regions of opposite charge have a pattern of travelling E- and B-fields associated with them. The E- and B-fields are perpendicular to each other and to the direction in which the pulse travels. Figure J32(b) shows how the two fields alone can be represented more simply.

If the source of energy is, say, an oscillator, as in demonstration J18a, then figure J32(c) shows how the continuous electromagnetic wave of travelling E- and B-fields might propagate.

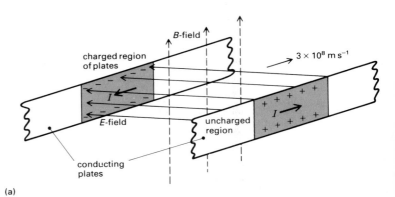

(a)

Figure J32 *(part)*
(a) Electromagnetic wave pulse.

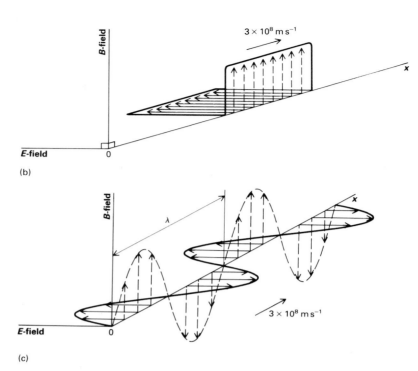

$3 \times 10^8\,\text{m s}^{-1}$

B-field

E-field

(b)

B-field

λ

$3 \times 10^8\,\text{m s}^{-1}$

E-field

(c)

Figure J32 *(part)*
(b) Graphical representation of (a).
(c) Sinusoidal e-m wave.

The free electromagnetic wave

The diagram of the moving *E*- and *B*-fields in figure J32(a) shows the fields directly associated with travelling charges. An electromagnetic wave propagating freely in air between transmitting and receiving dipoles has the same wavelength and speed as the 'tied' wave and yet, rather extraordinarily, has broken free of the waveguide and the charges which generated it.

Freely travelling electromagnetic waves are very much part of our everyday existence. Apart from light, which so much of life obviously depends on, many parts of the electromagnetic spectrum are vital to communications and modern technology of many kinds. We take the tied wave illustrated in figures J32(b) and (c) as a model for what a free wave might be like. A number of observations indicates that this might be a reasonable thing to do:

One is the common wavelength, speed, and method of detection of the 'tied' and free gigahertz waves.

Another is the fact that *all* members of the electromagnetic spectrum travel at exactly the same speed in a vacuum. The speed of an electromagnetic wave in a vacuum is one of the most important physical constants, and has been measured with great precision.

DEMONSTRATION J18b
Free waves

QUESTIONS 40, 41

Wavelength/m	Speed/10^8 m s^{-1}
5.4	2.9978 ± 0.0003
1.8	2.99795 ± 0.00003
1.0	2.99792 ± 0.00002
1.0×10^{-1}	2.99792 ± 0.00009
1.2×10^{-2}	2.997928 ± 0.000003
4.2×10^{-3}	2.997925 ± 0.000001
5.6×10^{-7}	2.997931 ± 0.000003
2.5×10^{-12}	2.983 ± 0.015
7.3×10^{-15}	2.97 ± 0.03

Table J1
The speed of electromagnetic waves.
Adapted from FRENCH, A. P. Special Relativity. *Nelson, 1968.*

J

The third is a theoretical derivation, based on the laws of electricity and magnetism, which allowed Maxwell (1831–1879) to predict the speed and properties of both free and tied electromagnetic waves before they had been measured experimentally. The analysis shows that the speed of all electromagnetic waves *in vacuo* is:

DEMONSTRATION J20
Speed of light

QUESTIONS 42, 43

$$c = \frac{1}{(\varepsilon_0 \mu_0)^{\frac{1}{2}}}$$

where ε_0 and μ_0 are, respectively, the permittivity and the permeability of free space (that is, a vacuum).

The fourth observation concerns the phenomenon of polarization. Both 'tied' and 'free' waves may be polarized and thus must be transverse waves.

Aerials

QUESTIONS 44, 45

An aerial is a device used to receive or transmit radiation in the radio wave region of the electromagnetic spectrum. For receiving wavelengths of the order of a metre a dipole is convenient. For longer wavelengths, 200 m to 2000 m (1.5 MHz 'medium wave' to 150 kHz 'long wave'), a coil is used. The coil is wrapped round a ferrite rod to increase the B-field and hence the alternating e.m.f. induced in the coil (figure J33). The rod should be oriented parallel to the B-field to maximize the flux through the coils.

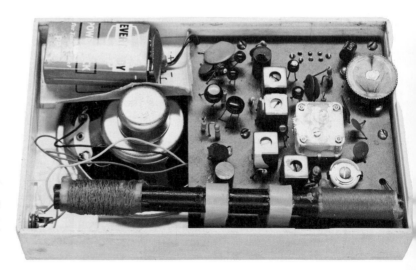

Figure J33
Portable radio with ferrite rod aerial.
Michael Plomer

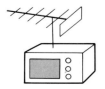

Figure J34
Television multi-element aerial array.

A dipole aerial can be improved by adding a metal reflector behind the dipole and/or one or more director rods in front of it. The principle of superposition is the key to designing such an aerial array: the waves reflected by the reflector and those scattered by the director rods must arrive at the dipole in phase with the original wave if the signal is to be increased. The more director rods an aerial array has the stronger the signal, but such an aerial must be accurately directed towards the transmitter. This behaviour could be compared with the increased brightness and improved resolution achieved when more slits of a diffraction grating are illuminated.

Polarization

A plane-polarized wave is one in which the varying E-field is only in one plane. The wave shown in figure J35 is plane polarized, with the electric vector vertical. (The waves illustrated in figure J32 are also plane polarized.) In an unpolarized wave the E-field has components in all directions perpendicular to the direction of propagation. The B-field is, of course, always perpendicular to the E-field.

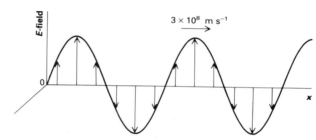

Figure J35
Polarized electromagnetic wave.

EXPERIMENTS J21a, b
Polarization

The aerial array illustrated in figure J34 is oriented to detect a polarized wave with the E-field horizontal. A dipole aerial receives no signal when it is at 90° to the transmitting dipole; the signal is maximum when the two dipoles are parallel. If a grid of wires is placed between the transmitter and receiver, no signal is received when the grid is parallel to the dipole rods. When the dipole transmits an electromagnetic wave with the electric field vector parallel to the rods, the grid does not transmit energy because the incident E-field sets the free electrons in the rods oscillating along the length of the rods, thus removing energy from the wave. The same phenomenon is displayed by the microwave equipment.

Polarization of light

QUESTIONS 46, 47

Light waves are usually generated by a large number of random, independent atomic processes, so they have no single plane of polarization and are said to be unpolarized. However, a material such as Polaroid transmits light with only one plane of polarization. Polaroid consists of long-chain molecules oriented parallel to each other; these act for light in much the same way as the parallel grid of rods does for microwaves.

EXPERIMENT J21c
Polaroid

The transmitted wave has no component of oscillating E-field in a direction parallel to the long-chain molecules in the material.

Polarization by reflection and scattering

EXPERIMENT J21d
Polarization by reflection and scattering

When unpolarized light is reflected by materials such as glass and water the light becomes partially polarized. This is because the component of the E-field parallel to the surface is reflected more strongly than the component perpendicular to the surface, the degree of polarization depending on the angle of incidence. The reflected beam is partly absorbed by Polaroid oriented to transmit light whose E-field is perpendicular to the surface. This is used to good effect in certain sunglasses, which reduce glare from such horizontal surfaces as the sea or a shiny road.

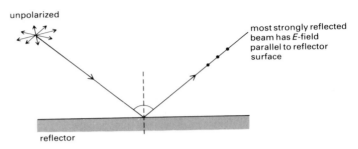

Figure J36
Polarization by reflection.

Light scattered through 90° is polarized. Sunlight scattered from the small particles in the atmosphere is partially plane polarized. Some insects, for example bees, have eyes which are sensitive to the plane of polarization and can use polarized light from the sky to navigate.

READINGS

MEASUREMENT OF RED BLOOD CELL DIAMETERS USING A LASER

(This article, by C. Bowlt, first appeared in *Physics education*, **6**, 1971, pages 13–15.)

Introduction

The experiment described here is not new, but the application of laser light to it, although obvious, does not seem to have been described. It seems to me to be sufficiently arresting to be introduced into optics teaching, either as a demonstration or as a laboratory experiment.

It has long been realized that if a beam of light passes through a not too dense but irregular array of small, uniformly sized particles, a concentric system of circular interference fringes will result. Newton observed coloured haloes around both the Sun and the Moon and attributed them to the action of small water globules in the air. The effect was also observed by Young over 150 years ago and he attempted to use it as a method for measuring the diameters of very small particles, including red blood cells. However, as a measuring technique the effect was not seriously investigated until 100 years later. The method requires a strong source of monochromatic light. Prior to the advent of the laser around 1960, such sources were not available and a number of the early investigators using non-monochromatic light concluded that the method was unreliable. In 1928 Allen and Ponder, using weak monochromatic light, showed that experimental results did accord with theory. The technique continued to be used for blood cell measurements for a number of years, but was eventually abandoned for clinical diagnostic purposes; principally, it would seem, because of the lack of an intense monochromatic light source.

The laser is a device producing a very intense beam of highly monochromatic, coherent light and is thus the ideal source for use with the method, providing a simple and elegant way for measuring the average diameter of a sample of several thousand blood cells or any other circular or spherical particles. At about the same time as the invention of the laser, the Coulter counter became available for the counting and measurement of small particles and the volumes of individual blood cells can now be found with ease using it. Had the laser been invented earlier, the diffraction method of measuring blood cells might not have been abandoned.

Theory

Diffraction of a parallel beam of light passing through a narrow slit produces on a screen (placed effectively at infinity) a series of line fringes centred on the straight-through position. The condition for a dark fringe to occur is $n\lambda/b = \sin\theta$, where n is the fringe order 1, 2, 3, ..., λ the wavelength of light, b the slit width, and θ the angular deviation of the diffracted beam.

For a circular hole, interference occurs between all rays from the whole area producing a series of concentric fringes. The exact solution in this case is more complicated, but turns out to be of the same form as for a slit, except that n is non-integer (that is, $n = 1.22, 2.23, 3.24, 4.24, 5.25, \ldots$).

Babinet's principle, which applies to any point outside the area illuminated by the undiffracted beam, states that the illumination is unaltered if the transparent parts of an aperture become opaque and the opaque parts transparent. Thus the same pattern of fringes will be produced by a circular hole in an opaque screen and by a circular disc of the same diameter as the hole, so that a single blood cell of diameter b will also produce a series of concentric fringes. In a blood smear there are many cells distributed randomly. The only effect of this is to enhance the intensity of the diffraction pattern due to a single cell.

If the angular deviation is small, $\sin\theta \approx \theta \approx S_n/L$, where S_n is the radius of the nth dark fringe and L is the distance between the diffracting particles and the screen, then $b = n\lambda L/S_n$ ($n = 1.22, 2.23$, etc.)

Experiment

The fringe pattern shown in figure J37 was produced on a screen by a parallel beam of light from a helium–neon gas laser passing through a

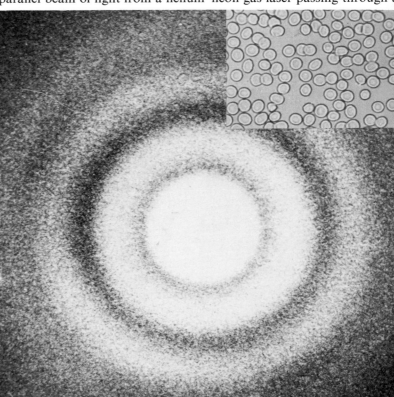

Figure J37
Interference fringes produced by diffraction of laser light by red cells.
Inset: A photomicrograph of a dried smear of red blood cells.

blood smear on a microscope slide. The great range in light intensity makes it difficult to show on a photograph all the orders observable by eye. The granular appearance of the fringe pattern is characteristic of laser light reflected from a surface. A very small quantity of blood was required and the only difficulty in producing a suitable smear was to spread the blood thinly enough to prevent the red cells overlapping (see inset, figure J37). Some adjustment of the position of the smear in the beam was required to find the area of the smear giving the most distinct fringes.

The thin film of blood will quickly dry unless covered with a cover slip. Fringes are produced by both wet and dry films, but it was found easier to produce distinct fringes with dry films. It should be borne in mind that the diameter of red blood cells shrinks about 10 per cent on drying. No focusing of the diffracted light was required. With the particular laser used, and with the distance between the blood smear and screen of the order of 20 cm so that the percentage error in its measurement was small, five fringes were visible. Best results were obviously obtained in a darkened room, but it was possible to see three fringes in ordinary lighting. Table J2 shows the diameters of the dark fringes at a distance (L) of 15.5 ± 0.15 cm from a dried blood smear obtained using laser light with wavelength (λ) of 6.328×10^{-7} m.

Figure J38 shows the fringe *diameters* plotted against n. Since theory requires a straight line passing through the origin, results such as these are a nice illustration that for diffraction by circular objects the orders (n) are non-integer, and that the values 1.22 and so on which are difficult to derive theoretically certainly produce a better fit. The slope of this line gives $n/2S_n$, and since

$$b = \left(\frac{n}{S_n}\right)\lambda L$$

$$b = (2 \times \text{slope})\lambda L$$

Dark fringe	n	Fringe diameter, $2S_n$/cm
1st	1.22	3.2
2nd	2.23	5.9
3rd	3.24	8.5
4th	4.24	11.4
5th	5.25	14.3

Table J2

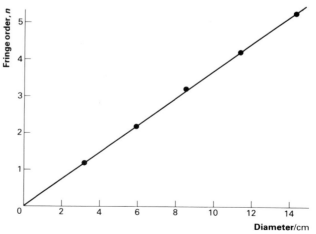

Figure J38
Plot of fringe diameter against fringe order, n.

This experiment gives the value $b = 7.3 \pm 0.2 \times 10^{-6}$ m. This is in agreement with Ponder's (1947) findings of 7.3 to 7.6×10^{-6} m, according to whom the actual value depends on the conditions of drying. It must be remembered that this is a mean diameter of a large number of cells. To produce such a result by direct measurement using a microscope would be very tedious, but a calibrated microscope can be used to show quickly that the diffraction result is certainly of the right order. An interesting point arises in contrasting these two methods of measurement. In using the microscope much care is needed to eliminate the diffraction rings from the field of view and obtain a sharp focus, whereas in the method described here it is these diffraction rings which provide the measurement.

Questions

a Explain what is meant by 'monochromatic' and 'coherent' (paragraph 3).

b i What fringe pattern would you get in the experiment if you did not use monochromatic light?
ii Explain why the calculation of blood cell diameter would thus be very difficult.

c How can 'the action of small water globules in the air' (paragraph 2) produce coloured haloes around the Sun and the Moon?

d With the help of a diagram, explain what is meant by 'fringe order' and 'angular deviation of the diffracted beam' (paragraph 4).

e According to Babinet's principle (paragraph 6), what would the fringe pattern caused by a straight human hair look like? To what condition must you adhere for this principle to apply?

f Taking values of n, λ, L, and S_n from the text, show that the calculated value of b is correct.

g If figure J37 is approximately life size, what is the minimum uncertainty in the measurement of fringe diameter expressed as a percentage?

h Is the value of cell diameter $b = 7.3 \pm 0.2 \times 10^{-6}$ m given in the passage consistent with your answer to question **g**? Explain.

SOME APPLICATIONS OF HOLOGRAPHY

The applications of holography cover an extremely wide range, from advertising on the one hand to scientific research on the other.

The capturing and subsequent comparison of minute movements in three dimensions has become possible using a technique called *holographic interferometry*. If, in the production of a normal transmission hologram the subject moves very slightly, then the superposition patterns on the hologram change. The reconstructed image then contains fringes which yield information about the object's movement. Such techniques have been used in, for example, a study of the vibrational characteristics of the fan blades in an aero engine; the investigation of distortion in the cone of a moving-coil high fidelity loudspeaker; the design of artificial hip joints; and in aerodynamics (see figure J39).

Figure J39
Double exposure holographic interferogram showing the flow field around an aerofoil, mounted in a wind tunnel.
Rolls–Royce Ltd

The capability of a hologram to store three-dimensional information may also be used to good effect. The microscopic examination and recording of cracks and flaws in the fuel elements from an Advanced Gas-cooled Reactor (figure J40) is carried out safely and conveniently using a holographic recording. The large storage space needed for millions of moulds of teeth has been reduced as the hologram replaces the dental mould for the purposes of inspection and analysis.

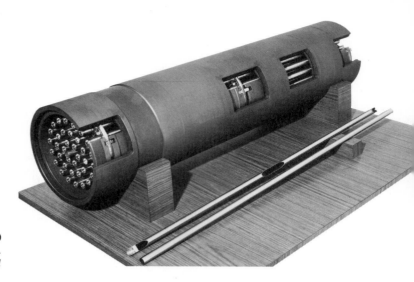

Figure J40
AGR fuel element.
Central Electricity Generating Board

Precious art objects reproduced as high quality images from a hologram make it possible for people in remote regions to experience cultural treasures in a most life-like form (see figure J41). Indeed, artists themselves have been quick to develop holography into an exciting new artform in its own right.

Figure J41
Holograms of icons and jewellery.
Hologram by NIKFI (USSR)
French Museum of Holography, Paris/Eve
Ritscher Associates Ltd

If a hologram is made of a scene incorporating a magnifying lens then the viewer of the hologram can look through the lens and see a magnified image of the subject that lies behind it, as if he were viewing the scene itself through the lens. This use of optical components in holography is finding increasing commercial application.

Devices to read bar codes on supermarket items are not new, but the laser scanner has made a considerable improvement. The beam detector can read the code within an angle of 180° of the scanning window, so the package need not be so carefully slid past the small window (figure J42). The scanner uses a spinning holographic optical element to split a laser beam into a large number of intersecting beams in space. It replaces the previous, cumbersome method which used rotating mirrors.

Figure J42
Scanned laser beam 'reading' the bar code on a product.
Richard Turpin. Courtesy of IBM United Kingdom Ltd

Figure J43
British Telecom Phonecard.
British Telecom/Landis & Gyr Ltd

In order to increase both the data storage capacity and the protection from forgery, credit card companies have begun to replace the magnetic strip on their credit cards with one which is holographically encoded (figure J43).

RELATIVITY

This article is concerned with some important, and perhaps surprising consequences of two pieces of experimental evidence about the speed of electromagnetic waves. The experimental evidence was graphically outlined by Einstein in 1920.

'There is hardly a simpler law in physics than that according to which light is propagated in empty space. Every child at school knows, or believes he knows, that this propagation takes place in straight lines with a velocity $c = 300\,000\,\text{km}\,\text{s}^{-1}$. At all events we know with great exactness that this velocity is the same for all colours, because if this were not the case, the minimum of emission would not be observed simultaneously for different colours during the eclipse of a fixed star by its dark neighbour. By means of similar considerations based on observations of double stars, the Dutch astronomer Willem de Sitter was able to show that the velocity of propagation of light cannot depend on the velocity of motion of the body emitting the light. ...

'... In short, let us assume that the simple law of the constancy of the velocity of light c (in vacuum) is justifiably believed by the child at

school. Who would imagine that this simple law has plunged th
conscientiously thoughtful physicist into the greatest intellectua
difficulties?'

From EINSTEIN, A. *Relativity: the special and the general theory*
Methuen, 1920.

Figure J44
Albert Einstein in 1905, the year in which
his paper which provided the Special
Theory of Relativity was published.
The Hebrew University of Jerusalem

The high but *finite* speed of $3 \times 10^8\,\mathrm{m\,s^{-1}}$ shared by all freely
propagating electromagnetic waves can have some surprising consequences as illustrated by this account of a dream Einstein is reputed to
have had. It is about one of the ideas that led him to his theory of special
relativity, though the theory itself is not involved here.

Einstein dreamed that he was in a field with six cows of an
unusually agile breed. Their grazing was controlled by an electric fence
to which a high-voltage pulse was applied every few seconds. But at the
time of Einstein's dream the battery had run down, and the cows had
become accustomed to touching the fence gently, and were grazing
right up to it. The farmer was replacing the battery at one end of the
fence and Einstein was standing near the other end of the fence
watching. When the farmer switched on Einstein saw the cows jump
back.

The farmer came across, and Einstein said to him, 'Your cows react very quickly. They all jumped back from the fence the instant you switched on, and they kept in a line perfectly parallel with the fence.' The farmer replied, 'They are better than that. The first had jumped back before the electricity had got to your end of the fence. Although they kept in a straight line, the line was at an angle to the fence after they had started to move.' He took some paper out of his pocket and sketched what he had seen – figure J45(a). Einstein drew a different sketch, shown in figure J45(b), and the farmer looked at it. 'Is this how you saw them at the same moment my sketch describes?' he asked.

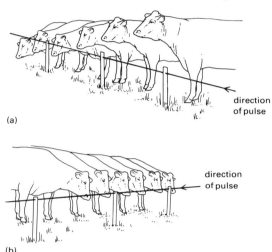

Figure J45
Einstein's dream.
(a) The farmer's sketch.
(b) Einstein's sketch.

How would you expect Einstein to have answered and explained it all?

Because the speed of light is finite, Einstein and the farmer gave two quite different descriptions of the same event.

The second piece of experimental evidence, is the perhaps surprising fact that the speed of light is constant and independent of the velocity of the emitter. Imagine that one is heading towards the Sun in a spacecraft, travelling very fast, at, say, $10^8 \, \text{m s}^{-1}$. Will sunlight go past at $4 \times 10^8 \, \text{m s}^{-1}$ (as it would if light were like any other object coming the other way)? No, all measurements show that light goes past everyone at the same speed, regardless of any relative motion between the source emitting the light and the observer.

As well as the experimental evidence of de Sitter, and also of Michelson and Morley, there are cogent theoretical arguments for the constancy of the speed of light. If it changed with the velocity of the emitter, it would be possible to determine the velocity of the emitter absolutely. But this would be at variance both with the laws of electromagnetism which had allowed Maxwell to predict c, but which dealt only in *relative* velocities, and also with the laws of mechanics, which are unchanged when a body moves with constant velocity and thus cannot be used to determine its absolute speed.

Einstein assumed that it can never be possible to measure th
absolute motion of a body. A direct consequence is that the velocity c
light must be the same regardless of the speed of the source and th
measurer. The Special Theory of Relativity is the mathematical workin,
out of Einstein's fundamental assumption. It concerns the description
which two observers (moving at constant velocity relative to on
another) give of the same event. We can see some of the surprisin,
predictions made by the theory by considering an imagined experimen
with two observers, A and B, on spaceships moving with a relativ
velocity, v. They communicate by sending radio signals.

We begin by asking how observer A might set about determining B'
speed. Both have clocks which are initially set to zero. At the momen
they pass each other, A and B both start their onboard clocks – figur
J46(a). Then, after waiting for a time t_1, A sends out a radio puls
towards B – figure J46(b). At some later time, B detects this pulse an
immediately reflects it back to A – figure J46(c). Eventually A receive
the reflected pulse at time t_2 – figure J46(d).

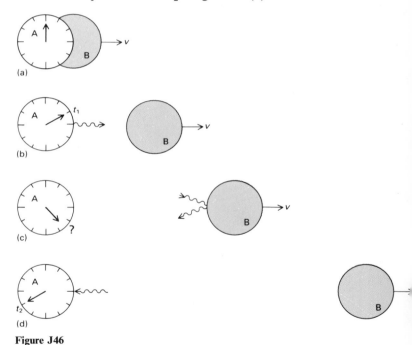

(a)

(b)

(c)

(d)

Figure J46

A makes the following calculation

If the pulse travels at the same speed in both directions (as indeed i
must) then A reasons that the pulse must have been reflected at a tim
midway between when she sent it out (t_1), and the time that she receive
the reflection (t_2). Hence she calculates that the reflection took plac
$\dfrac{(t_2 - t_1)}{2}$ after she sent the pulse, that is, at a time $\dfrac{(t_2 - t_1)}{2} + t_1 = \dfrac{t_1 + t}{2}$
after the spacecraft passed and A and B started their clocks.

The separation between the spaceships when the reflection occurs

= speed of the pulse × time the pulse takes to reach B

$$= c \times \frac{(t_2 - t_1)}{2}$$

Thus A calculates that B travels a distance

$$\frac{c(t_2 - t_1)}{2}$$

in a time

$$\frac{(t_1 + t_2)}{2}$$

and hence his speed is

$$v = \frac{c(t_2 - t_1)}{(t_1 + t_2)} \qquad [1]$$

What does B make of the experiment?

B records the arrival of the pulse at a time t_B on his clock. This is the only measurement he can make. t_B must be larger than t_1 because while the pulse is travelling from A to B the two spacecraft are moving further apart. (If, for example, the pulse travelled very slowly – c was very small – yet the relative speed of B was very large, then t_B would be much greater than t_1.)

Let us say that $t_B = k t_1$, where k depends on the pulse speed and relative speed of A and B.

What happens on reflection?

The speed of the pulse remains c regardless of relative motion. For both A and B the pulse moves away at the same speed, c; and both observe the other spacecraft receding at speed v. If this were NOT true then it would be possible for A and B to determine their absolute motions.

Thus when B measures the time of departure of the reflected pulse as t_B and A measures its time of arrival as t_2, then t_2 is larger than t_B by the same factor k as before.

Thus $t_2 = k t_B$

so $\quad t_2 = k^2 t_1 \qquad [2]$

The solution to equations [1] and [2] is:

$$k = \sqrt{\frac{(1 + v/c)}{(1 - v/c)}} \quad \Rightarrow \quad k = \frac{1 + v/c}{\sqrt{1 - v^2/c^2}}$$

Time dilation

From our imagined spacecraft experiment we can see an important consequence of the principle of relativity. *According to A the pulse arrives at spaceship B at time* $\frac{1}{2}(t_1 + t_2)$. Let us call this time t_A.

According to B the pulse arrives at time t_B:

Now $t_B = kt_1$ $\Rightarrow$ $t_1 = t_B/k$

and $t_2 = kt_B$ $\Rightarrow$ $t_2 = t_B k$

Hence $t_A = \frac{1}{2}(t_1 + t_2) = \frac{1}{2}t_B(k + 1/k)$

But $k = \sqrt{\dfrac{(1 + v/c)}{(1 - v/c)}}$

So $t_A = \frac{1}{2}t_B \left(\sqrt{\dfrac{(1 + v/c)}{(1 - v/c)}} + \sqrt{\dfrac{(1 - v/c)}{(1 + v/c)}} \right)$

$= \frac{1}{2}t_B \left(\dfrac{(1 + v/c) + (1 - v/c)}{\sqrt{1 - v/c}\,\sqrt{1 + v/c}} \right)$

$= t_B \dfrac{1}{\sqrt{(1 - v^2/c^2)}}$

$\Rightarrow$ $t_B = t_A \sqrt{(1 - v^2/c^2)}$

This is the time dilation equation. It says that t_B, the time interval *measured* by B with his clock, is always smaller by a factor $\sqrt{1 - v^2/c^2}$ than the time t_A of the equivalent time interval as *calculated* by A from measurements made with her own clock.

Figure J47 shows how the ratio t_A/t_B varies with the relative velocity v. Only when v is an appreciable fraction of the speed of light is the ratio t_A/t_B significantly different from unity. Such high velocities are not part of our everyday experience, and so time dilation and other relativistic effects seem surprising and perhaps hard to accept. But time dilation is tested every day in high energy physics laboratories where experiments using particles moving at speeds very close to c are routinely performed.

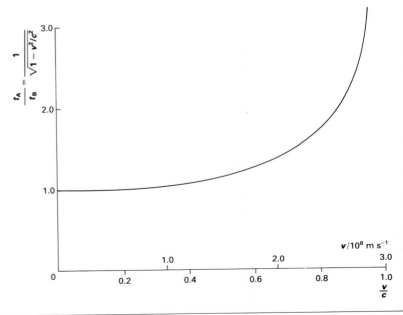

Figure J47

One particular example of time dilation is the unexpectedly long lives that rapidly moving π-mesons appear to have. π-mesons are unstable particles with a mass in between those of an electron and a proton. They are produced when rapidly moving protons bombard atomic nuclei in a target such as aluminium. Figure J48 is a plan of the proton accelerator at CERN (the European nuclear research laboratory) which was used in some experiments performed in the 1960s. This accelerator is quite small by today's standards, being about 200 m in diameter. A beam of particles, including π-mesons, was produced from targets placed in the proton beam in the accelerator ring. The π-mesons were detected in a bubble chamber (not shown in the diagram) beyond the experimental hall, more than 200 m from the point where they were produced.

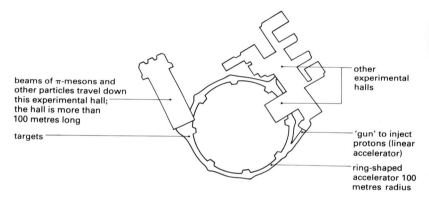

Figure J48
Plan of the proton accelerator used in the experiments with π-mesons.

π-mesons are unstable, and on average live for only 2.5×10^{-8} s (the lifetime being measured when the particles are at rest, or nearly so) before they decay into other particles. Moving at very nearly 3×10^8 m s^{-1} a π-meson will travel only 7.5 m in this time. This is an average value, but the fraction living for much longer is small. Yet the experimental hall is at least 100 m long, and the path laid out for the mesons is even longer. Were the designers very foolish, expecting the mesons to travel between ten and twenty times as far as an average meson could go before decaying? How many actually reach the bubble chamber?

In fact, the set-up does not waste a good beam of mesons. Because they are travelling so fast, they seem to us to live longer, and the effect is big enough for most of them to get to the far end of the hall. This is the time dilation effect predicted by relativity theory. In this case, the effect is by no means a small one: the mesons live much longer than they 'ought' to. We can use the time dilation formula to show how fast the π-mesons must be travelling to produce such a phenomenon.

t_B is the average lifetime of a π-meson measured by the π-meson itself and is thus equal to the lifetime measured when the particles are at rest. t_A is the time calculated by an observer in the laboratory from measurements made on the high speed π-mesons. If t_A is about $20 \times t_B$, then the speed of the π-mesons is given by v where:

$$t_B = t_A \sqrt{1 - v^2/c^2}$$

$$1 = 20 \sqrt{1 - v^2/c^2}$$

$$1/400 = 1 - v^2/c^2$$

$$v = 0.999c$$

(From the meson's point of view, however, the length of the experimental hall seems to be the few metres it could expect to travel in a normal lifetime.)

Other relativistic effects

Time dilation is just one of the surprising consequences of the fact that the speed of light is finite and the same for all observers. Other outcomes of the Special Theory of Relativity include mass increase and length contraction. A moving object appears to be more massive and shorter than the same object at rest in the laboratory. Like time dilation the size of these effects depends on v^2/c^2, so unless v is an appreciable fraction of c the effects are negligible.

Forces are altered too. For example, the force between a pair of electrons will seem to be reduced by about v^2/c^2 if they move together sideways relative to the instruments or observer investigating the force. This fact links electricity and magnetism. Although the velocities of charge carriers in electric currents are very small (see Unit B, 'Currents circuits, and charge') the fact that very large numbers of them are involved gives a sizeable effect. Magnetism is an everyday example of a relativistic effect.

The fact that the speed of light does not depend on the velocity of the source relative to the observer has to be taken into account in an analysis of the Doppler effect. This is the name given to the effect (well known before the theory of relativity was developed) whereby the frequency of light emitted by a moving source appears to depend on the relative motion of the source and the observer. If the source and observer are moving apart the frequency observed decreases. This is the well known red shift, widely used by astronomers to find the velocities of distant stars and galaxies. It has led to our present picture of an expanding Universe in which distant galaxies are receding at speeds proportional to their distances from us.

LABORATORY NOTES

EXPERIMENT
J1   Looking at a lamp through a slit and through a pin-hole

holder with two halves of a razor blade, to be used as a single slit
set of colour filters (red, blue, green)
aluminium foil
35 mm slide mounts
copper wire, 0.2 mm diameter, bare
steel or nichrome wire, 0.2 mm diameter, bare
lamp, holder, and stand
transformer

either
matt white reflecting screen
or
white card

mains lamp with 30 cm single filament and holder

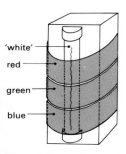

Figure J49
Single-filament lamp with colour filters.

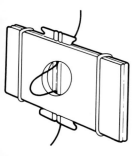

Figure J50
Adjustment of slit width to diameter of steel or nichrome wire.

Safety note: Razor blades are sharp! Take care not to get the adjustable slit too close to your face or eye. To avoid any possibility of injury, the side of the slit with the wire loop must be nearer to your eye than the side with the sharp ends.

Make as narrow a slit as possible from a pair of razor blades, by viewing the slit against an illuminated background while you adjust the blades. Hold the slit close to your eye and look at the lamp through it. Describe the patterns you obtain for one particular slit width with each of the colours, and for one colour with different slit widths.

Describe how the pattern depends *i* on the wavelength of light and *ii* on the width of the slit.

Make a circular aperture in some aluminium foil by pricking it carefully with the copper wire which has been stretched and broken. Make sure the wire is pushed through to its maximum diameter. Look at the lamp through the hole and note what you see.

As a final element in your experiment you can compare the patterns produced by a hole and slit of equal 'widths' by using the steel or nichrome wire to set the razor blade spacing equal to the hole diameter.

How are the patterns similar? How do they differ?

CIRCUS OF EXPERIMENTS
J2   Diffraction

J2a   Water waves going through a gap

ripple tank kit
illuminant
transformer
cell holder with two cells
rheostat, 10 to 15 Ω
hand-held stroboscope

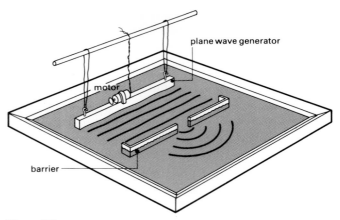

Figure J51
Diffraction of water waves at a gap.

How is the spreading of the wave affected by *i* the size of the gap and *ii* the wavelength of the waves?

You should be able to see the diffraction pattern itself; you could even make some measurements to show how the pattern depends on the wavelength and the gap size.

J2b Microwaves going through a slit

microwave transmitter
microwave receiver
general purpose amplifier
loudspeaker (if not part of above)
wax lens or plastic lens filled with paraffin (if available)
2 metal screens about 0.3 m by 0.3 m
metre rule
leads

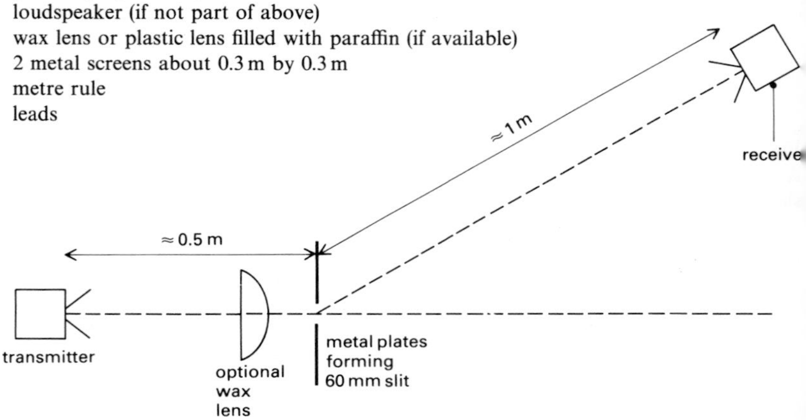

≈ 1 m

receiver

≈ 0.5 m

transmitter

optional
wax
lens

metal plates
forming
60 mm slit

Figure J52
Diffraction of microwaves.

It is important to have either the transmitter a long way from the slit or a correctly adjusted lens. Why?

Set the metal plates to form a slit 60 mm wide. By moving the receiver in an arc in front of the slit (figure J52), observe the diffraction pattern and measure the angle between the straight-through direction and that at which the first 'drop in intensity' occurs.

Try changing the slit size. How does this affect the pattern?

Why is this experiment likely to be of poor accuracy?

To see how 'less can mean more', place the transmitter and receiver as in figure J53. Slide the plate A into the beam until it cuts off the radiation to the receiver. Now slowly move plate B into the beam to vary the slit width from about 60 to 30 mm, until the receiver output increases. Less wave energy now passes through the slit, yet more energy is detected by the receiver. Why is this?

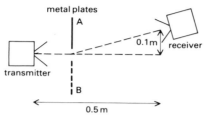

Figure J53
Superposition experiment.

J2c   Light through an adjustable slit

big stop to stand on bench
small translucent screen
eyepiece
adjustable slit
planoconvex lens, + 2D, diameter 37 mm
holder for lens of diameter 37 mm
2 holders (for eyepiece and adjustable slit)
set of colour filters (red, blue, green)
lamp, holder, and stand
transformer
holder and two halves of a razor blade
transparent ruler or 0.5 mm graticule

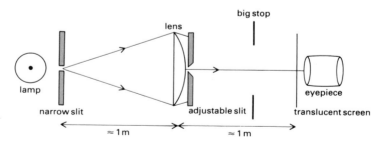

Figure J54
Diffraction of light by a single slit.

This experiment is really a rather more careful version of experiment J1.

Arrange the lamp, lens, and screen as shown in figure J54, to form a sharp image of the vertical filament on the screen. Use the big stop to prevent any light which has not passed through the lens reaching the screen. Adjust the razor blades to form a parallel-sided slit less than 1 mm wide. Put this against the lamp. Making sure that the narrow beam of light passes through the centre of the lens, move the lens a small distance further from the lamp to focus a sharp image of the slit on the screen. Put the adjustable slit just beyond the lens and gradually reduce its width until you see faint fringes on the screen.

To see the pattern more clearly, focus the eyepiece on the fringes, remove the screen, and position the transparent ruler so that its scale may be read easily. Measure the separation of a fixed number of minima or maxima for red, green, and blue light. The ratio of pairs of distances gives an approximate value for the ratio of pairs of wavelengths.

How does the diffraction pattern vary with wavelength?

J2d Ultrasound through a hole

ultrasound transmitter and receiver
milliammeter, 1 mA or 10 mA
metre rule
leads

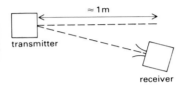

Figure J55
The diffraction of ultrasound.

Set up the transmitter and receiver about a metre apart (as shown in figure J55). Put them on the edges of two facing stools or tables to minimize troublesome reflections. Trial and error is the way to find the best arrangement.

The effective width of the aperture is the diameter of the piezo-electric transducer in the transmitter.

What is the function of the horn on the receiver?

It may be helpful to use the modulation facility for the transmitter – you will need to ask about this.

If the speed of sound in air is about $330 \, \text{m s}^{-1}$, what is the wavelength of the waves?

You should measure the diffraction pattern carefully, in particular the angle between the straight-through direction and the first minimum of intensity on either side.

EXPERIMENT
J3 Huygens's construction

A4 graph paper (*e.g.* 2 cm squares in 2 mm graduations)
pair of compasses
plastic ruler

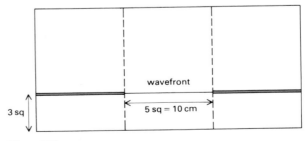

Figure J56

Mark out the barrier on graph paper and draw a wavefront which has just reached it, as in figure J56. Starting at one end of the wavefront, draw arcs from centres 1 cm apart with a radius of 3 cm into the region beyond the barrier.

Draw in the envelope of these wavefronts in ink, drawing extra arcs in any region where it is not clear.

Next, starting from this new wavefront, repeat the construction to produce a further wavefront 3 cm ahead. This process should be repeated until the 'frozen' picture of the diffracting waves becomes clear (figure J57).

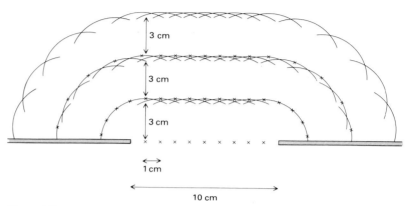

Figure J57
Huygens's construction.

DEMONSTRATION

J4 Wave amplitude and energy when waves superpose

signal generator
pre-amplifier
oscilloscope
2 loudspeakers
microphone
rheostat, 10 to 15 Ω
metre rule
3 retort stand bases, rods, bosses, and clamps
leads

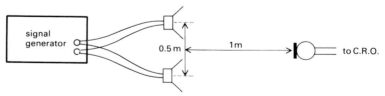

Figure J58
Amplitude and energy of a signal.

The frequency of the signal generator is set to 4 kHz and the two loudspeakers produce a superposition pattern. The loudspeakers and the microphone should be put on the edges of benches about a metre apart. The microphone is connected to an oscilloscope (via a pre-amplifier if necessary) and moved to the central maximum.

By how much is the height of the oscilloscope trace reduced if one loudspeaker is covered up? Does this show that the microphone is an 'amplitude detector'? You should be able to explain your answer.

If the oscilloscope were replaced by a resistor, how much less energy would be dissipated when one loudspeaker was covered up?

If the amplitude of the wave detected by the microphone doubles, by how much does the energy of the wave increase?

The eye and photographic film respond to intensity – the rate of arrival of energy per unit area. Intensity $\propto$ (amplitude)^2.

How is energy conserved in a superposition experiment like this, if energy seems to be created in some places and destroyed in others?

ALTERNATIVE DEMONSTRATIONS
J5 Measuring a single-slit diffraction pattern

In these demonstrations, the width of the central maximum of a diffraction pattern is measured to see if it conforms to the predicted value, given the slit width and the wavelength of the light.

J5a Using a laser

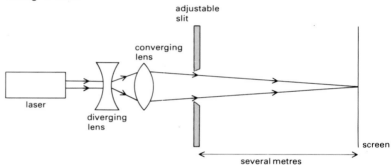

Figure J59
Measurement of single-slit diffraction pattern using a laser.

J5b Using a slide projector

either
holder for two halves of a razor blade, to be used as a single slit
or
single slit from set of slides

adjustable slit
small translucent screen
transparent ruler with mm graduations
metre rule
powerful slide projector

Whichever method is used to produce the diffraction pattern on the screen, the angle of the first order minimum, θ, is calculated from measurements of the separation of the two first order minima and the distance from the slit to the screen.

The width of the adjustable slit is measured by holding it in the plane of the carriage of a slide projector, and focusing and marking the position of the edges of its image on a distant screen. A transparent plastic ruler then replaces the slit in the projector and is moved until its image is in focus on the screen – the slit width is then read off. An alternative, for use with the laser, is to use steel or nichrome wire to set the slit width as in experiment J1.

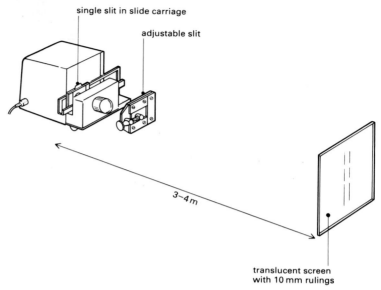

Figure J60
Measurement of single-slit diffraction pattern using a projector.

Use your values of θ and b, plus a value for the wavelength (taking either the value in the laser manufacturer's notes or an average value for white light) to check that the formula $n\lambda = b \sin \theta$ holds for the first order minimum.

DEMONSTRATION
J6 Diffraction and image recombination

J6a Diffraction at an aperture

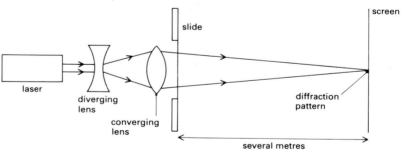

Figure J61
Diffraction at an aperture.

Diffraction patterns of slides with various apertures are obtained on the screen (figure J61). The diffraction patterns for a single slit and a small hole should be familiar to you from earlier experiments.

Try some slides of letters of the alphabet. The diffraction patterns become quite complex, but you should be able to deduce from them which letter produces which diffraction pattern.

J6b Recombination of a diffraction image

In figure J62 a more powerful converging lens is used (+ 10D), and the diffraction pattern of the slide is now very small and much closer to the slide. It may be located on a small translucent screen. The second converging lens produces an image of the slide on the screen which has been recombined from the diffraction pattern. Try some of the slides of letters from experiment J6a.

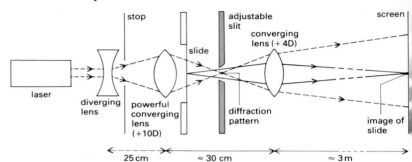

Figure J62

A phenomenon unique to diffraction imaging can be observed if an adjustable vertical slit is placed so as to cut off the higher orders of the diffraction pattern. What happens to the recombined image of the aperture on the slide as the diffraction pattern is increasingly restricted?

Why is the finer detail removed before the coarse detail? This sort of image degradation causes problems in optical systems with limited apertures.

The previous slide is removed and one consisting of an aperture with fine vertical lines is substituted (figure J63).

Figure J63

What happens to the image of the slide when the adjustable vertical slit is narrowed? Why is this?

This sort of image degradation can actually be used to *improve* image quality by the selective removal of certain unwanted features.

EXPERIMENTS

J7 Resolution

J7a Distinguishing lamps as separate

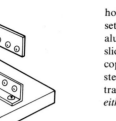

holder for two halves of a razor blade, to be used as a single slit
set of colour filters (red, blue, green)
aluminium foil
slide mounts
copper wire, 0.2 mm diameter, bare
steel or nichrome wire, 0.2 mm diameter, bare
transformer
either multiple light source with two lamps *or* 2 mounted festoon lamps

(a)

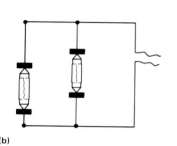

(b)

Figure J64
Resolution of two sources. (a) Multiple light source; (b) 2 filaments, vertically displaced.

Safety note: Razor blades are sharp! Take care not to get the adjustable slit too close to your face or eye.

Adjust your single slit to 0.2 mm using the steel wire. Hold the slit in front of your eye and view the two filaments with the green filter in place. Move back until these filaments can *only just* be seen as separate, that is, the two diffraction patterns overlap, but not so much as to make the source seem to have only one filament. Replace the green filter with firstly a blue and secondly a red filter, keeping the slit width and your distance from the lamps the same.

What do you notice? What does this tell you about the ability to resolve objects clearly and the wavelength of light used?

Try changing the slit width. What effect does this have?

Try changing the slit for a hole of equal size in aluminium foil. How does the resolution of the two lamps compare?

J7b Resolving detail with the eye

lamp, holder, and stand
transformer
card
plane mirror
transparent ruler with mm graduations

We always see through an aperture – the pupil of our eye. This experiment checks to see whether our ability to resolve closely spaced objects is limited by diffraction.

Draw two parallel, black lines, 2 mm apart, on some card. Illuminate the card and see how far away you can move before your eye fails to resolve the two lines. Try this for each eye separately.

The angular separation of the lines at your eye in radians is 2 mm/(distance between your eye and the card in mm). Calculate this value.

To calculate the limit of resolution predicted by the Rayleigh criterion, you will have to take an 'average' value for the wavelength of visible light ($\lambda \approx 5 \times 10^{-7}$ m) and measure the diameter of your pupil. This can be done by holding a ruler to your eye and looking at its reflection in a mirror. What is the predicted limit of resolution, λ/b?

J

How does this compare with your measured value? Suggest what factors other than diffraction might limit the ability of your eye to resolve detail.

DEMONSTRATION
J8 Model of a radio interferometer

microwave transmitter
microwave receiver
2 wax lenses (if available)
2 metal plates about 0.3 m square
general purpose amplifier
loudspeaker (if not part of above item)
metal plate (0.2 m square, bent to form two 0.2 m × 0.1 m surfaces at right angles)
table on wheels, or trolley, or sheet of hardboard

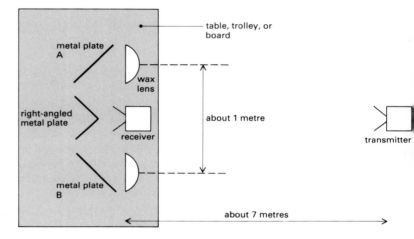

Figure J65
Microwave analogue of radio interferometer.

The receiver is pointed *directly* at the transmitter and the angle over which an appreciable signal is received is noted.

Then the receiver is positioned as in figure J65 and it is rotated together with the various reflectors (and lenses). What happens to the response of the system?

The two signals from the metal plates A and B are being superposed by the receiver. Suggest why the new arrangement gives improved resolution.

A radio interferometer at Cambridge uses several aerials spaced along a railway line. This idea has been taken further with MERLIN – Multi-Element Radio-Linked Interferometer Network – which consists of six individual radio telescopes with 25 m dishes linked electronically to a computer. It stretches across much of the West Midlands and East Wales, and gives the resolution equivalent to a 113 km dish. Having fifteen interferometer pairs of different orientations and baselines, it enables astronomers to make a detailed map of radio sources. (See figures J66 and J67.)

(a)

Figure J66
The tower next to the E-system dish at Knockin (a) transmits data to Jodrell Bank; the Wardle telescope (b) is one of MERLIN's older dishes.
Jerry Mason

(b)

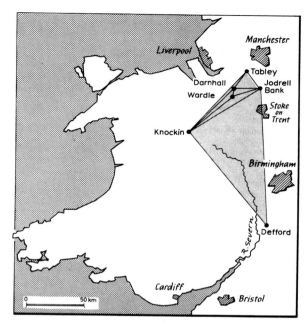

Figure J67
The network already covers much of the West Midlands, and it may be extended to include Cambridge.
*New Scientist, **96**, 1332, Nov. 1982, page 446*

CIRCUS OF EXPERIMENTS
J9 Looking through gratings

coarse grating, 100 lines mm^{-1}
fine grating, 300 lines mm^{-1}
neon (and/or hydrogen) spectrum tube (fluorescent tube will do)
e.h.t. supply
mercury discharge lamp (optional)
mains lamp with 30 cm straight filament and holder
set of colour filters (red, green, blue)
fine black chiffon (or umbrella material)

Hold each of the gratings and the chiffon in turn in front of your eye and look at the various light sources.

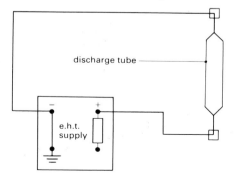

Figure J68

J9a Filament lamp. In what ways are the patterns produced by the colour filters different?

J9b Spectrum tubes (figure J68) or fluorescent tube. Make sure that the grating is parallel to the source. How many different wavelengths of visible light does the source emit? How many lines of the same colour are present?

J9c Mercury lamp. The lamp generates the spectrum produced by excited metal atoms. What do you see? Some mercury discharge lamps emit ultra-violet radiation: you should not look directly at such a lamp.

DEMONSTRATION
J10 The diffraction grating

single slit
set of colour filters (red, green, blue)
set of gratings
slide projector
translucent screen
microscope

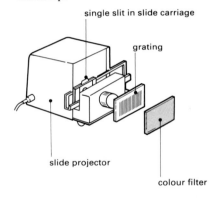
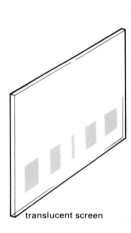

Figure J69

The projector must be focused so that (with no grating) a sharp image of the slit in the slide carriage is formed on the screen. The grating is then put in front of the projection lens.

How does the pattern on the screen differ from that given by a single slit?

How, in general, does the pattern depend on
i slit spacing
ii wavelength?

Look at one of the gratings under a microscope – the poorness of the lines may enable you to speculate how they were made.

J11 Ripple tank demonstration of grating pattern

ripple tank kit
illuminant
transformer
power supply for motor
rheostat, 10 to 15 Ω
hand stroboscopes

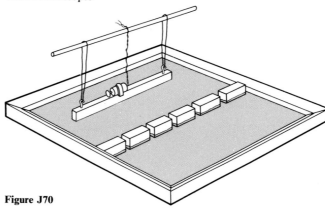

Figure J70

Look for semi-circular ripples emerging from the slits. If you try looking along the water surface you should be able to see a wave moving straight ahead, and waves moving at various angles either side of this one. This is sometimes difficult to see, so do take trouble over it.

What happens to the spacing of the strong reinforcement lines when the wavelength is changed?

It may help to use a stroboscope to freeze the pattern. Make sure you have tackled question **20**.

DEMONSTRATION/EXPERIMENT

J12 Sharpness of maxima depends on number of slits

Demonstration

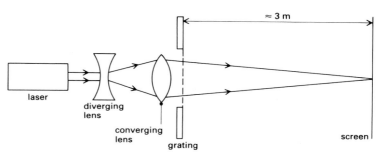

≈ 3 m

laser

diverging
lens

converging
lens

grating

screen

Figure J71

Experiment

lamp, holder, and stand
transformer
2 lenses, $+1D$
eyepiece
set of coarse gratings
set of parallel slits
slide holder
colour filters (red, green, blue)
small translucent screen

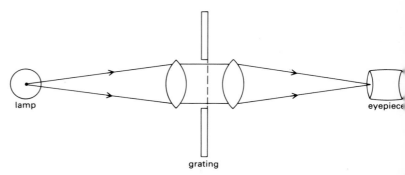

Figure J72

grating

The set of parallel slits contains slides with 1, 2, 3, 4, 5, and 6 slits. A[l]
have the same slit width and spacing as each other and as the coarsest [of]
the gratings.

Starting with this grating, describe what you see when you observ[e]
the diffraction pattern for red light through the grating, then in tur[n]
through 6, 5, 4, 3, and 2 slits.

Return to the coarsest grating in the set. Some of the higher order[s]
are missing. Suggest a reason for their absence. (*Clue:* look carefully a[t]
the very coarse grating pattern, then at the pattern given by the singl[e]
slit of the *same slit width.*)

EXPERIMENT

J13   Measuring the wavelength of light

J13a   Using a grating

fine grating, 300 lines mm^{-1} (or more)
lamp, holder, and stand
transformer
metre rule and 0.5 metre rule
red filter

Put the red filter in front of the lamp. Hold the grating in front of you[r]
eye (rulings parallel to the lamp filament) and look towards the lam[p]
from a distance of 1 m.

Measure the distance, x, from the middle of the central maximum t[o]
the middle of the first order maximum. You will need to use a pointe[r]
and it may help to have the services of a friend. From x, L (the grating t[o]
screen distance), and s (the grating spacing), calculate λ_{red}. What is th[e]
uncertainty in your value?

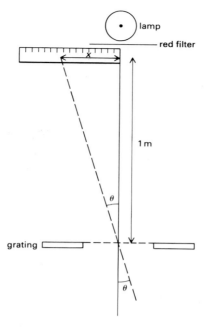

Figure J73

J13b Using Young's double slits

lamp, holder, and stand
transformer

either
microscope slide
colloidal graphite
slide holder for ruling slits
needle
or
slide with two slits

translucent screen
hand lens
set of colour filters (red, green, blue)
transparent millimetre scale
0.5 metre rule
holder with two halves of a razor blade

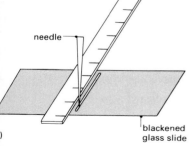

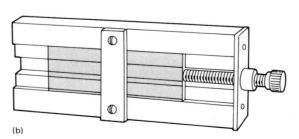

Figure J74

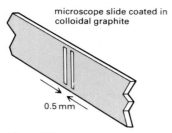

microscope slide coated in colloidal graphite

0.5 mm

Figure J75

This double slit can be made by coating a microscope slide with colloidal graphite (*e.g.* Aquadag), then ruling a pair of lines on the opaque, but not too thick coating. The lines can be made with a blunt needle or razor blade and a ruler – figure J74(a). They should be parallel and about 0.5 mm apart. It may help to make several such pairs of lines; the best pair may then be selected by trial and error.

Alternatively, put the slide in the special holder – figure J74(b). Rule one slit with a blunt needle, move the slide 0.5 mm by turning the screw once, and then rule the second line.

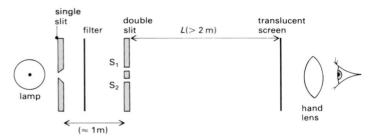

single slit
filter
double slit
$L(> 2\,m)$
translucent screen
S_1
S_2
lamp
hand lens
$(\approx 1\,m)$

Figure J76

Make sure that the vertical filament, slits, and screen are in line and that the adjustable (razor blade) slit provides enough light to cover the double slit.

The fringes may be viewed closer than 2 m from the slits if a magnifying lens is used, and there may then be no need for the screen.

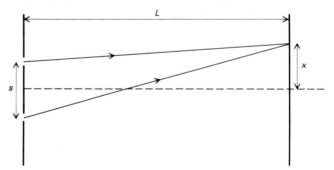

L

s

x

Figure J77

The fringe separation, x, can be found by putting the transparent scale in front of the viewing lens so that the scale divisions are in sharp focus and superimposed on the fringe patterns.

To find the slit separations, put the transparent scale by the double slits and view both simultaneously through the hand lens.

Alternatively, a slide projector can be used to produce an image of the scale and the slits at the same magnification on a distant screen.

$$\lambda = \frac{xs}{L}$$

Obtain a value for the average wavelength transmitted by the filter and estimate the uncertainty in your result.

Observe and explain what happens to the pattern if the following changes are made.

i The distance L is halved.

ii The single slit is moved sideways in the plane of the diagram (figure J76).

iii The double slit is moved sideways, the single slit having been returned to its original position.

iv The single slit is moved towards the double slit. What may happen, eventually, if the two become too close? Why?

DEMONSTRATION
J14 A spectrum using a concave reflection grating

holder with two halves of a razor blade
concave reflection grating
transformer
lamp, holder, and stand
phototransistor
cell holder with one cell
ammeter, 1 mA d.c.
infra-red and ultra-violet filters
white screen (non-fluorescent)
fluorescent paper (green)
leads

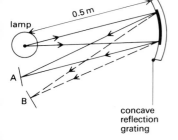

Figure J78
Concave reflection grating.

The grating is stuck to a concave spherical surface so that it both produces a conventional grating diffraction pattern by reflection and focuses it at the same time. In figure J78, the image of the filament is formed at A on the screen. If the screen is moved to B, first and higher order spectra should be visible. An additional benefit is that the reflection grating does not absorb any ultra-violet (u.v.) or infra-red (i.r.) radiation, whereas most other gratings do. Why is this?

Why are special methods needed to detect u.v. and i.r. radiation?

Over what part of the spectrum is the phototransistor sensitive to radiation? To which wavelength of radiation is it most sensitive?

Over what part of the spectrum is the fluorescent paper sensitive?

What sort of detectors might be used for radiation beyond i.r. and u.v.?

DEMONSTRATION
J15 Reflection grating at glancing incidence

either
LP gramophone record
multiple light source and festoon lamp
transformer
hand lens

Figure J79
Reflection grating at glancing incidence using a gramophone record.

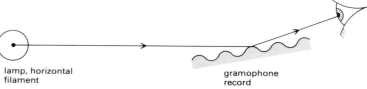

lamp, horizontal
filament

gramophone
record

or

metal rule with 0.5 mm divisions
laser
adjustable height stand (Labjack)
white screen
Plasticine

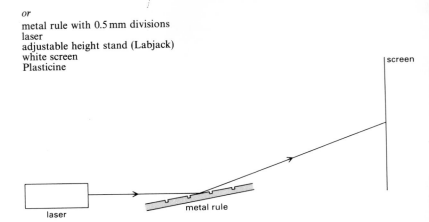

Figure J80
Reflection grating at glancing incidence using a laser and metal rule.

Both the record and the rule act as diffraction gratings for light even though the grooves are very many wavelengths apart. The pattern can be seen if the light strikes the 'grating' at an angle of incidence of very nearly 90°. (*N.B. DO NOT* look down the laser beam but look at the pattern on the screen.) Describe what you see.

i Look at a record with the hand lens. Estimate how many wavelengths of visible light would fit into one groove spacing.

ii Explain how a grating with such a relatively large spacing manages to form a diffraction pattern.

iii The same method is used to measure the wavelength of X-rays, using a grating ruled for use with visible light. Why is it necessary to use the grazing angle method?

DEMONSTRATION
J16 Diffraction at complex gratings

i What does the diffraction pattern of a grating with 80 lines per mm look like?

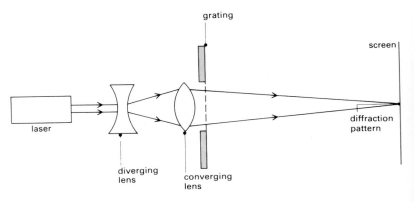

Figure J81

ii Sandwich two such gratings together, with their rulings perpendicular. Sketch the diffraction pattern. It is *not* merely a single row of vertical and horizontal dots as you might expect. Suggest a reason for the increased complexity.

iii Try the piece of black chiffon that you used in experiment J9. It has a square weave but is much coarser than the gratings used above. How could you tell this from its diffraction pattern? Another feature of its diffraction pattern is the absence of spots in certain regions of the pattern. What might cause this?

iv The two crossed gratings form an array of regularly spaced square holes – figure J82(a). The diffraction pattern produced by such an array is simply a scaled version of the pattern produced by the chiffon. By looking at the diffraction patterns produced by the arrays shown in figures J82(a), (b), (c), (d), and (e) try to identify which characteristics of an array determine

a the pattern and spacing of the dots

b the relative intensities of the dots in its diffraction pattern.

The same factors determine the arrangement and intensities of the dots in the X-ray diffraction pattern produced by an array of atoms, as in a solid.

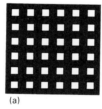

(a)

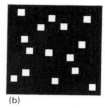

(b)

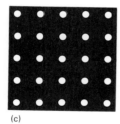

(c)

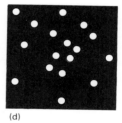

(d)

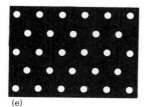

Figure J82
Aperture arrays.

(e)

DEMONSTRATION

J17 Reconstructing the image from a hologram

The production of a hologram is extremely difficult in school using a low power laser. A schematic layout of the apparatus is shown in figure J83(a).

A glass plate acts as a beam-splitter and the object is illuminated by the laser light reflected by the plate. The reference beam produces a uniform patch of light on the photographic plate. Light scattered from the object, the signal beam, strikes the plate and forms a complex superposition pattern with the reference beam which is recorded on the photographic plate.

The reconstruction process shown in figure J83(b) is quite straightforward to carry out in schools and consists, essentially, of illuminating the hologram with a laser from the same direction as the reference beam in the production stage. To view the hologram you should look for the reconstructed virtual image *behind* the plate and *not on* the plate. It helps to locate the image if you move your head from side to side looking through the plate all the time.

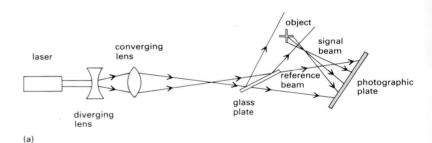

(a)

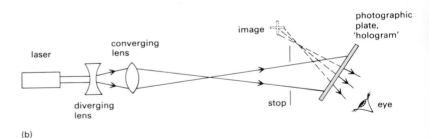

(b)

Figure J83
(a) Production of a hologram (not to scale).
(b) Reconstruction of the image (not to scale).

Keep your eyes focused on the image but change your direction of view – what happens?

Try using a piece of card with holes in as stops placed near to the hologram both to reduce the illuminated area and to select particular parts of the hologram. Clearly there is altogether less light but the effect on what is seen is very surprising.

How might this result be useful in high-density information storage?

DEMONSTRATION
J18a   Guided or 'tied' waves

15 cm dipoles and oscillator
sensitive galvanometer

either
2 long retort stand rods
or
2 metre rules covered with aluminium foil

2 crocodile clips
leads

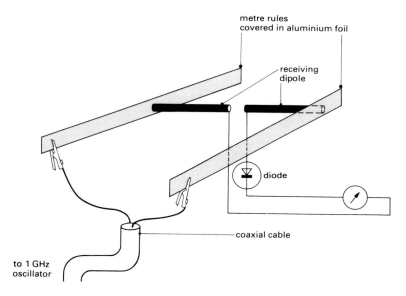

Figure J84

How does the signal vary as the receiving dipole is moved along between the conductors?

What suggests to you that this is a 'standing wave' phenomenon? What happens to the wave when it reaches the ends of the conductors?

By measuring the separation of maxima, calculate the wavelength.

Calculate a value for the speed of the waves if the frequency is assumed to be 1 GHz.

DEMONSTRATION
J18b   Free waves

Apparatus as for demonstration J18a plus
large metal sheet, about 30 cm × 30 cm

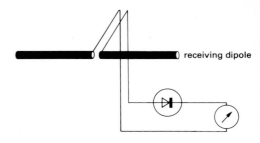

receiving dipole

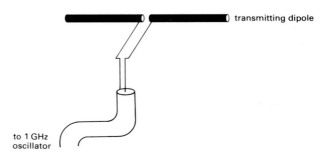

transmitting dipole

to 1 GHz
oscillator

Figure J85

Remove the long rods used in demonstration J18a and attach the usual transmitting dipole to the oscillator as in figure J85.

Despite the absence of the long rods a strong signal is still detected by the receiver. This wave is freely propagating in the laboratory.

Use a large sheet of metal to reflect the wave and set up a standing wave pattern. Measure the wavelength and so calculate the speed of the wave.

What is the difficulty in measuring the speed of this wave *directly* (that is, timing its travel over a known distance)?

DEMONSTRATION
J19 The speed of a pulse along a coaxial cable

200 kHz pulse generator
200 m drum of coaxial cable
double-beam oscilloscope
2 resistors, 68 Ω
2 clip component holders
1 kΩ potentiometer
leads

The pulse generator switches a p.d. on and off 200 000 times a second across the end of a long length of coaxial cable. This is rather like demonstration J18a, except here the pair of conducting rods is very long and the signal is a pulse instead of a sinusoidal wave.

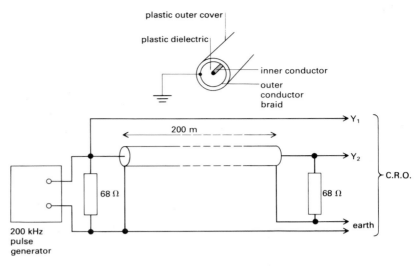

Figure J86

How long does the pulse take to travel along the cable?

What is the speed of the pulse?

What happens to the reflected pulse if the 68 Ω resistor at the far end of the cable is:

i removed, or *ii* replaced by a short-circuit?

Does this behaviour agree with results from other wave experiments?

DEMONSTRATION

J20 Speed of light

apparatus to measure the speed of light
double-beam oscilloscope, $0.1\,\mu s\ div^{-1}$ or better
2 cell holders with 6 cells (or other 9 V d.c. supply)
leads

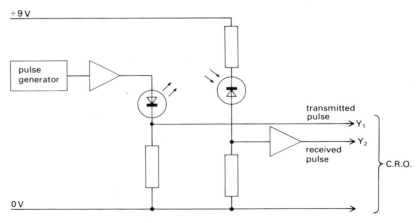

Figure J87
Measurement of the speed of light.

Short pulses, produced by a 1 MHz oscillator, are fed to a light-emitting diode. These pulses are fed by a fibre optics cable of known length to a receiver, a photodiode. The received signal is amplified and fed to one input of the oscilloscope, the transmitted pulse being displayed on the other trace.

There are several points of detail to think about in interpreting the time delay between the pulses seen on the screen.

Is the 'received pulse' in fact due to light which has travelled along the optical fibre, or might it be a purely electrical signal within the system? How could you check this?

Is the delay due only to the time of flight of the light pulse, or are there other parts of the system which might be causing a delay and so introducing a systematic error? If so, how might this difficulty be tackled?

When you have obtained a value for the speed of light in the polymer fibre you should estimate the uncertainty in your value and consider how the experiment might be improved.

By careful use of lenses and a mirror, it might be possible to adapt this method to measure the speed of light in air. What distance would a light pulse have to travel for you to have a chance of measuring the time of flight?

CIRCUS OF EXPERIMENTS
J21 Polarization

J21a Microwaves

microwave transmitter
microwave receiver
general purpose amplifier
loudspeaker (if not included in amplifier)
metal grille

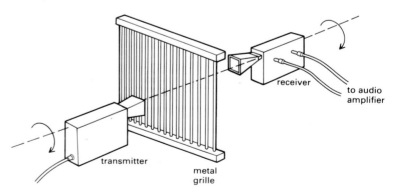

Figure J88
Polarization of microwaves.

What happens to the received signal when the transmitter and receiver are rotated with respect to each other as shown in figure J88 (but without the metal grille in place)? Does this result suggest that the wave from the transmitter is plane polarized or unpolarized?

Put the metal grille between the transmitter and receiver and observe what happens when the grille is rotated about the axis shown in figure J88.

Now put the receiver on its side so that the receiver and transmitter are 'crossed'. What now happens when the grille is rotated?

Electrons in the metal rods of the grille are set in motion by an electric field parallel to their length. Use this to determine the plane of the electric field of the waves generated by the transmitter.

Suggest how it is possible, by using the grille, to receive waves even when the receiver and transmitter are 'crossed'.

J21b   30 cm or gigahertz waves

15 cm dipoles and oscillator
sensitive galvanometer
leads
several metal rods 15 cm long (or short retort stand rods)
40 cm square rotatable platform (hardboard or similar)

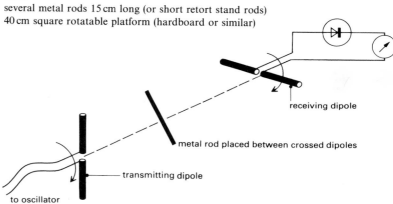

receiving dipole

metal rod placed between crossed dipoles

transmitting dipole

to oscillator

Figure J89
Polarization of 30 cm waves.

With this equipment you can do the same experiments and answer the same questions as with the microwave equipment – see experiment J21a above. Use a 15 cm metal rod in place of the grille of rods.

Aerials and the reception of radio waves

This experiment also enables you to see how the sensitivity and directivity of an aerial system depend on the arrangement of the component parts of the system.

from transmitter

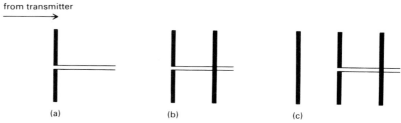

Figure J90
Aerial systems.

(a)   (b)   (c)

Put the receiver – figure J90(a) – in the middle of a rotatable platform on the edge of one bench facing the transmitter on the edge of another about 1 m away. Reflections are unavoidable, but their effect can be minimized by reducing unnecessary movement and, if possible making the final adjustments from a distance using a metre rule.

What happens to the received signal as a rod is brought up behind the receiver dipole as in figure J90(b)?

Bring up a rod in front of the dipole as in figure J90(c). Suggest a reason for the changes in signal.

Adjust the multi-element array of figure J90(c) until it produces the biggest signal. Rotate the whole array until the signal has fallen by a factor of between 5 and 10. Now remove the front and rear rods. What happens to the signal? Return the receiver to its original position facing the transmitter and note the size of the signal. How does the directivity of the simple dipole compare with that of the three-element array?

By considering the rods as sources of secondary wavelets, use the principle of superposition to suggest how the array has increased sensitivity and directivity. In what way could the behaviour of an aerial array compared with a single dipole be said to be like that of a diffraction grating compared with a single slit?

Examine a multiple-element television aerial and compare it with the arrangement in figure J90(c). Estimate the wavelength and hence calculate the frequency that the aerial is designed for and identify the plane of polarization. Try to compare your result with data from the local BBC or IBA transmitter.

What is the required orientation of a ferrite rod and coil, such as in a radio (figure J91), relative to a transmitter for it to be effective as an aerial?

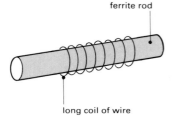

ferrite rod

long coil of wire

Figure J91
Ferrite rod aerial.

J21c   Polarization of light by Polaroid

3 polarizing filters (Polaroid)
lamp, holder, and stand
transformer
transparent adhesive tape
cellophane paper
microscope slides

Look at the lamp, on its own, through a polarizing filter (Polaroid). Try rotating the filter about an axis parallel to the light beam. What effect does it have?

Try looking at the lamp through two pieces of Polaroid and rotating one relative to the other. What effect does this have on the light transmitted?

What can you say about the light
i from the lamp, and
ii transmitted through a piece of Polaroid?

Look through two pieces of Polaroid in the 'crossed' position. Add a third Polaroid between these two, and rotate it. What do you see? How can you explain this? (It may help to think about the direction of the electric vector transmitted by each of the successive Polaroids.)

You may already have seen how polarized light can be used to detect strain, for example when polythene is stretched between crossed polarizers. Transparent adhesive tape or cellophane wrapping material also give beautiful colour effects when viewed between crossed polarizers. Try it.

J21d Polarization of light by reflection and by scattering

2 polarizing filters (Polaroid)
rectangular plastic tank
lamp, holder, and stand
housing shield
2 barriers
plano-cylindrical lens, + 7D
transformer
small sheets of glass, polythene, and metal (*e.g.* aluminium foil)
milk or powdered milk

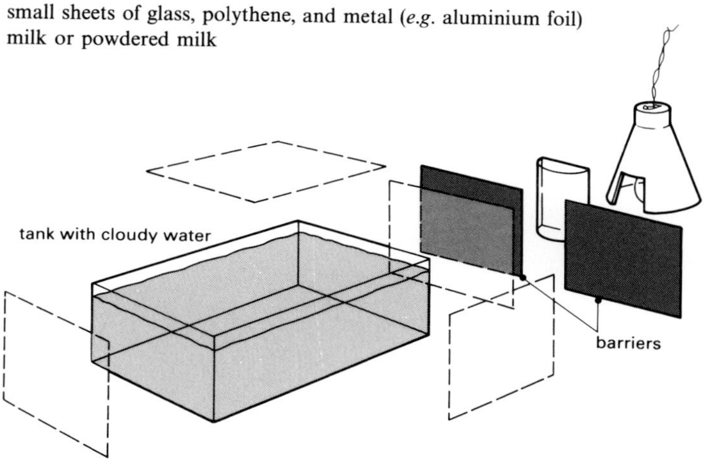

Figure J92
Scattering by cloudy water. (Broken rectangles show positions for a Polaroid filter.)

Using just one Polaroid sheet look at light reflected from
i the bench,
ii a sheet of glass,
iii a shiny metal surface, and
iv a polythene sheet.

Try different angles of reflection. In each of the cases, is the reflected beam polarized?

Send a beam of light through a tank of water as shown in the figure J92. Tap water may contain enough suspended matter to scatter the light. If not, add just one drop of milk – no more, otherwise too much scattering is produced.

Figure J92 shows various positions for the polarizing filter. Try rotating the filter. What happens to light scattered through 90°? The same effect cannot be produced if clouds of small water droplets are used as the scattering centres. Suggest a reason for this.

HOME EXPERIMENTS

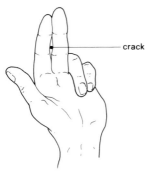

Figure J93

JH1   A homemade slit

Hold your first and second fingers together so that there is a narrow crack between the middle parts of the two fingers, although they touch at the top, as in figure J93. Look at a distant small lamp through the crack, and press the two fingers gently together. As the crack closes, the lamp appears dimmer (obviously), but when the crack is very narrow the lamp also seems to get wider. Why?

JH2   Simple spectroscopy

You can make a simple spectroscope and look at a reflection of sunlight from a piece of white card (*NEVER* look directly at the Sun), or at shop signs and street lights. In what ways are the spectra of the Sun and of a glowing filament different?

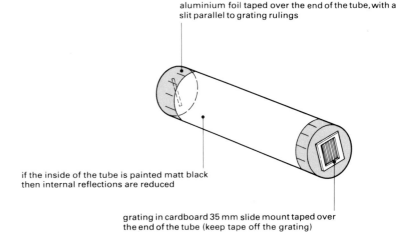

aluminium foil taped over the end of the tube, with a slit parallel to grating rulings

if the inside of the tube is painted matt black then internal reflections are reduced

grating in cardboard 35 mm slide mount taped over the end of the tube (keep tape off the grating)

Figure J94

Light from the hot outer surface of the Sun has to pass through the Sun's cooler (though still hot) atmosphere. This atmosphere contains atoms and ions of many different elements, which absorb radiation at the same frequencies as those at which they emit. Since the emitted radiation is in all directions, the Sun's 'white light' spectrum has light missing from it at a number of frequencies. If the spectrum is formed from a slit, the spectrum seems to be crossed by narrow dark lines. These lines in the absorption spectrum were found by Fraunhofer, and are often named after him.

JH3   Ear and eye

This experiment is about an interesting difference between what your ears and eyes do to signals containing more than one frequency.

physicist would say it shows that your ear is a 'Fourier analyser', but that your eye is not.

Get someone to play you three or four notes on a piano, one at a time. Give them arbitrary names, say P, Q, R, etc. Then get your helper to play two at once, and see if you can say which two notes are being played.

Now supply your eyes with two colours of light simultaneously, as follows. Stand in front of a pair of electric lamps with a diffraction grating held over your eye, and move about until part of the lefthand first-order spectrum from one lamp seems to fall over part of the righthand first-order spectrum from the other lamp. Suppose red overlaps blue: do you see 'red and blue', or some other, single colour?

Both eye and ear were supplied with a complex oscillation made up of at least two frequencies. Your ear and brain, at least partially, separate the complex oscillation into its constituent frequencies. A diffraction grating does the same for light, sending different frequencies off at different angles. Both analyse the input sent to them. Your eye is not an analyser, however, and sees one colour for each complex light input.

JH4 Polarized light

The 'Polaroids' used in this experiment could be a pair of 'lenses' taken from a pair of Polaroid sunglasses.

Stick a piece of transparent adhesive tape onto a piece of glass, put it between 'crossed' Polaroids, and look through the sandwich. Try turning the Polaroids together, keeping them crossed. Make whatever suggestions you can about what the tape does to polarized light passing through it. You may like to go on to try several thicknesses of tape, and to try rotating just one Polaroid.

You may recall, from Unit A, 'Materials and mechanics', that materials like polythene sheet which do not behave like the tape can be made to do so if they are strained. Try cutting a V-shaped notch in the side of a long strip of polythene, and pull it longways between crossed Polaroids.

On a sunny day, stand so that the Sun is on your right or on your left, and look at a patch of blue sky through a piece of Polaroid. Choose a patch of sky from which the light to your eye is at right angles to the direction from it to the Sun.

Rotate the Polaroid, and try to explain what you see. (*Harder.*) Refer to question **46**, and try to decide along which direction in your Polaroid sheet the iodine-loaded, long-chain polymer molecules generally lie.

QUESTIONS

Superposition

1(I) Figure J95 shows circular ripples on water, produced by a disturbance of the water surface.

In what sense do the ripples not affect one another? In what sense do the ripples affect one another? Explain what physicists mean when they say that waves 'superpose' on one another. You may be able to think of an example where water waves do not superpose, at least not in the simple sense intended by physicists when they use the term.

Figure J95
Ripples on water.
Barnaby's Picture Library

Figure J96
Morro Bay, California.
University of California

Diffraction

2(I) Figure J96 is an aerial photograph of a narrow harbour mouth formed by two angled jetties, open to the sea.

How can there be waves inside the harbour, well within the 'shadow' of the jetty which runs parallel to the waves in the open sea? Make a sketch showing what you expect to see in a ripple tank if straight waves reach a barrier which blocks off half the tank.

Huygens's construction

3(L)a Figure J97 is based on one in Huygens's *Treatise on light* (1690), and is part of his explanation of how a wave theory of light could explain the fact that light is reflected from a flat, mirror-like surface at an angle equal to that at which the light strikes the surface.

AB is the flat mirror, seen edge on. Identify the lines AC and NB.

The distance CB is drawn equal to the distance AN. Suggest how Huygens used this diagram to advance his explanation.

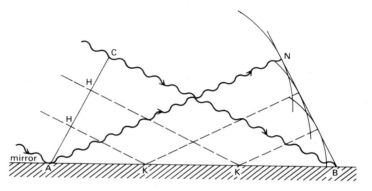

Figure J97

b Figure J98 is part of Huygens's explanation of the refraction of light as it passes from, say, air into water or glass. AB is the flat surface of, say, water. Identify the lines AC, HK, and NB.

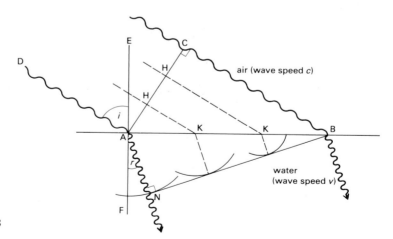

Figure J98

Suggest how Huygens explained refraction, particularly the fact that the ratio of the sines of angles DAE and FAN is constant for any one pair of materials. You will need to know that light travels more slowly in water or glass than it does in air.

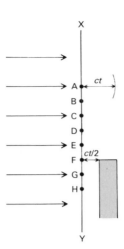

Figure J99

c Show that $\sin i/\sin r = c/v$, where i and r are the angles of incidence and refraction (angles DAE and FAN respectively in figure J98). This ratio, the ratio of the speed of light in air (strictly in a vacuum) to its speed in the transparent material is called the refractive index of the material.

4(L) A single wavefront is represented by a line XY in figure J99. The circular arc is a secondary wavelet drawn from A with radius ct. The obstacle is distance $ct/2$ from the wavefront. Copy and complete the diagram by drawing a series of secondary wavelets from B, C, D, etc., and sketch the shape of the wavefront after time t. Also sketch the shape of the wavefront after $2t$.

Superposition

5(l)a Two loudspeakers are stood on stools out-of-doors on a rough, grassy, non-reflecting surface. They are mounted about a metre apart, and each produces the same musical note, and oscillates in phase with the other. How will the sound heard from the two speakers change as you move about in front of them?

b Using only one loudspeaker in a room, you can get effects similar to those obtained with two speakers outside. How do you explain this?

Diffraction at a slit

6(L) This question is about the wave energy diffracted in a particular direction at an angle θ to the straight-through direction when a plane wavefront, wavelength λ, is incident at a slit, width b (figure J100).

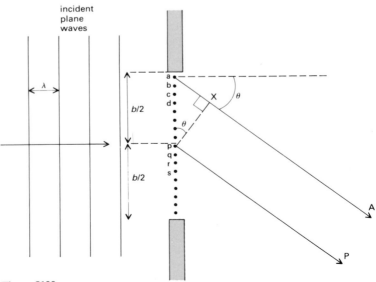

Figure J100

a Consider the plane wavefront reaching the slit to consist of a row of secondary wavelet sources a, b, c, etc. (as in Huygens's construction). All the sources are equally spaced, and p is just over half way across the slit. What is the distance between a and p, b and q, and c and r in terms of the slit width b?

b What is the path difference (aX) between waves from a and p travelling in the directions A and P at an angle θ to the original direction? Express this in terms of b and θ.

c If the path difference between a and p at a particular angle θ_1, is $\lambda/2$, what will be the effect of superposing waves from a and p?

d What will be the effect on a distant screen of light coming from the pairs of sources b and q; c and r; d and s; etc. all travelling in this same direction θ_1?

e The effect on the screen of light from the whole slit can be found by adding up the waves from all the pairs of secondary wavelets $b/2$ apart. What is the effect on the screen for waves diffracted in the direction θ_1?

f Write down an expression linking b, λ, and θ_1.

g Give a reason for thinking that at all angles less than θ_1 there will be some light reaching the screen.

h Suppose that light travelling from pairs of secondary sources $b/4$ apart has a path difference of $\lambda/2$ at another angle θ_2. What is the relationship between b, λ, and θ_2, and what will be seen on the screen at this angle?

i Write down a general equation predicting the directions of minima in a single-slit diffraction pattern.

7(P) A plane microwave of frequency 10 GHz is incident on a large piece of metal in which there is a slit 10 cm wide. The diffracted wave is detected beyond the metal and readings of intensity and angular deviation are taken.

Draw a sketch to show how the intensity varies with angle. Show the angles at which intensity minima are detected.

8(P) A loudspeaker in a cabinet produces sound waves which pass through an aperture, forming a diffraction pattern. A loudspeaker manufacturer wishes to investigate this effect and uses the equipment shown in outline in figure J101. From his results, he plots what is called a polar response diagram (figure J102).

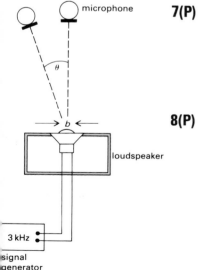

microphone

θ

b

loudspeaker

3 kHz

signal
generator
and amplifier

Figure J101

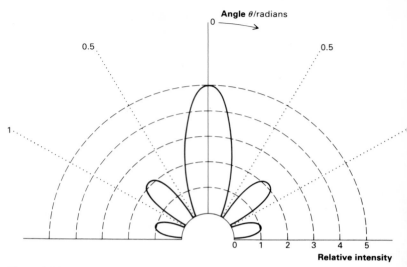

Angle θ/radians

Relative intensity

Figure J102

a Figure J103 shows the same data, plotted in a form familiar from earlier work. Explain how it is related to figure J102. Why may figure J102 be more useful?

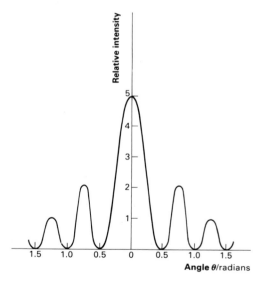

Relative intensity

Angle θ/radians

Figure J103

b From the results shown above, calculate the effective diameter (b) of the loudspeaker aperture. (Speed of sound in air $= 330\,\mathrm{m\,s^{-1}}$.)

c Such an experiment really requires reverberation-free or anechoic conditions. Say why this is important and briefly suggest how you would produce a suitable environment.

d If the effective diameter of the loudspeaker aperture is reduced by a factor of ten, what effect will this have on the polar response? Why is this advantageous to the faithful reproduction of music in the domestic setting?

The polar response is a very important property of many wave systems: microwave transmitters and receivers, radio and television aerials, as well as loudspeakers and microphones. (See 'Aerials', page 168.)

9(P) Diffraction patterns of six letters of the alphabet are shown in figure J104.

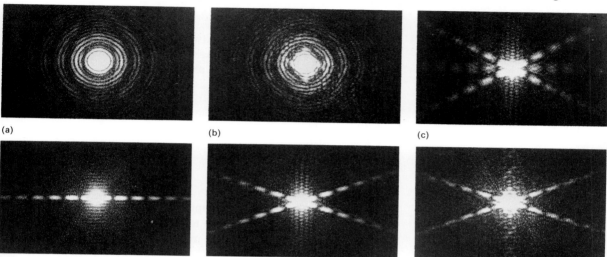

(a)

(b)

(c)

(d)

(e)

(f)

Figure J104
Diffraction patterns of some letters of the alphabet.
Dr A. Winter

Though not in order, the letters are: A, I, O, Q, V, Y. By considering the single-slit and circular hole diffraction patterns, try to decide which pattern belongs to which letter.

10(R) Figure J105 is used to illustrate an argument which shows that for diffraction from a single slit, the intensity first falls to zero when $b \sin \theta = \lambda$.

Here are three deductions made from this result.

1 If a longer wavelength is used the main diffraction peak will be broader.
2 If white light is used the edges of the main diffraction peak will be coloured.
3 If a slit with smaller b is used the main diffraction peak will be broader.

Which of these deductions is/are true?

A 1 only.
B 2 only.
C 1 and 2 only.
D 1 and 3 only.
E 1, 2, and 3.

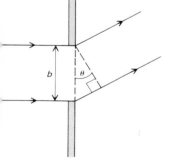

Figure J105

(Coded answer paper, 1970)

Resolution

11(R)   The image of a star so distant as to be a point source appears in a telescope as a fuzzy disc, because of diffraction at the objective aperture of the telescope.

If the diameter of the objective aperture is halved, which of the following statements correctly describes aspects of the resulting effect?

1   The fuzzy disc becomes about twice as wide.
2   The light energy coming through the aperture is halved.
3   The brightness of the image is reduced.

A   1 only.
B   1 and 2 only.
C   1 and 3 only.
D   2 and 3 only.
E   1, 2, and 3.

(Coded answer paper, 1977)

12(P)   The World's largest optical telescope has a mirror of 5 m diameter whilst the 'mirror' of a large radio telescope may be as large as 80 m across. Why is the radio telescope mirror so much bigger?

13(L)   A telescope is set to view a star. The image at the focus of its main lens, when viewed through an eyepiece or when photographed, is not a sharp point of light, but is blurred out into a disc surrounded by some fainter rings. Figure J106(a) suggests the way the intensity varies across the pattern. A line from point X on the pattern to the middle of the lens makes an angle θ with a line from point Y at the middle of the pattern to the lens.

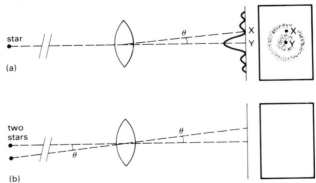

(a)

two stars

(b)

Figure J106

a   If the pattern shown is obtained with red light, what difference would it make, if any, if a blue filter were used instead of a red one?

b   The same telescope is pointed at a pair of stars which happen to subtend at the lens the angle θ mentioned above, as indicated in figure J106(b).

Make a rough sketch of what the pattern of light at the focus of the telescope would look like now, supposing that the stars are equally bright.

c The telescope is pointed at a planet whose diameter subtends this same angle θ at the telescope. Would the pattern shown in figure J106(a) be altered much?

14(P) Figure J107 shows the dish-shaped reflector and aerial of the radio telescope at Dwingeloo in the Netherlands. It was used to plot the distribution of hydrogen gas in our galaxy by detecting the characteristic radiation (wavelength 0.21 m) emitted by hydrogen atoms in space. The galaxy has a flattish, multiple spiral structure with the Sun about two-thirds of the way from the centre in one of the spiral arms.

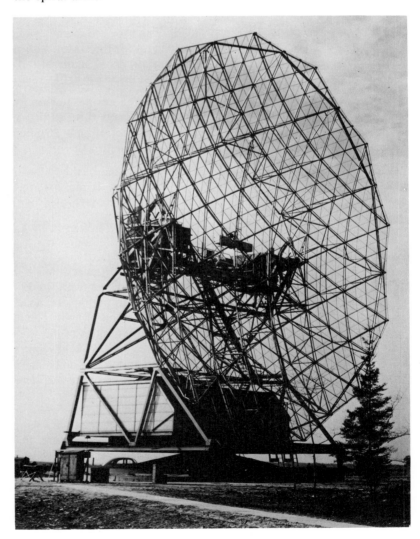

Figure J107
The radio telescope at Dwingeloo in the Netherlands.
By courtesy of the Royal Netherlands Embassy

a Suppose that the reflecting dish of diameter 25 m is equivalent to a slit of this width (actually, it is more nearly equivalent to a slit 25/1.22 m wide). Over what angle either side of the central position will the telescope detect an appreciable intensity when directed towards a 'point source' of 0.21 m radiation?

b A region of our galaxy under examination might be about 2×10^{20} m ($\approx 20\,000$ light years) from the telescope. What is the minimum separation of two hydrogen 'clouds' if the telescope is to be able to resolve them as separate sources?

c It is proposed that a similar telescope be built with a dish diameter ten or a hundred times bigger than that at Dwingeloo. You will see from figure J107 that this telescope can be steered to point at different places in the sky. What arguments might there be for and against this proposal?

15(P)a Taking 2 mm for the diameter of the eye pupil and 500 nm (5×10^{-7} m) for the wavelength of light, estimate the limit of resolution or visual acuity of the eye due to diffraction (that is, the smallest distinguishable angular separation).

b In practice, the normal human eye has a limit which is about twice this. If two objects subtend this angle at the eye and the distance from eye lens to retina is 20 mm, how far apart are the two images formed on the retina?

c In the central area of the retina the light receptors are about 5×10^{-6} m apart. Is this spacing adequate to enable the eye to resolve two objects separated by the angle which you calculated in **b**?

d What other factors do you think may limit the ability of the eye to see fine detail?

16(E) When the planet Venus appears as the Morning Star it is about 150×10^6 kilometres from the Earth. It looks perceptibly different from a true star, perhaps because the unaided eye sees it as a disc rather than a point of light. The diameter of Venus is about 12 000 km. Using rough estimates of the wavelength of light and of the diameter of the pupil of your eye at low light intensity, do you think this suggestion is plausible, or does the difference in appearance between the planet and a star require some other explanation?

17(P) Figure J108 illustrates the value of good resolving power in a radio telescope. The radio source Cygnus A seems to be located near the blurred object at the centre of the photograph, which may be an exploding galaxy. It is believed to be 5×10^{21} km (500 million light years) from the Earth.

A sufficiently good radio telescope can show that the radio source corresponding to this visual object is actually a pair of sources. The figure shows contours of radio intensity, obtained with a radio telescope at Cambridge University. The two sources are some 3×10^{18} km apart.

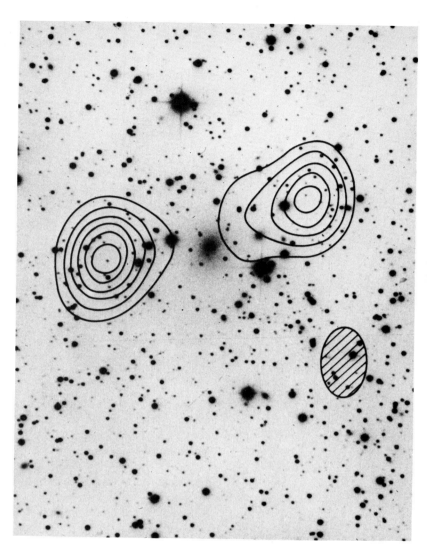

Figure J108
The radio source Cygnus A, showing radio intensity contours superimposed on a photograph of the same part of the sky, taken with the 5-metre Palomar telescope in California.
MOFFET, A. T. Annual review of astronomy and astrophysics, **4**, *149, 1966.*

a What angle do the two sources subtend at the Earth?

b The ellipse in the lower righthand corner of the picture shows the size of the area within which pairs of radio sources cannot be resolved by the telescope at the distance of Cygnus A. Estimate the mean diameter of this region in km, and the angle subtended by this diameter at the Earth.

c Estimate the diameter of the dish aerial (such as that in question **14**) which would be needed to resolve sources as well as the telescope used to obtain the result in figure J108, at a wavelength of 0.15 m. Explain why a dish aerial was not used.

18(L) The ability of a radio telescope to resolve two sources is limited by its aperture, see question **14**. Even one with a dish 100 m across has much poorer resolution than the human eye. One way around this problem is to use two small telescopes a long way apart and to superpose the signals to produce a superposition pattern whose spacing is finer than the fringe spacing of the diffraction pattern from either small telescope on its own (this is like Young's double slits, experiment J13b). Such a device is called a *stellar interferometer*.

In Australia, a stellar interferometer has been constructed by placing an aerial array on top of a 100 m high cliff near the entrance to Sydney Harbour. The system was designed for the study of 1.5 m wavelength radiation emitted from the Sun.

a Figure J109 shows the Sun's rays when the received intensity at A is a maximum. On a copy of the figure, mark a point Y on the direct ray from the Sun to A, such that AX–AY is an odd number of half wavelengths. (The phase is reversed on reflection by the sea.)

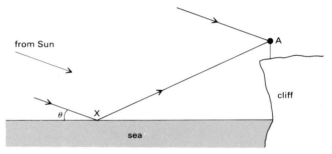

Figure J109

b As the Sun sets, the angle θ gradually changes. Explain how and why the intensity at A will vary as the Sun sets. You may be able to derive a formula for the path difference in terms of θ to predict at which angles maxima occur.

19(R) This question revises ideas about diffraction by an aperture.

The passage below presents two sets of ideas about diffraction. For each of the sections **i** and **ii** you are asked to write a more complete explanation of the ideas. Your explanation may include:

fuller explanations of the theory;
quantitative calculations to illustrate the ideas;
discussion of possible experiments.

i Light from a point source appears to cast sharp shadows and this leads to the familiar idea that it travels in straight lines. However, this is not exactly true: the shadows are not perfectly sharp, although special experiments are needed to show the effect because it is so small. This unfamiliar property is called diffraction and is explained by a wave model of light.

ii The consequence is that the eye, or a camera, or even the best possible telescope, doesn't produce a perfect image. Instead it gives an image which is slightly blurred. When we try to make a telescope magnify more to show finer details of the stars this blurring effect can become an obstacle.

(Long answer paper, part question, 1980)

Waves through gratings

20(L) Figure J110(a) shows how waves emitted by several sources of the same frequency and in phase combine to produce superposition patterns. When thinking about a diffraction grating, the first step is to imagine that each slit in the grating acts as such a source.

By looking obliquely along figure J110(a) from the bottom edge of the page, or by laying a transparent ruler over the figure, you should be able to see a clear set of wavefronts parallel to the line of slits. This undeviated set of waves is called the zero order and is shown in figure J110(b). Now look along the figure from the lefthand corner. You should be able to see the first order waves – figure J110(c). Further changes of angle reveal the subsequent orders. Note that there is a set of first order waves on both sides of the undeviated zero order set, similarly for second, third, etc. orders.

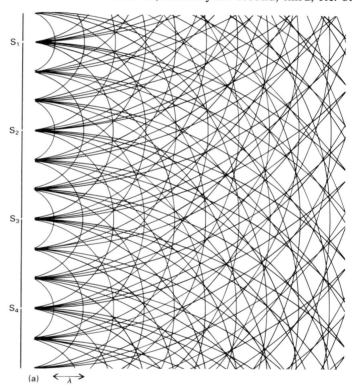

(a)

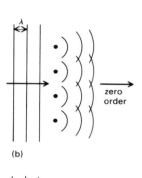

(b)

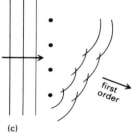

(c)

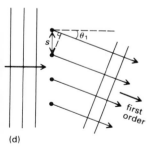

(d)

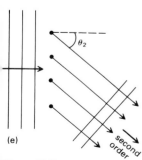

(e)

Figure J110

a Lay a rule along this first order wavefront. What is the path difference between waves from consecutive sources? (This is, of course, why they are 'in phase'.)

b Figure J110(d) is a modified figure, drawn to make clear the path differences between waves. Use this figure to explain why the constructive superposition (maximum) occurs when $\lambda = s \sin \theta_1$. (It may help to refer back to question **6**.)

c Use figure J110(e) to explain in a similar way why there is another maximum for $2\lambda = s \sin \theta_2$.

d   Write down a general equation for the angles θ at which maxima will occur for waves of wavelength λ incident on a grating spacing s. (This assumes that the angle of incidence is zero.)

21(P)   A grating composed of many narrow slits in an otherwise opaque sheet gives, with a monochromatic source of light, a set of bright lines. Then every other slit is blocked out. What happens to the positions and intensities of the bright lines?

        What do you think might happen if half the slits were blocked out but selected at random rather than regularly? (An intelligent guess – don't spend too long on it.)

22(E)   At roughly what frequency would a slatted wooden fence (or, if you prefer, iron railings) be a good diffraction grating for sound waves? The speed of sound in air is about $330\,\mathrm{m\,s^{-1}}$; make any other estimates you need.

23(E)   Comment on the following statement.

        'Diffraction by a grating is not the same as diffraction at a single slit. In the second case, the light just spreads out; in the first, the radiations from many slits are superposed and can interfere with one another, as can the radiations from a pair of slits.'

24(P)   A diffraction grating is illuminated with a parallel beam of light of wavelength $550\,\mathrm{nm}$. The first order maximum is in a direction making an angle of $20°$ with the straight-through position.

    a   Calculate the slit separation in the grating.

    b   Calculate the wavelength of light which would give a second order maximum at $\theta = 32°$.

25(L)   This question is about how the sharpness of spectral lines produced by a grating depends on the number of slits in that grating.

        Figure J111 shows a $10\,000$-slit grating, each slit $10^{-6}\,\mathrm{m}$ from the next. Light of wavelength $5 \times 10^{-7}\,\mathrm{m}$ falls perpendicular to the grating.

    a   Use the grating formula to calculate the angle θ for the first order maximum of intensity.

    b   What is the path difference (in terms of λ) between waves from adjacent slits?

    c   What is the path difference (in terms of λ) between waves from 1st and 5001st slit? This is equal to BC.

    d   Why are all waves emerging along line AC in phase?

    e   Now consider waves emerging at a slightly larger angle, θ', with the condition that path difference $BC' = BC + \lambda/2$, as shown in figure J112. What is the path difference (in terms of λ) between waves from the 1st and 5001st slit now?

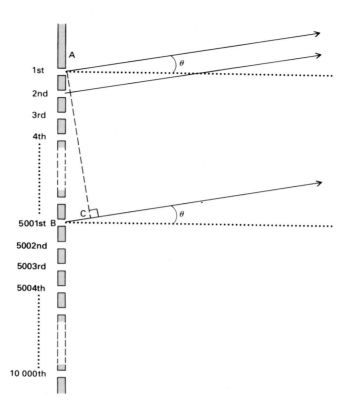

Figure J111

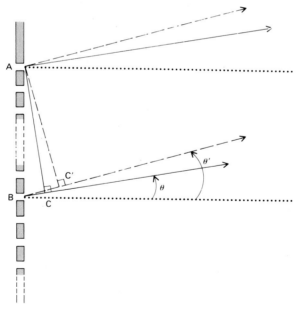

Figure J112

f What is the resultant of the waves from all the slits in this new direction?

The determination of the positions of no light is similar to the analysis of single-slit diffraction (question **6**). The first principal maximum has a pattern of light and dark fringes as drawn in figure J113. What was previously considered to be a single position of constructive superposition is seen to be spread out and to have substructure.

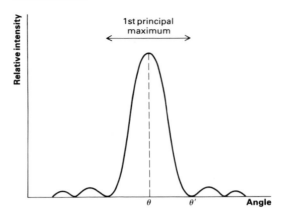

Figure J113

g If only 100 slits of the grating were illuminated, then the angle θ for the 1st maximum would remain the same but θ' would now be very much larger. Why is this?

A grating with many slits contributing to the diffraction pattern produces brighter and sharper maxima than one with fewer slits.

h Suppose that the incident light contains another wavelength, λ', slightly greater than λ, which produces a 1st order maximum at θ' just where the original wavelength gives no resultant. According to Rayleigh's criterion, we can say that the two maxima are *just resolved*; see figure J114.

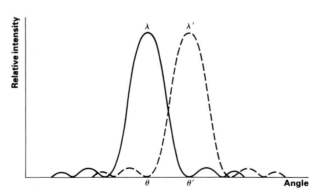

Figure J114

If there is to be a maximum at θ' for λ', write down an expression for BC′ in terms of λ' (calculated as in part **c**).

i Write down the two expressions for BC′ from parts **e** and **h** and show that

$$\frac{\lambda' - \lambda}{\lambda} = \frac{1}{10\,000}$$

for the two maxima to be just resolved.

j What would happen to the grating's ability to resolve the two wavelengths if only 100 slits contributed to the diffraction pattern?

The grating can resolve two wavelengths with a fractional difference in wavelength $\dfrac{(\lambda' - \lambda)}{\lambda}$ equal to $\dfrac{1}{\text{number of slits}}$. A good grating is one which can resolve two very close wavelengths and is thus able to show two close spectral lines as distinct maxima. This property is vital in spectroscopy and is achieved by ensuring that as many slits as possible contribute to the diffraction pattern.

Young's double-slit experiment

26(L) A diagram for the Young's double-slit experiment is shown in figure J115. It is important to note that it is *NOT* to scale; typically x_1 might be a few mm if $s \leqslant 1\,\text{mm}$ and $L \geqslant 1\,\text{m}$; θ_1 is much smaller than shown here.

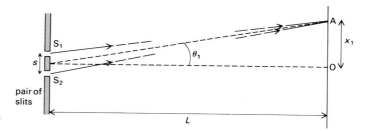

Figure J115

a We assume that the rays from S_1 and S_2 are parallel, yet they are drawn meeting at A to produce the first maximum or bright fringe. Why are we justified in doing this?

b Use the techniques from earlier work on gratings to find the relationship between θ, s, and λ.

c Use tables or a calculator to compare the values of $\sin\theta$ and $\tan\theta$ for $\theta = 10^{-2}$ radian. You should now feel justified in writing $\sin\theta_1 = x_1/L$ and be able to substitute this into your answer to **b**. What equation do you get?

d Suppose that the $(n+1)$th fringe is measured, giving a new value of $OA = x_{n+1}$. What is the grating formula now?

e Show that if x is the fringe separation, $\lambda/x = s/L$.

27(P) Light from a colour filter is used to produce Young's double-slit fringes. The slit separation is 0.4 mm. The distance between the slits and the screen on which the fringes are formed is 1.4 m, and the distance between successive dark spaces (or bright fringes) is 1.7 mm.

a Find the average wavelength of the light used.

b Why 'average'?

28(P) Light of wavelength 500 nm from a very small source falls on a pair of slits 0.1 mm apart, and forms fringes 2.5 mm apart on a photographic film, 0.5 m from the slits.

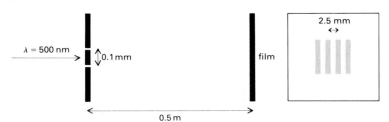

Figure J116

a What would the fringe spacing become if light of wavelength 250 nm were used? Would the fringes be visible if you looked at a screen placed where the film was held?

b The slits are replaced by a pair with half the spacing, still using the shorter wavelength. What is the fringe spacing now?

c An experiment has been done, using this arrangement, to test whether electrons have wave properties. The expected wavelength was about 10^{-10} m. The fringes could be detected if they were at least 10^{-2} mm apart. Approximately what slit spacing would have to be used if the film were still 0.5 m from the slits?

X-ray diffraction

29(L) This question is about the diffraction of X-rays by a crystal and its optical analogue.

In 1912 Max von Laue suggested that, just as a grating with a periodic array of apertures produces a diffraction pattern when illuminated by radiation of comparable wavelength, so the regular arrangement of atoms in a crystal should also give a diffraction pattern when illuminated appropriately – in this case with X-rays. It was hoped that the analysis of such diffraction patterns would yield much useful information about the structure of crystals.

Figure J117 shows a photograph of an X-ray diffraction pattern for a crystal of ZnS taken with the X-ray camera shown in figure J118. The essential geometry of the rather complex apparatus is shown in figure J119.

Figure J117
X-ray diffraction pattern for ZnS.
Professor C. A. Taylor

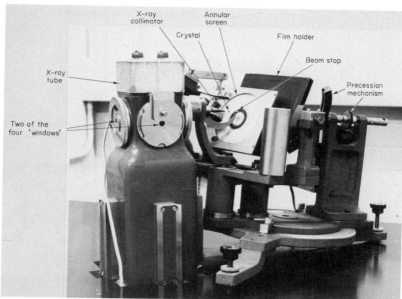

Figure J118
X-ray camera used to achieve figure J117.
Professor C. A. Taylor

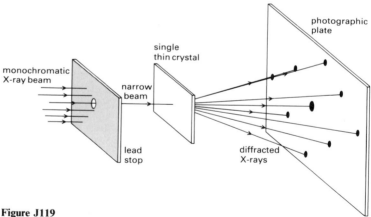

Figure J119
Simple geometry for X-ray diffraction.

a As we have seen in demonstration J6, the diffraction pattern contains all the information necessary to enable an enlarged image of the crystal to be produced by recombination. Why cannot this be done using X-rays?

b Not only can an image of the crystal not be formed, but it proves very difficult to determine its structure by analysing the diffraction pattern directly. A way forward is to make an optical analogue of the experiment. It is possible to make an informed guess at the crystal structure from its chemical and physical properties. A 'ball-and-stick' model is constructed and a mask made of dimensions suitable for diffracting light, where each aperture represents an atom in the model, as seen in a shadow to simplify the detail (figures J120 and J121).

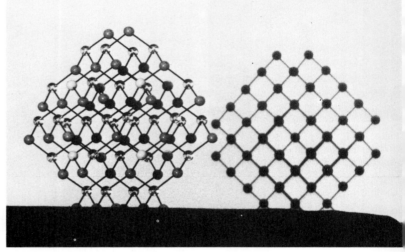

Figure J120
Ball-and-stick model of ZnS, with the 'shadow' corresponding to the position which produces the diffraction pattern shown in figure J122.
Professor C. A. Taylor

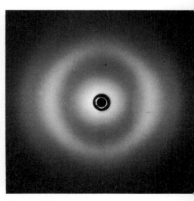

Figure J121
Optical diffraction grating of holes from ZnS model.
Professor C. A. Taylor

If the model is an accurate representation of the crystal, the diffraction pattern produced when the negative is illuminated with monochromatic light, usually from a laser, should be similar to the pattern produced with the crystal using X-rays. Compare the two patterns in figures J122 and J117 and say why you think the model of ZnS is a good one or not.

c Figure J123 shows the diffraction pattern for distilled water. From demonstration J16, what might be a reasonable interpretation of the arrangement of molecules in water?

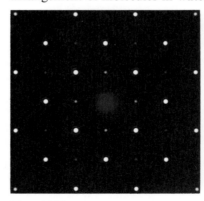

Figure J122
The optical diffraction pattern, with the direct beam removed.
Professor C. A. Taylor

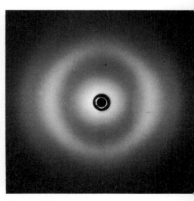

Figure J123
Distilled water (X-ray diffraction).
Pilkington Brothers P.L.C.

d Figures J124 and J125 show the diffraction patterns produced from unstretched and stretched rubber. Compare the photographs; what do they suggest about the difference in molecular arrangement between the two examples?

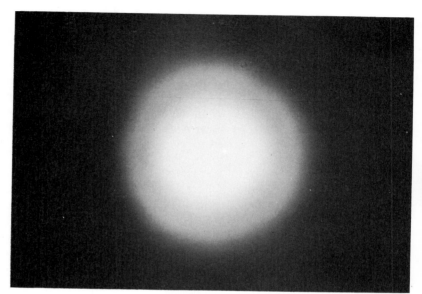

Figure J124
Diffraction pattern formed by unstretched rubber.
The Malaysian Rubber Producers' Research Association

Figure J125
Diffraction pattern formed by stretched rubber.
Professor E. H. Andrews, Department of Materials, Queen Mary College, University of London

Holography

30(L) Imagine that in the production of a hologram the object consists of just a single small point.

a What shape would the scattered wavefronts which constitute the signal beam have?

b If the reference beam is virtually parallel, what shape do the reference wavefronts have?

c In figure J126 the scattered and reference waves are shown superposing along a line where the photographic plate has been put. In the diagram the waves are shown frozen in time. What happens at A, B, C, D, and E? Explain your answer.

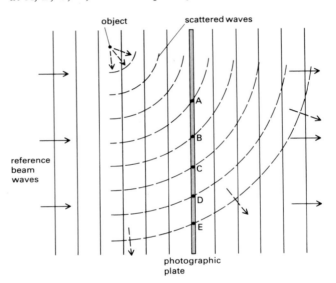

Figure J126

d What happens between these points on the plate?

e Why does this superposition pattern remain the same even as the waves advance?

f The reference beam must have a constant phase relationship between all its waves, that is, it must be coherent. Explain why this is important.

g A real object would consist of many such points, each scattering waves in slightly different directions, and each scattered wave would produce its own superposition pattern with the reference wave. The photographic plate records an enormous number of such diffraction patterns, for all the illuminated parts of the object. The developed plate is called a hologram.

In the reconstruction stage the developed plate is illuminated by the reference beam from its original direction. Each of the diffraction patterns on the plate produces a diffraction image of the original scattering point and in this way a complete image of the original object is recombined.

If the viewpoint is changed, then light is received from a changed direction and consequently from a different set of diffraction patterns on the hologram. Thus a different set of images is recombined, with the new overall image corresponding exactly to the viewer's changed perspective of the object.

Each part of the hologram contains some contribution from *every* part of the object. Explain why this is so, and why it is possible to recombine a complete image from a small (though not too small) piece of the hologram.

Revision questions on slits and gratings

31(R) A parallel beam of light of wavelength 7.0×10^{-7} m falls normally on to an opaque screen in which there are two parallel and identical slits, S_1 and S_2, 3.5×10^{-4} m apart, as shown in figure J127. (Note that the drawing is not to scale.)

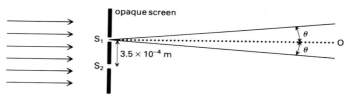

Figure J127

If slit S_2 is covered up, the variation of the intensity of the light transmitted by slit S_1 on both sides of the line $S_1 O$ parallel to the incident light will vary with $\sin \theta$, as shown in figure J128.

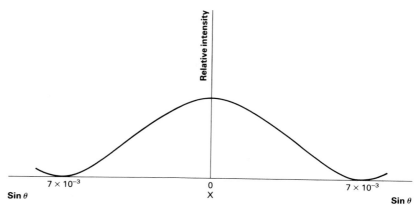

Figure J128

a Calculate the slit width, showing your working.

b *i* If slit S_2 is now uncovered, there is still a maximum at X, where $\sin \theta = 0$. Copy figure J128 and mark with Xs other places where there are now maxima. Show how you calculate these positions.
ii Now show how the intensity of the light transmitted by both slits varies with $\sin \theta$, indicating also how the intensity scale may need to be changed.

c State two ways in which the graph you have drawn in **b**ii would differ if the width of each slit were doubled, their distance apart remaining unchanged.

(Short answer paper, 1978)

32(R) A narrow parallel beam of light of wavelength 5.0×10^{-7} m falls normally on to a diffraction grating with a spacing of 12.5×10^{-7} m. Diffracted beams are observed on the other side of the grating from the light source.

a Calculate the angle between the first order diffracted beam and a line perpendicular to the grating. Show how you arrive at your answer.

b Calculate the angle between the second order diffracted beam and a line perpendicular to the grating. Show how you arrive at your answer.

c Explain why no third and subsequent orders are produced when this grating is set up as described.

d A third order diffracted beam can be produced by tilting the grating so that the incident beam is no longer normal to the grating. Copy and complete figure J129, and add whatever further written explanation is necessary to explain how the tilted grating can produce a third order diffracted beam.

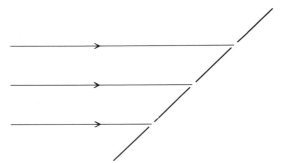

Figure J129   (Short answer paper, 1976)

33(R) Light from a distant point source falls on a single slit, and also on a double slit, as shown in figure J130 parts (a) and (b).

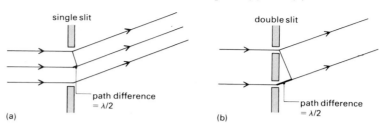

Figure J130

If the path difference indicated in each diagram is half a wavelength, which one of the following correctly describes for both what will be observed at the angle shown?

	single slit	double slit
A	darkness	darkness
B	brightness	brightness
C	darkness	brightness
D	brightness	darkness
E	edge between bright and dark	brightness

(Coded answer paper, 1979)

34(R) Figure J131 shows three slits from each of two diffraction gratings X and Y. The open slits of grating X are twice as wide as those of grating Y, otherwise the gratings are identical. Both gratings have the same slit spacing and the same large number of slits.

Which of the following statements about the first order spectrum of white light from the two gratings is/are true if the gratings are used with the same lamp and lens system?

1 The angle between red and blue is smaller for Y than for X.
2 The spectrum from Y is dimmer than that from X.
3 Red light is diffracted by Y through twice as large an angle as it is by X.

A 1 only.
B 2 only.
C 3 only.
D 1 and 2 only.
E 1, 2, and 3.

(Coded answer paper, 1976)

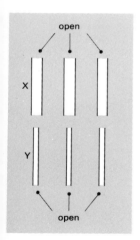

Figure J131

'Tied' and travelling waves

35(P) The hollow tube of rectangular cross-section in figure J132 has a slot cut in the top to allow a diode receiver probe to be inserted. The sides of the tube behave in the same way as the rods in demonstration J18 and guide the wave down the tube. Minima are detected every 15 mm along the guide. Explain in terms of superposition why there are such minima and from the values given calculate the speed of the microwaves in the waveguide.

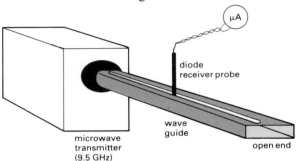

Figure J132

36(L) This question suggests some links between the 'tied' electromagnetic wave, moving charges, and travelling E- and B-fields. It uses a very simple geometrical arrangement similar to that in demonstration J18a, but with the essential difference that the signal applied to the guide is not oscillating; it is a step pulse produced when a battery is connected across the nearer ends of a pair of long metal rods, by closing the switch in the circuit shown in figure J133.

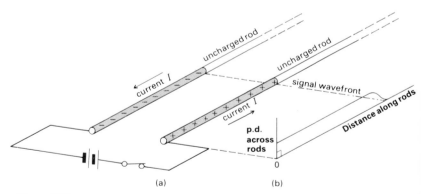

Figure J133
Signal travelling along a pair of metal rods.

a When the switch is closed, positive charges move off the lefthand rod and flow onto the righthand rod, leaving them charged negatively and positively respectively. Figure J133 shows the charged regions a short time after the battery had been switched on. The speed of charge carriers in metal was discussed in Unit B, 'Currents, circuits, and charge'. What is a reasonable estimate for the drift speed of individual charges in the rods? This diminutive value is *not* the speed of the signal wavefront, however, as the edges of the charged regions move forward at a speed approaching $3 \times 10^8 \, \mathrm{m\,s^{-1}}$.

b On a copy of figure J133, draw the electric field lines between the rods in the region where they are charged.

c Why must there be a current I in the metal rods between the signal wavefront and the battery?

d Draw the magnetic field lines associated with these currents in a contrasting colour on your answer to **b**.

e At what speed are these E- and B-fields spreading into the region which was previously uncharged?

The signal moving along the guide is an electromagnetic pulse. The pattern of E- and B-fields which constitutes the pulse is associated with moving regions of charge and propagates at a speed of $3 \times 10^8 \, \mathrm{m\,s^{-1}}$ in a vacuum. The individual charges drift along very much more slowly.

37(R) Figure J134 shows a length of coaxial cable, made with an outer sheath of conductor wrapped round a long roll of insulator, inside which is a conducting wire running along the axis of the whole cable. The capacitance of each metre of cable is $200 \times 10^{-12} \, \mathrm{F}$. Some time before the instant shown, the switch S was switched to the 1.5 V battery for $10^{-9} \, \mathrm{s}$ and then back to the position shown. At the time shown, the inner wire carries positive charge in the region BC and the outer conductor carries negative charge. The regions AB, CE are uncharged.

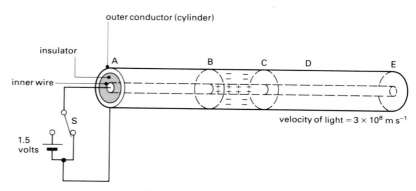

Figure J134

a Give a reason why no electricity has yet reached the distant place E.

b Estimate roughly the length of the charged region BC (the insulator actually reduces the velocity, but you may ignore this).

c Make a sketch showing the directions of the electric field around the central wire within the region BC.

d Explain why the charge on each conductor in the region BC is about 9×10^{-11} C (again neglect any effect of the insulator).

e What do you think will happen when the charged region reaches the end of the cable beyond E if the conductors end abruptly and are not connected to anything else or to each other?

(Paper I, 1970)

38(R) The signal from a receiving aerial is brought by coaxial cable to the input of a television set. The spot where the electron beam meets the television screen sweeps across the screen at 10^4 m s^{-1}. Another length of coaxial cable is also connected to the aerial, in parallel with the first, but the far end of this second cable is left free and unconnected. When this is done, a second, fainter picture appears on the screen, 10^{-2} m to the right of the first.

a Suggest a reason for the existence of this second picture.

b If the second cable is 125 m long, how fast does the signal travel along the cable?

c It is suggested that the lengths of otherwise identical coaxial cables remaining on a number of big, partly-used reels could be estimated by measuring the displacement of the second picture. Explain, using appropriate numerical estimates, how accurate this method is likely to be.

(Short answer paper, 1972)

39(E) Advances in solid state electronics, in particular the production of integrated circuits, have made it possible to design computers which can process data in times of the order of a nanosecond.

a One limitation on the speed of operation of a computer is connected with the physical size and layout of the circuits. Explain this.

b In a certain experiment it is necessary to delay the passage of an electrical pulse by 2 ms. Suggest a simple way of doing this and give some practical details.

40(P) The output power of a space probe's radio might be about 100 W. Its signal can be detected from as far away as the Moon's distance from Earth (380 000 km) by a dish aerial about 10 m in diameter.

a Use this information to set a limit on the power that modern receivers can detect.

b If you assume that the power follows an inverse-square law, what are you supposing about the space probe's aerial?

c The receiving dish aerial is strongly directional. Does this fact make the use of an inverse-square law in **a** invalid?

41(E) *For discussion*

A television programme may be received in one of two ways:

1 The signals are transmitted from an aerial, and picked up in a receiving aerial connected to a television set. (In the Direct Broadcast Satellite television system, developed in the early 1980s, the transmitter aerial is an orbiting satellite.)

2 The signals are transmitted along a coaxial cable which is connected directly to the television set (there may be an amplifier somewhere in the transmission line). This is commonly called the Cable Television system.

Describe how each system conveys the programme information and explain how it is that the final results are very similar.

The speed of electromagnetic waves

42(L) This question is about the speed of an electrical signal along a pair of long, flat conducting plates (see figure J135). It is very similar to the geometry of the 'guided' or 'tied' wave demonstration J18a and question **36**, but the gap between the plates is very much smaller than their width, so that any length of the plates behaves like a parallel plate capacitor. The electrical signal applied to the guide is not oscillatory but merely a step pulse produced by switching on a battery across one end. This electrical signal travels at speed v leaving behind a charged region – the left plate is negatively charged and the right positively charged.

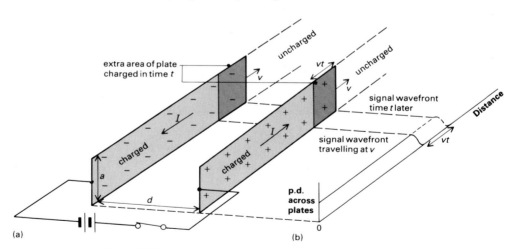

Figure J135

a The wavefront travels a distance vt along the plates in time t, thus an extra area of plates becomes charged in time t. Where does this extra charge come from?

b Why must there be electric current I flowing in the left and right plates between the battery and the signal wavefront?

c   If the current is I, what charge flows onto the extra area of plate in time t?

d   Over what area will the charge in **c** be spread, if the width of each plate is a?

e   Treating the two newly charged regions as a parallel plate capacitor $\left(\text{capacitance } C = \dfrac{\varepsilon_0 A}{d}\right)$, write down an expression for the electric field E between the plates in terms of the current I using the answers from parts **c** and **d** (figure J136).

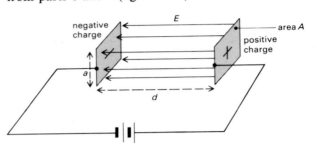

Figure J136

f   If the plates carry current there must be a B-field between them. To help visualize how the plates produce a B-field, and to link up with work on solenoids, it is useful to think of the plates as rather like a flat solenoid in which the many wires wound around a solenoid have become one wire – the plates themselves. In figure J137(a), if the solenoid has N turns in width a, the B-field inside it and well away from its ends is given by:

$$B = \mu_0 N I / a$$

(Note that the drawing is *not* to scale, the plates have to be much closer to satisfy the conditions for a flat solenoid.)
What will the B-field be in figure J137(b) when there is *one* turn in width a?

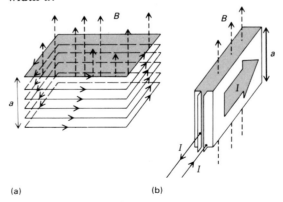

(a)   (b)

Figure J137

g   Use the answers to **e** and **f** to write as simple an equation as you can, giving B in terms of E.

h   Your answer to **g** should show that the larger the speed, v, the larger the B-field for a given E-field. The E-field is fixed by the battery p.d. and is just that p.d. divided by the plate spacing. Why is B larger if the speed, v, is larger? (Think about how much current must flow.)

i   Wherever currents flow in the plates there will be a B-field near the plates. Currents flow up to the present position of the travelling leading edge of the pulse. Thus the B-field extends further and further along the plates, just as the E-field does, while the pulse is propagating along the plates. Into what new length between the plates does the B-field extend in time t?

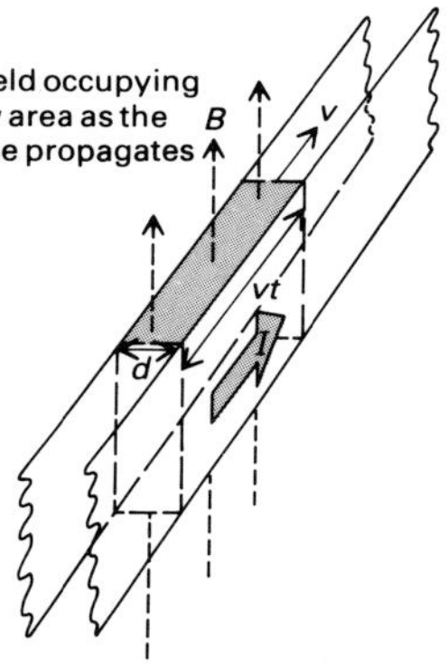

j   Figure J138 illustrates the B-field occupying new area as the pulse propagates. An area dvt has new B-field at right angles to it in time t. What is the new flux through this area? What is the rate of change of flux?

k   A p.d., equal to the rate of change of flux, is needed to increase the magnetic flux in a region of space. What p.d. across the plates produces the rate of change of flux found in **j**?

l   If there is a p.d. V across the plates, there is an electric field E between them, equal to V/d. Write an expression for this electric field, E, in terms of B, using the answer to **k**.

m   In **g**, the electric field between the plates was found to be related to the B-field between the plates by:

$$B = \varepsilon_0 \mu_0 E v$$

The larger the speed, v, the bigger the B-field, because a greater current would be needed to deliver the same charge per unit area at a faster rate to new parts of the plates. In **l**, the E- and B-fields were related by a second condition

$$E = Bv$$

The bigger the speed, v, the faster the magnetic flux must be produced in new area. The speed v is limited by both equations. Eliminate B between these two equations, and obtain an expression for speed v.

n   Use

$$\mu_0 = 4\pi \times 10^{-7}\,\mathrm{N\,A^{-2}} \quad \text{and}$$

$$1/4\pi\varepsilon_0 = 9 \times 10^9\,\mathrm{N\,m^2\,C^{-2}}$$

to obtain the value of the speed v.

o   Show that the units of $1/\sqrt{\varepsilon_0\mu_0}$ are $\mathrm{m\,s^{-1}}$, using the units given in **n**.

p   Why does the speed, v, remain the same even if the size of the plates, their spacing, or the battery p.d. are changed?

B-field occupying new area as the pulse propagates

Figure J138

43(P) In an experiment to measure the speed of light in air, light from a laser is shone through one of the holes of a stationary disc and is reflected back from a mirror 5 km away through the adjacent hole. It is received by a photosensitive detector behind this hole.

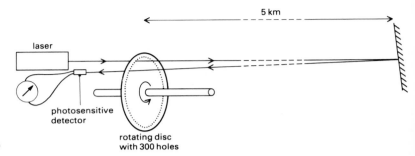

Figure J139

a The wheel is then made to rotate and the detector reading gradually falls. Why is this?

b As the speed increases, there comes a point when the detector reading again reaches a maximum. Explain why this is so and calculate a value for the speed of light if this rotational speed is 100 rev s^{-1}.

The speed of light *in vacuo* is one of the fundamental constants and can now be measured with an uncertainty of ± 100 m s^{-1}, *i.e.*, to better than 1 part in 10^6. Early attempts at its determination were astronomically based, relying upon a deduction from the time light took to travel a relatively large distance, for example Rømer's method of 1676. Later attempts, similar to the one in the question above, utilized either a toothed wheel (Fizeau, 1849) or a rotating mirror (Foucault, 1850, and Michelson, 1926) to chop up or modulate a continuous beam into pulses. By measuring the time interval separating pulses which have travelled a known distance, the speed can readily be calculated.

Aerials

44(R) A television programme is broadcast at a frequency of 600 MHz with the electric vector vertical. Figure J140 illustrates the waves at a considerable distance from the transmitter.

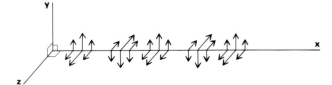

Figure J140

a Make a rough copy of the diagram, label the axes, and explain how it is meant to represent the waves.

b Draw another diagram to show what this wave would look like 5×10^{-10} s later. ($c = 3 \times 10^8$ m s^{-1}.)

c Show on another diagram
  i how you would place a short straight wire so as to get the maximum e.m.f. induced in it,
  ii how you would place a small loop of wire so as to get the maximum e.m.f. induced in it,
  iii where you would place a large metal sheet so as to increase the e.m.f. in *i*.

d What features of the diagram of the wave indicate that the wave is polarized? How would you decide whether the waves carrying a particular television broadcast were polarized?

(Paper I, 1970)

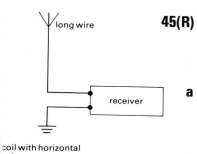

long wire

receiver

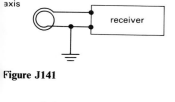

coil with horizontal axis

receiver

Figure J141

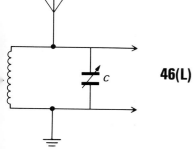

C

Figure J142

45(R) A medium wave radio receiver may have two kinds of aerial, as shown in figure J141: either a long straight wire or a coil. (The coil is actually wound on a ferrite rod and is usually enclosed within the receiver.)

a Reception of a particular station using the long straight wire aerial is best with the wire vertical. Explain how the radio waves cause alternating currents in the aerial, and why it matters that the wire is vertical.

b Reception of the same station using the coil aerial is good when the axis of the coil is at right angles to the direction of the transmitter and poor when the axis of the coil points at the transmitter. Why?

c The aerial currents produce alternating currents in the tuning circuit of the receiver (figure J142). Why can turning the knob which varies *C* tune in a particular signal?

(Short answer paper, 1979)

Polarization

46(L) Figure J143 (page 246) shows how much light 'ideal' Polaroid transmits. In figure J143(a), the electric field of the incoming light is at right angles to long polymer chains, to which iodine atoms are attached. The presence of the iodine allows electrons to migrate along the chains, so that the chains behave like a very fine grid of conducting wires. With the electric field perpendicular to the grid, all the incident light is transmitted.

In figure J143(b), the electric field is parallel to the grid, and no light is transmitted.

In figure J143(c), the electric field makes an angle θ with the direction it had in figure J143(a). A component $E \cos \theta$ lies along that original direction, and is transmitted. (A component $E \sin \theta$ lies along the direction in figure J143(b), and is not transmitted.)

The amplitude of the transmitted electric field oscillation in figure J143(c) is $E \cos \theta$, if the amplitude of the incoming wave is E. The brightness, or intensity, of the transmitted light is proportional to the square of the amplitude, and so to $\cos^2 \theta$.

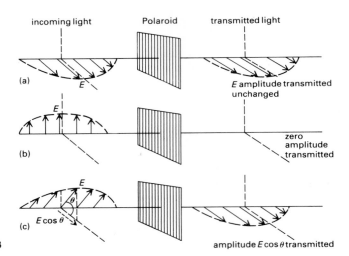

Figure J143

In figure: incoming light / Polaroid / transmitted light

(a) E — E amplitude transmitted unchanged

(b) E — zero amplitude transmitted

(c) E / θ / $E\cos\theta$ — amplitude $E\cos\theta$ transmitted

a Sketch a graph of the variation in brightness of the transmitted light if plane-polarized light falls on a sheet of ideal Polaroid, which is rotated through 360°.

b If unpolarized light, containing a random assortment of polarization directions, with no direction favoured, falls on ideal Polaroid, by what factor is the brightness of the light reduced by Polaroid? (You should recall something about an average value of $\cos^2\theta$ from work on alternating currents in Unit H, 'Magnetic fields and a.c.'.)

47(R) Which of these remarks about the use of plane-polarizing material (such as Polaroid) with light is/are correct?

1 If the light falling on the material is unpolarized, it emerges from the material with unchanged intensity, but is then polarized.

2 If two sheets of the material are put one in front of the other, and one is turned, the light transmitted is a minimum twice in each complete revolution.

3 If plane-polarized light falls on the material, it is transmitted with equal intensity whatever the orientation of the material.

A 1 only.
B 2 only.
C 1 and 3 only.
D 2 and 3 only.
E 1, 2, and 3.

(Coded answer paper, 1982)

Unit K
ENERGY AND ENTROPY

Jon Ogborn
Department of Science Education, University of London, Institute of
Education

K

SUMMARY OF THE UNIT

INTRODUCTION

Change at the molecular level

Much of physics deals with single lumps of matter, whether on a large or small scale, and tells us why things happen: how the pull of the Earth's gravity makes the Moon orbit the Earth, or how the charge on a nucleus deflects an alpha-particle passing close by. But physics has also to deal with changes involving large numbers of particles, such as diffusion or Brownian motion, thermal conduction, or electric current. For these, regular and predictable behaviour on the laboratory scale has lying behind it the random, chaotic, unpredictable motions of a multitude of particles. The problem is to see how the chaotic does in fact lead to the predictable: how, for example, the random motion of molecules results in scent diffusing across a room, in spite of the fact that it is absurd to suppose that the individual molecules could care which way they go. This Unit looks at how molecular chaos leads to large-scale regularity, even certainty.

Section K1 introduces the idea of *entropy*, and gives one example of how to calculate an entropy change. The entropy change is seen to be connected with energy changes and with temperature.

Section K2 shows how to understand the entropy change when energy is given to matter at a certain temperature. This involves rethinking what temperature itself means.

Section K3 is more practical, showing how the Boltzmann factor helps us to understand such things as rate of evaporation, rate of flow and rate of reaction.

Section K4 is about how entropy changes predict the direction of processes, and about how to exploit entropy changes to control events.

The whole Unit is just an introduction to these ideas. One important reason for studying them is that they are very different from ideas met elsewhere in physics, so that they help to complete a picture of what science is like. A second reason is their fundamental importance and very wide application, the latter illustrated by the variety of examples in Sections K3 and K4. These ideas apply, not just to one kind of process, but to any kind of process. They are thus important to physicists, chemists, biologists, and to engineers of all kinds.

Section K1 WHAT IS ENTROPY?

When ice melts or water boils, there is no sense in talking of the individual molecules 'melting' or 'boiling'. They just move about somewhat differently. No hidden guiding hand directs those motions to ensure that the result is boiling or melting.

Now physicists, chemists, and engineers *do* want to direct what happens. A physicist may want many atoms in a gas to be ionized. A

I am the undertow
Washing tides of power
Battering the pillars
Under your things of high law.

I am a sleepless
Slowfaring eater,
Maker of rust and rot
In your bastioned fastenings,
Caissons deep.

I am the Law
Older than you
And your builders proud.
I am deaf
In all days
Whether you
Say 'Yes' or 'No'.

I am the crumbler: tomorrow.

From Chicago poems *by Carl Sandburg, copyright 1961 by Holt, Rinehart and Winston, Inc.; renewed 1944 by Carl Sandburg.*
Reprinted by permission of Harcourt Brace Jovanovich, Inc.

1 in 6.5 million

Figure K1
Four aces.

$k = R/L = 1.38 \times 10^{-23}\ \mathrm{J\ K^{-1}}$
Unit A, 'Materials and mechanics'

QUESTIONS 1 to 3

$\Delta S = k\,\Delta \ln W$

QUESTIONS 4 to 7

Unit A, 'Materials and mechanics'
random walk

chemist may want many hydrogen and nitrogen molecules to combine to make ammonia for fertilizers. An engineer may want water to boil under pressure to provide steam for a turbine. All need to be able to predict when such things will happen, so as to be able to choose the conditions under which the random behaviour of many molecules will have the desired effect.

When the underlying behaviour is random, what happens most frequently is simply that which happens in most ways. If you deal a hand of cards, you hardly ever get all cards of one suit, simply because a mixture of suits can be dealt in more ways. So we have to count the numbers of ways in which events can happen: to know, for example, when one gas diffuses into another, whether the number of ways of arranging the molecules changes or not.

Suppose W is the number of ways of arranging the molecules of some piece of matter, at a certain pressure, temperature, and so on. Then we define a quantity called its *entropy*, S, related to W, by

$$S = k \ln W$$

The entropy is just the logarithm of the number of ways of arranging the molecules, multiplied by the Boltzmann constant k. The units of entropy are the same as those of k: joules per kelvin.

It is often enough just to calculate by how much W changes, and so to consider only entropy *changes* ΔS,

$$\Delta S = k\,\Delta \ln W$$

In some simple cases we can say directly in what direction events will go. We know that gas molecules will mix and diffuse, and once mixed will not of their own accord separate again. We know that the energy of a bullet hitting a target will spread out amongst the molecules of the target, warming it, and that this energy will never 'come together' and send the bullet flying back again. When the gas molecules mix, the number of ways of arranging molecules amongst molecules increases; when the target warms up the number of ways of arranging energy amongst molecules increases. The reverse processes, which do *not* occur, would decrease the number of ways.

Some examples of numbers of ways

Rubber consists of chains of isoprene molecules, with C—C bonds around which rotation can occur. So a chain follows a zig-zag path. In unstretched rubber, the chains zig-zag a lot, so that the places at which they cross-link to other chains are close together (figure K2). In stretched rubber, the chains are more straightened out. There are fewer ways a chain can be arranged between two points far apart than between two points close together. The number of chain arrangements for a given stretch can be calculated; and it contributes to the entropy of the rubber.

Figure K2
Paths between cross-links.
(a) Many paths.
(b) Fewer paths.

(a)

(b)

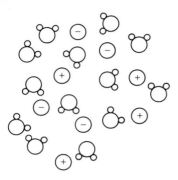

Figure K3
Water molecules and ions in solution.

In salt water, there are sodium and chloride ions (figure K3). For a given saltiness, it doesn't matter where exactly the ions are. They can change places with water molecules without our tongues tasting the difference. The number of ways of interchanging ions and molecules can be calculated, for a given concentration; and it contributes to the entropy of the salty water.

In a piece of metal near absolute zero, many atoms will have the least energy possible. There are then rather few ways of choosing which atoms have what energy. At a higher temperature, more atoms will be at various energies and there are more ways of sharing out the energy (figure K4). Changes in the numbers of ways in which atoms share energy, for a given rise in temperature, can be calculated; and they contribute to the change in entropy.

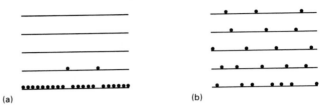

(a)   (b)

Figure K4
Collections of particles with different total energies.
(a) Most particles at lowest energy.
(b) Particles with many different energies.

In each case we are talking about some system which has a certain large-scale state (stretch, concentration, temperature). Consistent with that state, the particles of which it is composed can vary in their detailed state (position, energy, orientation, etc.). W is the number of such different detailed states which are possible given the large-scale state. $S = k \ln W$ is a convenient quantity to describe this degree of variability.

Calculation of an entropy change: particles spreading out

GAME K1
Particle shuffling

A game in which counters are shuffled between two halves of a box gives an example of an entropy change which can be calculated. The result can be applied to the expansion of a gas or to the dilution of solutions.

If N counters move between two halves of a box, there are 2^N ways of arranging them between the two halves (figure K5). Only one of these ways has all N counters in one half (say the left). If we start with all counters in one half, and move them purely at random, there is a tendency for the counters to become spread between the two halves. If N is large (100 is enough), there is essentially no chance that all the particles will concentrate again in one half.

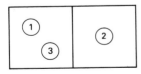

Figure K5
One of 2^3 arrangements.

QUESTIONS 8 to 11

Doubling the space open to N particles multiplies the number of ways W of arranging them by 2^N, if all the space is equally likely to be occupied and the position of a particle is not affected by the positions of others (figure K6).

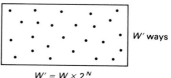

$$W' = W \times 2^N$$

If there is one mole of particles, the factor 2^N has the unimaginably large value

$L = 6 \times 10^{23}\,\mathrm{mol}^{-1}$
(L is the Avogadro constant)

$$W'/W = 2^{6 \times 10^{23}}$$

(where W' is the new, larger number of ways).
The entropy change is

$\Delta \ln W = \ln(W'/W)$
$\ln 2^{6 \times 10^{23}} \approx 4 \times 10^{23}$
$k \approx 1.38 \times 10^{-23}\,\mathrm{J\,K}^{-1}$

$$\Delta S = k\,\Delta \ln W$$
$$= k \ln 2^{6 \times 10^{23}}$$
$$\approx 6\,\mathrm{J\,K}^{-1}$$

QUESTION 12

which is a much more 'thinkable' number. A modest entropy change corresponds to a large addition to $\ln W$, and to an enormous factor multiplying W. (If written out, the number representing the factor would stretch beyond the nearer stars.)

When there is no change in the number of ways (for example particles moving about at random in a constant volume) $W' = W$, and $W'/W = 1$. Since $\ln 1 = 0$, it follows that $\Delta S = k \ln(W'/W) = 0$ when there is no change in the number of ways, *i.e.* at equilibrium.

K

Expansion of a gas

QUESTION 13

The entropy change $\Delta S \approx 6\,\mathrm{J\,K}^{-1}$ is in fact rather a good approximation to the entropy change when a gas doubles its volume. (This is so, even though gas molecules, unlike counters, cannot be distinguished from one another.) The number 2 in 2^N was just the ratio of volumes before and after. In general, if the volume changes from V_1 to V_2, we can write V_2/V_1 in place of the number 2 in 2^N, since we believe that a molecule is just as likely to be in one part of the total volume as in any other. This gives:

$S_2 = S_1 + Nk \ln(V_2/V_1)$
$S_2 = S_1 - Nk \ln(p_2/p_1)$

$$\Delta S = kN \ln(V_2/V_1) = kN\Delta \ln V$$

for any volume change, as long as the temperature is constant.

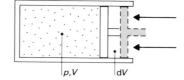

Figure K7
Expansion of a gas.

p, V dV

If the gas expands by an infinitesimal amount dV, then the change in entropy is

$$dS = kN\,d(\ln V)$$

$$\frac{d}{dx}(\ln x) = \frac{1}{x}$$

But $d(\ln V) = dV/V$, the fractional change in volume, so

$$dS = kN\, dV/V$$

QUESTIONS 14 to 17 There is a relation between the entropy change dS and the work $p\,dV$ involved in the expansion of the gas (figure K7, page 251). Since

$$pV = kNT$$

we have

$$p\,dV = kNT\,dV/V$$

entropy change = energy transfer/temperature

Comparing the equations for dS and $p\,dV$, we obtain the result

$$p\,dV = T\,dS$$

The value of k depends on the (arbitrary) size of a degree on the scale of T. Using k in the definition of entropy means that for a gas expanding at a given temperature, $T\,dS$ is numerically equal to the work $p\,dV$.

units of entropy JK^{-1}

The relation $p\,dV = T\,dS$ only holds for an ideal gas, for which there are no changes in internal energy. But it shows why we give entropy, via the Boltzmann constant, the units of energy divided by temperature.

Section K2   ENTROPY, ENERGY, AND TEMPERATURE

The connection of entropy with energy arises because, just as molecules can be arranged in space in many ways, so they can share energy in many ways.

Particles and energy levels

Unit L, 'Waves, particles, and atoms' energy is quantized

The energy of any bound particle is *quantized*: its energy can have only discrete values. Thus we can think about counting the number of particles at each energy level, and so think about counting the number of different arrangements of particles on the various levels, sharing out the total energy in different ways.

QUESTIONS 18 to 20

Figure K8
Ways of sharing energy.
(a) All the ways for 2 particles sharing 2 quanta.
(b) All the ways for 2 particles sharing 3 quanta.

Suppose, for simplicity, that particles have equally spaced energy levels. In going from one level to another they then exchange energy in lumps or quanta equal to the level difference. Consider just two such particles which happen to share two quanta of energy. There are just three possibilities: both can have one quantum each, or either can have two and the other none – figure K8(a).

More energy means more sharing possibilities. If the two particles share three quanta, there are four ways W of sharing the energy – figure K8(b). For three particles sharing three quanta, $W = 10$. For ten sharing ten, it is $92\,378$. For 100 sharing 100, it is 8×10^{59}.

Energy shuffling

GAME K2
Energy shuffling

QUESTION 21

A game in which counters representing particles exchange energy, moving up or down a ladder of equally spaced levels, shows how likely it is to find particles at the various levels, if they share the fixed total energy in all possible ways.

Even with only a few particles, it is rare for a particle to be at the highest possible level: that is, for one particle to have all the energy and the rest none. It is most common to find a particle on the lowest possible level. Going up the levels, the chance of a particle getting that much energy steadily decreases.

COMPUTER SIMULATION K3
Equilibrium distribution of energy

QUESTIONS 22 to 24

A computer program can play the game with many particles. With (say) 200 particles sharing 200 quanta, it is rare for a particle to get as many as 10 quanta, common for it to have one or two, and most frequent for it to have none. The distribution fluctuates around an *exponential* form: one in which the number on any one level is a constant fraction of the number on the next lower level (figure K9).

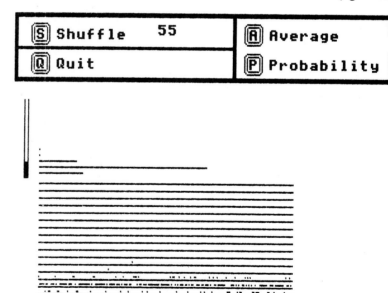

Figure K9 *(part)*
Computer simulation of energy shuffling between 200 particles. Lower part of display shows individual particles on energy levels; above that total number of each level and average energy per particle.
(a) Soon after starting with all on one level.

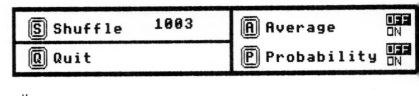

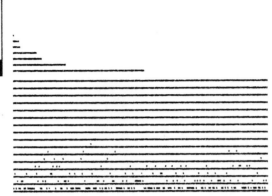

Figure K9 *(part)*
Computer simulation of energy shuffling between 200 particles.
(b) After a considerable number of moves.

For equal (and large) numbers of particles and quanta, it happens that the ratio of numbers in adjacent levels is just 1/2. Thus if a particle has a certain chance of being at any one level, it has twice the chance of being one level lower and half the chance of being one level higher.

If the same number of particles share more energy, more of them climb higher on the levels. The pattern is still exponential, but steeper. If the particles share less energy, fewer reach the higher levels. The pattern is again exponential, but less steeply graded (figure K10).

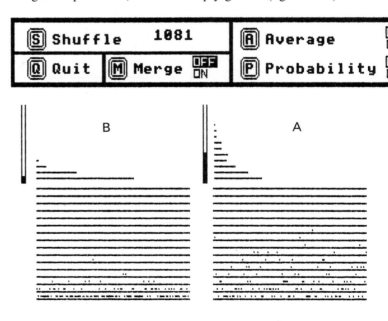

Figure K10
Two isolated systems, with different energies per particle.

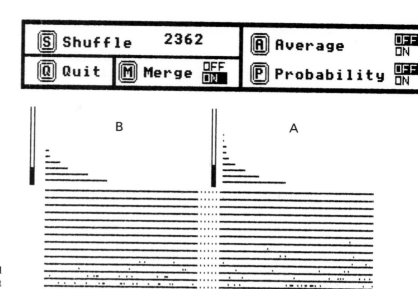

Figure K11
The two systems of figure K10 in contact and nearing equilibrium.

Energy shuffling and ways of sharing energy

Let f be the fraction

$$f = \frac{\text{chance of finding a particle at a given level}}{\text{chance of finding a particle at next lower level}}$$

f is the Boltzmann factor, Section K3

for your information:
$$f = n/(N + n)$$
for N particles sharing n quanta
(if N and n are large)

in the equilibrium distribution. For a given distribution, f is a constant, less than unity.

Figure K12 shows one particle, exchanging energy with a number of others. As expected, the probability of finding the lone particle at each level matches the probability of finding particles at each level in the larger set.

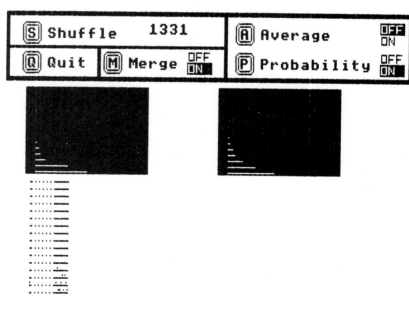

Figure K12
One particle sharing energy with ten others. Display shows that probability of finding a particle at a particular level is the same for the single particle (on the left) as for the set of ten particles (right).

The lone particle spends less time at higher levels because to get there it must take energy from the others. If it does so, the others have less energy to share, and so fewer ways W of sharing energy. Let taking one quantum from the set of particles reduce the number of ways from W to W'. Then

$$f = W'/W$$

since f gives the relative likelihood that the lone particle will be at any particular level rather than at the next lower level, and the frequency of events happening at random is in proportion to the number of ways in which they can occur.

QUESTIONS 25, 26 The entropy change when just one quantum is removed is

$$k \ln (W'/W) = k \ln f.$$

(f is less than one, so $\ln f$ is negative and the entropy falls.)

Entropy change and temperature

COMPUTER SIMULATION K4
Thermal equilibrium

Temperature differences are just what decide the direction of thermal flow of energy: from hot to cold and not from cold to hot. Since entropy changes decide the direction of change, we expect a connection between entropy change, energy change, and temperature.

The energy-shuffling simulation can be used to look at energy flow between two sets of particles (figures K10 and K11). System A (figure K10) must have been hotter than system B, because energy went spontaneously from A to B when they were in contact (figure K11). When they reach equilibrium, they must be at the same temperature, and energy then passes equally in both directions.

Suppose one quantum goes from A to B, when they are at temperatures T_A and T_B (figure K13). The entropy of A is reduced:

$$\Delta S_A = k \ln f_A$$

but, since energy is added to B, the entropy of B increases:

$$\Delta S_B = -k \ln f_B$$

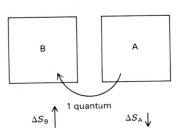

Figure K13
One quantum passing from one system to another.

To take a specific example, suppose $f_A = 0.8$ and $f_B = 0.5$. Then $\ln f_A = -0.22$ and $-\ln f_B = +0.69$. The increase in the entropy of B is more than the decrease in the entropy of A. The net effect of one quantum going from A to B is to increase the total number of ways of sharing energy in the two systems. But a quantum going from B to A reduces the number of ways. Thus quanta more often go from A to B than from B to A.

At equilibrium, $f_A = f_B$ and one quantum going in either direction has no effect on the total number of ways. Energy therefore passes equally often in both directions.

Temperature T can be defined in terms of $\ln f$. At low temperatures, adding or removing a quantum must have a large effect on the number of ways, whilst at high temperatures the effect must be small. Thus $\ln f$, and so the entropy change, should be inversely related to temperature.

In the case of a gas, the entropy change associated with an energy change has the form

entropy change = energy change/temperature

In the present case, the energy change is $-\varepsilon$ (remove one quantum). This suggests writing

entropy change $= k \ln f = -\varepsilon/T$

T is defined so that the *lower* the temperature, the *larger* will be the effect of removing a quantum on the number of ways, and so the effect on f. This gives

$$\ln f = -\varepsilon/kT$$
$$f = e^{-\varepsilon/kT}$$

Thermal transfer of energy

QUESTIONS 27 to 30

Working – raising a mass or speeding up the rotation of a wheel – does not necessarily alter the entropy. But a thermal transfer of energy from hot to cold does always increase the total entropy. When one more quantum of energy ε, enters a system at temperature T, the entropy increases by ε/T. If many quanta enter, with total energy Q transferred thermally, the increase in entropy is

$$\Delta S = Q/T$$

so long as the energy Q is small enough not to raise T appreciably. The entropy increases simply because more energy means more ways to share energy. In moving towards thermal equilibrium, if a hot body A gives energy Q to a cold body B, their entropy changes are

$$\Delta S_A = -Q/T_A \qquad \Delta S_B = +Q/T_B$$

and

$$\Delta S_{total} = \Delta S_A + \Delta S_B > 0$$

Energy-rich systems give up energy easily because doing so makes little difference to the number of ways in which they share energy internally. Energy-poor systems suck up energy greedily because adding a little energy greatly increases the number of sharing possibilities.

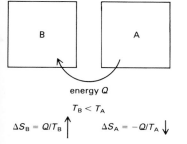

$T_B < T_A$

$\Delta S_B = Q/T_B \uparrow \qquad \Delta S_A = -Q/T_A \downarrow$

energy Q

Figure K14
Thermal transfer from hot to cold.

Thermodynamic temperature

The rather special arguments above, about particles on equally spaced energy levels, are merely the simplest possible form of a general argument about systems with any set of levels. Naturally such arguments are more complex, but in fact they lead to the same basic result, that temperature T is definable in terms of the ratio f of the chances of finding a particle in states differing by energy ε, with

$$f = e^{-\varepsilon/kT} \qquad \text{or} \qquad \ln f = -\varepsilon/kT$$

For these reasons, the definition of temperature and its relationship to entropy change are general, not special. Temperature defined in this way is called *thermodynamic temperature*. It is also chosen so as to agree with temperature defined on the ideal gas scale, by making the constant k the Boltzmann constant.

Section K3   THE BOLTZMANN FACTOR

Activation processes

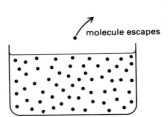

Figure K15
Evaporation as an activation process.

Puddles of water evaporate because a few molecules acquire enough energy to break free from the surface (figure K15). Silicon conducts electricity, and so transistors and microchips can work, because a few electrons get enough energy to be mobile.

Processes like these, which depend on a few particles acquiring enough energy to do something, are called *activation processes*. If the necessary energy E is to be acquired by chance from the particles of the material all sharing energy randomly at temperature T, then the Boltzmann factor

$$f = e^{-E/kT}$$

QUESTIONS 31 to 33

is often a good guide to the probability that a particle will gain the excess energy E, especially if E is large compared with the energy kT. The Boltzmann factor can be interpreted as the fraction by which the number of ways of sharing energy in the material is multiplied, when energy E is removed from the material and taken by a single particle.

The Boltzmann factor is not necessarily a precise guide to the chance of a particle acquiring energy, because energy levels of real systems are not in general equally spaced.

Experimental study of activation processes

In studying an activation process experimentally, one can measure the rate of the process, which depends on the number of particles with large enough energy E, and how the rate varies with temperature. Sometimes the energy E can be obtained directly, so that a relation like

$$\text{rate} \propto e^{-E/kT}$$

can be checked empirically. Sometimes a value of E has to be found from the variation of rate with temperature. It is common to plot $\ln(\text{rate})$ against $1/T$:

$$\ln(\text{rate}) = \text{constant} - E/kT$$

A number of processes to study are suggested below. You are not expected to consider more than one in detail.

Vapour pressure of water

EXPERIMENT K5
Vapour pressure of water

The energy E is the energy needed to get a molecule out of the liquid:

$$E = \Delta H_{\text{evap}}/L$$

ΔH_{evap}, in joules per mole, can be measured directly with an electrical heater. The fraction of molecules in the vapour is indicated by the pressure of the vapour, so we expect

$$p \propto e^{-\Delta H_{evap}/LkT}$$

(see figure K16).

QUESTIONS 34, 35

The Boltzmann factor is the reason why only a modest temperature rise produces a large increase in pressure in a pressure cooker.

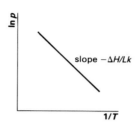

Figure K16
$\ln p$ against $1/T$.

Current in a semiconductor

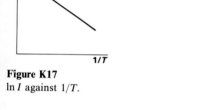

Figure K17
$\ln I$ against $1/T$.

EXPERIMENT K6
Current in a thermistor

The energy E is that needed to free an electron which is bound to an atom (leaving also a mobile 'hole') in the semiconductor. The current I at a given potential difference is approximately proportional to the number of free charge carriers. Thus we expect

$$I \propto e^{-E/kT}$$

The Boltzmann factor is the reason why (pure) semiconductors conduct at all, and why they are rather temperature sensitive, so that devices like a thermistor can be used to monitor temperatures.

Viscosity

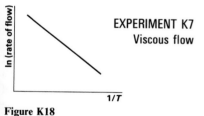

Figure K18
$\ln$ (rate of flow) against $1/T$.

EXPERIMENT K7
Viscous flow

Liquids flow because molecules acquire enough energy to break out of the 'cage' temporarily formed by their nearest neighbours, moving to a nearby 'cage'. The energy E is the average energy needed to push aside neighbouring molecules.

If we measure the rate of flow of a liquid under a fixed pressure gradient, we might expect approximately

$$\text{flow rate} \propto e^{-E/kT}$$

Creep

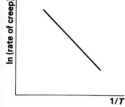

Figure K19
$\ln$ (rate of creep) against $1/T$.

EXPERIMENT K8
Creep

Solids can flow under stress, usually less rapidly than liquids. For an atom or molecule to move past its neighbours, an extra energy E is needed, so we might expect approximately, for a given stress,

$$\text{rate of creep} \propto e^{-E/kT}$$

For both liquids and solids, the energy E depends on the external stress, which supplies molecules with energy when they are displaced.

Rate of reaction

Some chemical reactions require an energy barrier to be overcome before two or more molecules can combine, with the particles passing through a short-lived, high-energy activated state. The chance of getting the activation energy E_A from random energy exchanges may be given by the Boltzmann factor, and we may expect

rate of reaction $\propto e^{-E_A/kT}$

Other factors, notably the rate of collision of molecules, also matter, but are often less important than the Boltzmann factor. The larger the activation energy, the slower the reaction, and the more sensitive it is to temperature change. The Boltzmann factor explains why food cooks so much more quickly in a pressure cooker. It is also a reason why our bodies need such careful temperature control.

Figure K20
ln (rate of reaction) against $1/T$.

Importance of the Boltzmann factor

The Boltzmann factor is very sensitive to the ratio E/kT. For an energy twice kT it is around 1/10, but for an energy twenty times kT it falls to about 10^{-9}.

This sensitivity is fundamental to the possibility of life. We live on a planet at a temperature of some 300 K. Covalent bonds, like those in rocks, need an energy of several hundred times kT to break them, so rocks last a long time and do nothing. People, by contrast, must be held together by bonds which break often enough for reactions such as digestion to occur, but not so easily that life is over in a flash. The most important bond in biological material is the hydrogen bond, with breaking energy around ten times kT. Amongst other essential things, hydrogen bonds play an important role in holding the two strands of DNA together.

At very high temperatures, the energy E can be large and still allow an appreciable fraction of particles with high energy. Thus in the Sun, the rate of the nuclear reaction of hydrogen fusing to helium is in part controlled by the small fraction of protons which acquire enough energy to 'touch' despite their electrical repulsion. In the early stages of the birth of the Universe (the 'Big Bang'), it was hot enough for some protons to gain enough mass-energy to exist as neutrons, and the temperature at that time decided the present ratio of protons to neutrons in the Universe.

Less dramatic examples of applications of the Boltzmann factor include lasers, ionization in flames, the emission of electrons from a hot cathode in a television tube, and the occurrence of defects in solids.

In all such examples the Boltzmann factor tells how chance sharing of energy works out.

Section K4   EXPLOITING ENTROPY CHANGES

The Second Law of Thermodynamics

When energy is transferred thermally from hot to cold, the entropy increases. The idea is quite general:

All changes occur in the direction for which the total entropy change is an increase.
The total entropy never decreases.
At equilibrium, the total entropy change is zero.

The word 'total' refers to all entropy changes produced. The entropy of part of the system can decrease, but if so there must be a bigger increase elsewhere if the process is to happen (figure K21).

It is the Second Law which explains our feeling that, despite the First Law (energy conservation), energy is in fact easily 'lost'. A moving car comes to a halt, because its kinetic energy is shared out in many more ways amongst warmed-up road and brakes. A warm room cools off as energy spreads through the walls and windows, again being shared in more ways by more particles. What is lost is not energy, but the potential for further change.

Any spontaneous change in an isolated system (such as a mixture of liquids in a stoppered vacuum flask) must increase the number of arrangements of molecules and their energy. The number of ways could only decrease if the molecules were to avoid getting into certain of the arrangements which they could in fact get into. But this would mean that their behaviour was not random.

More interesting are cases where entropy increases in one part of the system are exploited to achieve entropy decreases in another part. Thus letting carbon dioxide out of a cylinder increases the entropy by expanding the gas, and this permits the smaller entropy decrease involved in cooling and even solidifying some of the carbon dioxide (figure K22). An increase in one kind of numbers of ways can pay for a decrease in another.

This is how entropy changes can be exploited, in nature or by human intervention. Any process which is going to happen depends on the existence of some disequilibrium, and will involve an entropy increase as it moves towards equilibrium. By some device, it may be possible to use the process to run another which produces a desirable entropy decrease, as long as the *total* entropy still increases. Thus entropy increase both permits and sets limits to exploiting natural processes.

In this way we get combustion to run engines, extract pure metals from their ores, desalinate sea-water, freeze food for storage, or make chemical reactions in batteries run electric motors.

Second Law of Thermodynamics

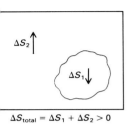

$\Delta S_{total} = \Delta S_1 + \Delta S_2 > 0$

Figure K21
Total entropy increases in a closed system.

QUESTIONS 40 to 42

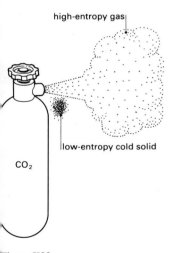

high-entropy gas

low-entropy cold solid

CO_2

Figure K22
Entropy increase can 'pay' for a decrease.

K

The inefficiency of engines

Unit G, 'Energy sources', efficiency of power stations

It was in studying steam engines, so important for the Industrial Revolution, that the science of thermodynamics began. The French engineer Carnot (1796–1832) argued that all such engines, no matter what their design, must be inefficient to some extent.

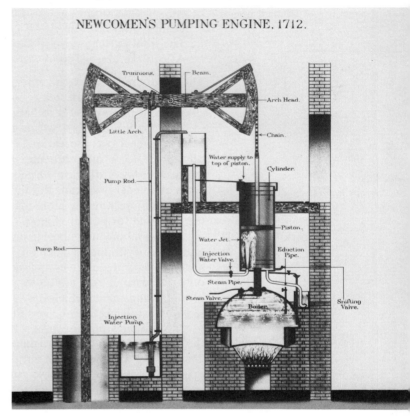

Figure K23
Drawing of Newcomen's pumping engine *circa* 1712.
Reproduced by permission of The Trustees of the Science Museum, London.

A whole variety of engines work by making some substance (often steam) hot, getting it to expand and do work, and then restoring it to its original state, making it hot again, and repeating the process. They are all called *heat engines*. They work only because energy goes from hot to cold: the steam gets energy from the furnace because it is colder than the furnace. So a heat engine is a way of exploiting a thermal disequilibrium.

A thermal transfer of energy across a temperature difference increases entropy. If energy Q is transferred thermally from a furnace at temperature T_{hot} to the atmosphere at T_{cold}, the net entropy change is

$$\Delta S = Q/T_{\text{cold}} - Q/T_{\text{hot}}$$

Only because $T_{\text{hot}} > T_{\text{cold}}$ does the energy flow occur, and the entropy increase.

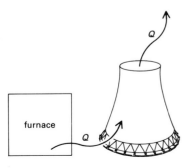

Figure K24
A power station merely heating the countryside.

A heat engine is a way of diverting some of the energy flow, so that it does useful work. In the long run, this energy still goes to the surroundings, but it is channelled through whatever dissipates energy in the job the engine does – whether driving a car, pumping water as Newcomen's engine did, or driving machinery. In the long run the entropy increases as much as if the engine wasn't there, but in the short run there is a smaller increase.

The best we could possibly do would be to have the entropy stay constant in the short run. If the engine was well designed we could

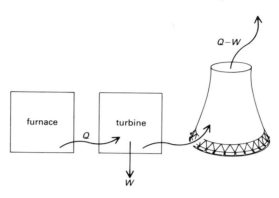

Figure K25
A power station not increasing entropy more than is necessary.

imagine diverting work W usefully, so that only energy $(Q - W)$ was delivered immediately to the cool surroundings (figure K25). The entropy change would then be

$$\Delta S = (Q - W)/T_{cold} - Q/T_{hot}$$

ΔS cannot be less than zero, so the best that can be done is to have

$$(Q - W)/Q \geqslant T_{cold}/T_{hot}$$

or

$$W/Q \leqslant 1 - T_{cold}/T_{hot}$$

But W/Q, the ratio of useful energy output to total energy input, is the efficiency of the engine. If T_{hot} is 1000 K and T_{cold} is 300 K, at least 3/10 of the energy from the furnace must be delivered to the surroundings and the efficiency cannot exceed 70 %.

QUESTIONS 43 to 45

The argument is very general, and it may seem as if there ought to be some ingenious way round it. But there isn't, *because* it is so general. It depends on nothing more than the fact that (as Carnot put it) in getting motive power from fire, the substance which gets energy from the fire must be cooler than the fire.

Further applications

The further applications which follow all use the idea of entropy. You should study at least one.

EXPERIMENT K10

Entropy changes in a gas

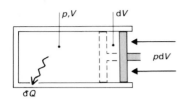

Figure K26
Compressing a gas.

Unit A, 'Materials and mechanics'

QUESTION 46

QUESTIONS 47, 48

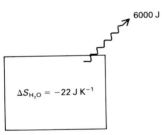

Figure K27
Freezing a mole of water.

$$-22 + \frac{6000}{250} = +2$$

$$-22 + \frac{6000}{300} = -2$$

$$-22 + \frac{6000}{273} = 0$$

Energy and entropy changes in a gas

If a gas is gently compressed or expanded, the smallest change in the force on the piston can bring it to rest. So the system is always very close to equilibrium, and the entropy change should approach zero.

But if the gas is compressed, its entropy falls:

$$dS_{gas} = Nk\,dV/V$$

A conducting cylinder can keep the gas at a constant temperature. As soon as the gas is warmed slightly by the compression, a small amount of energy đQ is transferred thermally to the walls of the cylinder (figure K26), contributing to raising the total entropy by

$$dS_{cylinder} = đQ/T$$

Since the gas is at constant temperature, its internal energy is constant, and

$$đQ = -p\,dV = -NkT\,dV/V$$

Thus

$$đQ/T = -Nk\,dV/V = -dS_{gas}$$

showing that the two entropy changes are then equal and opposite.
Of course, if there is friction on the piston, or turbulence in the gas, đQ is numerically larger than $p\,dV$ and there is a net entropy increase.

Equilibrium

At equilibrium, the total entropy change is zero. But we do have to take into account all entropy changes. Consider the freezing of water. When water changes to ice, its entropy decreases by $22\ \text{J K}^{-1}\,\text{mol}^{-1}$, as a result of the formation of the ice crystal structure. But at the same time, $6000\ \text{J mol}^{-1}$ are liberated to the surroundings, increasing the total entropy on that account, by an amount depending on the temperature of the surroundings (figure K27).

	$\Delta S/\text{J K}^{-1}\,\text{mol}^{-1}$
water to ice	-22
surroundings at 250 K	$+24$
surroundings at 300 K	$+20$
surroundings at 273 K	$+22$

Table K1

At 250 K the entropy increase Q/T of the surroundings is larger than the decrease due to the change in structure. There is a net entropy *increase* of $2\ \text{J K}^{-1}\,\text{mol}^{-1}$. Such an event can happen, and it does: water at 250 K freezes.

At 300 K the entropy of the surroundings increases by less than that of the water decreases. There is a net entropy *decrease*. Such a thing cannot happen, and indeed water does not freeze at 300 K.

At 273 K the two changes are equal, and freezing and melting are in equilibrium. The net entropy change is *zero*.

The example seems trivial, but just this reasoning is used to determine whether any change can happen, and where its equilibrium will lie.

Another example: hydrogen is dissociated in the Sun, but not on Earth. If hydrogen dissociates, there are two particles where before there was one, and so an increase in entropy, in fact of $100 \, J \, K^{-1} \, mol^{-1}$. But to dissociate H_2 means breaking bonds, taking energy from the surroundings, amounting to $430 \, kJ \, mol^{-1}$.

$$+100 - \frac{430 \times 10^3}{6000} > 0$$

Taking this energy from the Sun at $6000 \, K$ gives an entropy decrease of $430 \times 10^3/6000 = 72 \, J \, K^{-1} \, mol^{-1}$. The increase outweighs this decrease, and the hydrogen dissociates.

$$+100 - \frac{430 \times 10^3}{300} < 0$$

On Earth, taking the same energy at $300 \, K$ would decrease the entropy by $430 \times 10^3/300 = 1400 \, J \, K^{-1} \, mol^{-1}$. There would be a net entropy decrease, and so hydrogen does not dissociate. At this temperature, what does happen is the reverse process, for which the total entropy increases, and the hydrogen on Earth is strongly associated.

$$-100 + \frac{430 \times 10^3}{300} > 0$$

$T = d\,(\text{energy})/d\,(\text{entropy})$

It follows from all this that if you want a process which absorbs energy from the surroundings to occur, it is best to make the surroundings hot. Hot surroundings give up energy for little entropy decrease.

If you want a process which gives out energy to the surroundings to occur, it may be best to make the surroundings cool. Cool surroundings have a large entropy increase for the receipt of given energy. On the other hand, making things cool also slows down reactions, so although the reaction may be possible it may not happen fast enough to be useful. Then you may need a catalyst, to reduce any energy barrier.

A cell which runs on entropy

A difference in concentration between two beakers of copper sulphate solution, is enough to produce an e.m.f. (figure K28).

The electrode in the more concentrated solution is positive. Cu^{2+} ions have arrived from the solution, so making the solution more dilute. At the negative electrode, Cu atoms go into solution, making it more concentrated. This is of course the direction in which the concentrations would have changed if the solutions just diffused.

At the molecular level, the particles in the solution are continually moving about, changing places with one another. In how many more ways can they be arranged if we dilute a solution? Suppose we dilute the solution by doubling the number of solvent molecules (figure K29).

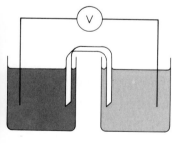

Figure K28
e.m.f. from a concentration difference.

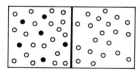

Figure K29
Doubling the dilution.

Each solute molecule (or ion) can now change places with a solvent molecule in twice as many ways as before. Doubling the dilution multiplies the number of ways of arranging N solute particles amongst solvent particles by the factor 2^N. Just as for expanding a gas,

$$W' = W \times 2^N$$

$$\Delta S = kN \ln 2$$

The number 2 is now the ratio of two dilutions. The general form of the relation is

$$\Delta S = -kN \ln (\text{concentration ratio})$$

with entropy increasing as concentration falls. In real solutions, the entropy change may be given approximately by such an expression.

QUESTIONS 49, 50   The action of the cell is equivalent to taking some of the more concentrated solution, diluting it, and putting it in the dilute solution. Thus the equation also gives the net entropy increase if N ions of Cu^{2+} are removed from the concentrated side, and produced at the dilute side. The concentration ratio is now the ratio of concentrations in the two parts of the cell. But the entropy need not increase: it must simply never decrease. The cell can take energy from the surroundings and do electrical work.

If the cell e.m.f. is $\mathscr{E}$, then the maximum energy it can deliver when N ions pass is $2eN\mathscr{E}$ (two electrons pass for each Cu^{2+} ion). If the entropy decrease of the surroundings balances the entropy increase in the cell, then

$k/e \approx 8.6 \times 10^{-5} \, \text{J K}^{-1}\text{C}^{-1}$ $2eN\mathscr{E}/T = -kN \ln (\text{concentration ratio})$

$\ln\left(\frac{1}{10}\right) = -2.3$ $\mathscr{E} = -(kT/2e) \ln (\text{concentration ratio})$

$\mathscr{E} \approx 30\,\text{mV}$

This gives a few tens of millivolts for a concentration ratio of 10 to 1 at $T = 300\,\text{K}$. The e.m.f.s from such concentration differences are an important part of the means by which our nerves create and transmit electrical signals.

The calculation is nothing like so exact as that for a gas, solutions being much more complex. In fact, experiments like this are used the other way round – from observations of the e.m.f. to work out the entropy change, to learn about the molecular structures of solutions.

READING

LIFE IN THE UNIVERSE

The Universe is a place of dramatic extremes: dense, white-hot stars set in the cold, black emptiness of space. It is clearly very far from equilibrium. We, the human race, live on a planet populated with an immense variety of kinds of biological pattern, from viruses through algae and plants to the animals. Yet all this must have come about through the universal tendency of things to decay; to become more, not less even.

The story begins with the birth of the Universe. Three simple facts lead us to suppose that the Universe is not infinitely old nor infinitely big, so that there must have been such a birth. These facts are:

the sky is dark at night
there are stars in the sky
there is matter in the Universe.

The German astronomer Olbers (1758–1840) pointed out that if the Universe were infinite, we should see a star in every direction we looked, so that the sky would be as white hot as the surface of a star. But, as Newton realized, if matter occupies only part of space, its gravitational attraction will pull it all together. The Universe is either infinite, but would then be white hot, or not infinite and not stable. The Universe cannot be infinitely old, because it only takes a finite time for a system to reach equilibrium, so the bright stars we see would not be there.

We now think that the Universe is 'young', and expanding. Friedmann showed in 1922 that Einstein's equations of General Relativity, replacing Newton's Laws of Gravitation, share the problem of stability, so that a Universe containing matter must either expand or contract. Recently, Hawking and Penrose have shown that space–time itself is gravitationally unstable, and that the Universe must contain at least one 'singularity' (point of collapse).

In the 1930s Hubble showed that the distant galaxies were running away from us, at a rate indicating a compressed origin about 16 billion years ago. Gamow in the 1940s used nuclear physics to work out how the elements might have been built up in that compressed state. He found that to get the observed preponderance of hydrogen with some helium, he had to suppose that the early Universe was very hot – the 'hot Big Bang'.

In 1965 what is thought to be the faint glow of that bang was found by accident by the radio engineers Penzias and Wilson, who discovered cosmic microwave radiation filling space and travelling equally in all directions. As the Universe expands, the wavelength of radiation stretches in proportion and its temperature falls ($\lambda T = $ constant). At present, the radiation has a temperature of about 3 K, a wavelength of a few centimetres, and an intensity equivalent to about 10^9 photons per cubic metre throughout space. This compares with about one proton mass per cubic metre. Tracing back the size and temperature, we can reconstruct the thermal history of the Universe (figure K30).

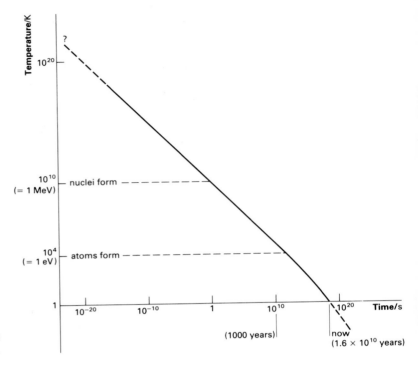

Figure K30
Cooling of the Universe.

At about time 1 second after the birth of the Universe, the temperature was high enough for protons to be converted into the more massive neutrons, by randomly acquiring the extra energy needed. But at about this time, the expansion meant that the particles got too far apart to collide often enough, so the reaction effectively stopped and the present proportion of neutrons to protons (around 1 to 10), and so of hydrogen to helium, was 'frozen' into the composition of the Universe.

After about 100 000 years, the temperature was low enough (about 1000 K) for electrons to combine with protons to make hydrogen atoms. Before this, the intense radiation kept matter from collapsing, but now with matter in the form of neutral atoms, gravity could begin to magnify local irregularities and clump the gas into clouds which became the galaxies.

But gravitational attraction delivers energy, so the collapsing matter grew hot, nuclear reactions began, and there were stars. The first stars were made of hydrogen and helium, but as they grew old, there was time (as there had not been in the 'Big Bang') to synthesize heavier nuclides, such as carbon and oxygen. Still heavier nuclides, like iron and up to uranium, were made in the explosive death throes of such stars (novae and supernovae). The dust and gas from such dead stars could again be collapsed by gravity, and new stars like our Sun formed, probably with planets like Earth made of the heavy-element ashes of ancestor stars.

The thermal disequilibrium of our present Universe thus came from gravitational instability as a source of increasing entropy. Then the thermal disequilibrium acted as a further source of increasing entropy, driving further change. So far as we understand it, this is how life began.

The Sun's photons arrive at the Earth at a radiation temperature of about 6000 K, and are re-radiated at about 300 K. With photons delivering 1 kW per square metre, the entropy increase per square metre per second is about $3\,\mathrm{J\,K^{-1}}$. This is enough to drive reactions such as the photosynthesis of sugars or cellulose from carbon dioxide and water by plants. We and other animals profit by eating these low-entropy forms so as to drive other reactions in our bodies. We live by the Second Law of Thermodynamics, not in spite of it.

Life has another special property: self-replication. All organisms on Earth use the same method, a genetic code-carrying molecule (DNA) which replicates itself. The ingredients of DNA have already been made in the laboratory just by exposing more primitive chemicals known to exist in the Universe to heat and light. Nobody knows how the first self-replicating molecule arose, though von Neumann has proved that sufficiently complicated structures are capable of it. Once self-replication happens, the inevitability of mistakes, due again to the Second Law, gives it enormous power. Poor copies which replicate a little more slowly are rapidly suppressed, but if conditions change and what was a poor copy has an advantage, it soon takes over. In this way, given a Sun delivering energy and a continual entropy increase for a few billion years, structures could grow and evolve, which may be the reason that we are now here to wonder at it all.

K

Questions

a Prove that Olbers was right. Assume n stars per unit volume, and write down the number of stars dn in a spherical shell of radius r, thickness dr. Use the inverse-square law to write down the intensity dI contributed by this shell. Why do all such shells, no matter what their radius, contribute the same intensity? Why does this mean that Olbers was right?

b What is the energy per cubic metre in the cosmic background radiation, if its wavelength is about 5 cm? How does this compare with the energy mc^2 of one proton mass per cubic metre?

c If the temperature of the cosmic radiation is now 3 K, how many times smaller was the Universe than it is now, in the year 100 000 when the temperature was about 1000 K ($\lambda T = \text{constant}$)? How many proton masses were there per cubic metre at that time? How many per cubic metre at time 1 s, when the temperature was about $10^{10}\,\mathrm{K}$?

d Use $\Delta E = c^2 \Delta m$ to find the energy equivalent of the mass difference between neutrons and protons. At what temperature, according to the Boltzmann factor $e^{-\Delta E/kT}$, would their numbers have been in the ratio 1 to 10?

($m_\mathrm{p} = 1.672\,65 \times 10^{-27}\,\mathrm{kg}$; $m_\mathrm{n} = 1.674\,95 \times 10^{-27}\,\mathrm{kg}$)

e It requires about 20×10^{-19} J to ionize a hydrogen atom. What, from the Boltzmann factor, is the probability of an atom acquiring this energy by random collisions if the temperature is *i* 10 000 K *ii* 1000 K?

f Study of the dynamics of the expansion of the Universe suggests that as the early Universe expanded and cooled, its density ρ and temperature T at time t were given by

$$\rho t^2 = 3/(32\pi G)$$

$$T^4 = 2 \times 10^{31}\rho$$

Estimate the density and temperature at $t = 1$ s.

g Show, using $Q(1/T_{Earth} - 1/T_{Sun})$ and data in the Reading, that 1 kW of sunlight per square metre corresponds to an entropy increase of about $3\,J\,K^{-1}\,m^{-2}\,s^{-1}$.

h Suppose cells of an early life-form (say blue–green algae) can reproduce once by cell division in one hour. How many copies are made in 24 hours, if none die? Suppose a genetic 'mistake' increases the time to reproduce by 10 per cent, to 66 minutes. How many generations are produced in 24 hours? How many fewer descendants than the original does the mutation have in 24 hours? What happens if changed conditions mean that the mutation has an advantage and reproduces in 10 per cent less time, 54 minutes?

LABORATORY NOTES

GAME
K1 Particle shuffling

6 counters
die
graph paper

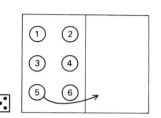

Figure K31
Counters in a box.

Draw a box with two equal halves on squared paper. Place six numbered counters in one half. Throw the die, and move the counter whose number comes up to the half it is not presently occupying. Continue moving, recording how many counters are in each half.

What *must* happen on the first throw? What is likely to happen on the second throw? What distribution of counters between the halves happens most often?

Is it possible that all the counters will go back into the half they started in? Is it likely?

GAME
K2 Energy shuffling

20 counters (or more)

either
2 dice
or
other means of picking counters at random

graph paper

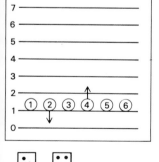

Figure K32
Counters on 'levels'.

Rule lines for 'energy levels' on a sheet of paper. Put numbered counters down in some initial pattern (for example, all on level 1). Start with just six counters; then try a larger number – 20 or more.

The rules of the game are:

1 Pick a counter at random and move it down one level. (If the counter you pick is on the lowest level, pick again.)
2 Pick a counter at random and move it up one level.
3 Repeat.

Record how many counters are on each level, after making several moves. A class average should show a graded distribution.

Given your initial pattern, what is the highest level any counter can reach? Why is it rare for a counter to get high up on the levels?

How does the rule of the game conserve 'energy'?

COMPUTER SIMULATION
K3 Equilibrium distribution of energy

microcomputer
program 'Quantum shuffling'

The program should let you:

split the particles into two groups;
merge the two groups into one;
show instantaneous, or time-averaged distributions, or probabilities;
place particles initially anywhere on the lower levels.

a Firstly, have one group of particles. Try first placing all (say 200) on the lowest level but one (level 1). Observe the form around which the instantaneous distribution fluctuates. Try with fewer particles.

b Make two groups of particles, say 100 in each, and start one group off with particles on low levels, and the other with some particles on rather higher levels. Compare the two distributions. After the distributions become fairly steady, switch to time-averaged distributions for a clearer comparison.

COMPUTER SIMULATION
K4 Thermal equilibrium

microcomputer
program 'Quantum shuffling'

See experiment K3 for notes on the program.

Make two groups of particles, about 125 in each, starting one group with a larger mean energy per particle. Observe them reach equilibrium independently, with the two groups isolated.

Now merge the two groups, to allow energy to pass from one to the other. What happens to the two distributions?

It is instructive to start one group with all its particles on the lowest level (level 0). Why do these particles *not* alter levels when the groups are isolated? What *must* happen when the groups are merged?

Then have just *one* particle in the first group, and 10 or 20 in the second. Merge the two groups to allow energy to be exchanged between them. Watch the display of probabilities to see how long the single particle spends on each level.

EXPERIMENT
K5 Vapour pressure of water

K5a Energy needed to evaporate water

vacuum flask
balance, resolution 0.1 g
immersion heater
l.t. variable voltage supply

either
joulemeter
or
ammeter, 10 A a.c., and voltmeter, 25 V a.c.

leads

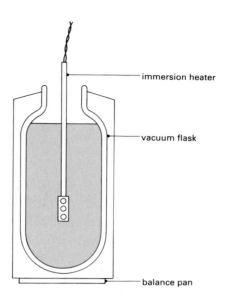

immersion heater

vacuum flask

balance pan

Figure K33
Boiling water in a vacuum flask.

Safety note: Do not use an immersion heater that has a cracked seal, or allow the heater to cool while it is immersed in water.

Use the immersion heater to boil away water in a vacuum flask, resting on a top-pan balance. Record the mass of water boiled away in (say) 20 minutes, and the energy supplied electrically. Calculate the energy needed to evaporate one mole (18 g) of water. How much energy is that per molecule?

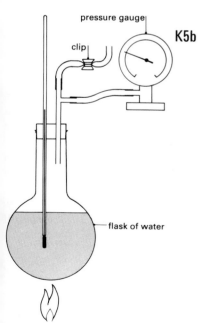

pressure gauge

clip

flask of water

Figure K34
Measuring vapour pressure with a pressure gauge.

K5b Variation of vapour pressure with temperature

round-bottomed flask
thermometer, −10 to 110 °C
T-tube
Bourdon gauge
pressure tubing
Hoffmann clip
tripod
gauze
Bunsen burner
safety spectacles
retort stand base, rod, boss, and clamp

Safety note: You must wear safety spectacles for this experiment.

In this experiment you measure the vapour pressure as water in the flask and vapour above it cool, starting with the water boiling at atmospheric pressure and the flask full of vapour.

Half fill the flask with water and heat it to boiling *with the clip open.* Continue boiling with the clip open for some minutes to displace air. Remove the flame, close the clip, and allow the flask to cool. At intervals, warm the water *gently* with a *small flame* until it just boils: record the pressure and temperature.

Is the plot of $\ln p$ against $1/T$ linear? How does its slope compare with $-\Delta H_{evap}/Lk$?

EXPERIMENT

K6 Current in a thermistor

thermistor (*e.g.* RS Components TH3)
cell holder with two cells
milliammeter, 10 mA d.c.
milliammeter, 100 mA d.c.
2 crocodile clips
thermometer, -10 to $110\,°C$
tripod
gauze
Bunsen burner
beaker, 250 cm^3
retort stand base, rod, boss, and clamp
leads

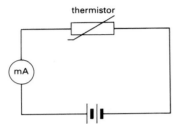

Figure K35

Measure the current in the thermistor for a fixed potential difference. Heat the thermistor by suspending it in water heated in a beaker.

Is the plot of ln I against $1/T$ linear? From its slope, what is the energy E in $e^{-E/kT}$? Why would differences in how easily electrons move at different temperatures also affect the results?

EXPERIMENT

K7 Viscous flow

Ostwald viscometer
stopwatch
tall beaker
thermometer, -10 to $110\,°C$
tripod
gauze
Bunsen burner

Any method suited to measuring the rate of flow of a liquid at different temperatures will serve. The Ostwald viscometer is convenient. Other possibilities include measuring the torque on a drum suspended in a rotating can of liquid, the torque needed to stir a liquid, or the time taken for a vessel to empty through a small outlet.

For many liquids, including water, the dependence of rate of flow on temperature is governed by the Boltzmann factor. Certain oils, with complex molecules, may not show this behaviour.

If the method used measures the time of flow, t, for a given quantity, the rate is proportional to $1/t$. Is a plot of ln $(1/t)$ against $1/T$ linear? If you have measured viscosity η, plot ln $(1/\eta)$ against $1/T$.

EXPERIMENT
K8 Creep

polythene strip
hanger and slotted masses, 10 g
2 plane mirrors
laser (or compact light source and lens)
screen (*e.g.* piece of white paper on wall)
75 mm diameter tube (*e.g.* drain pipe)
supports (*e.g.* retort stand rods, short)
hair dryer
thermometer, − 10 to 110 °C
Plasticine

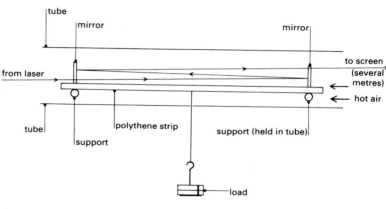

Figure K36
Apparatus to study creep.

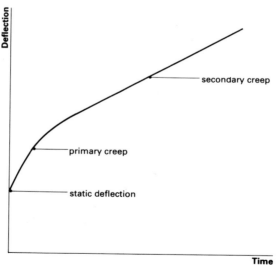

Figure K37
Primary and secondary creep.

Safety note: If you use a laser make sure that the beam cannot enter your eye, either directly or after reflection from a mirror.

You can study creep if you bend a polythene strip by hanging a load at its centre. Mirrors on each end of the strip tilt as it bends, and deflect a beam of light cast on a screen several metres away (figure K36).

The beam first deflects as soon as the load is applied (static deflection) and then creeps rather rapidly for a time (primary creep).

Then it settles down to a linear rate of creep (secondary creep). It is this secondary rate of creep which you should investigate (see figure K37).

The temperature can be controlled by enclosing the strip in a tube (which can carry supports for the strip), and blowing hot air from a hair dryer down the tube.

The experiment is lengthy, and you may only be able to study the creep at two or three temperatures.

EXPERIMENT
K9 Rate of reaction

sodium disulphate(IV), 5 g
sodium sulphite (anhydrous), 1 g
methanal, 10 cm³
phenolphthalein, 20 cm³
2 measuring cylinders, 100 cm³
2 beakers, 250 cm³
2 volumetric flasks, 1 dm³
safety spectacles
thermometer, −10 to 110 °C
stopwatch or clock
plastic bucket or basin
supply of hot water

Safety note: Wear spectacles.

Use freshly made-up solutions, kept in stoppered flasks:
solution A   5 g sodium disulphate(IV) and 1 g sodium sulphite in 1 dm³ water
solution B   10 cm³ methanal and 20 cm³ phenolphthalein made up to 1 dm³ with water.

Mix 100 cm³ of each solution, and measure the time before the solution goes pink. Warm the solutions in hot water (and/or cool in ice), and measure the rate of reaction at different temperatures.

Plot ln (1/time of reaction) against $1/T$.

What information can be obtained from the graph?

EXPERIMENT
K10 Entropy changes in a gas

gas energy transfer apparatus
aluminium block
immersion heater
l.t. variable voltage supply
low-voltage smoothing unit
ammeter, 0–5 A d.c.
voltmeter, 0–15 V d.c.
sensitive galvanometer
copper wire, 0.28 mm diameter (bare)
constantan wire, 0.28 mm diameter (covered)
G-clamp
slab of expanded polystyrene
transparent adhesive tape
measuring cylinder, 100 cm³
balance, resolution 0.1 g
stopwatch or clock
leads

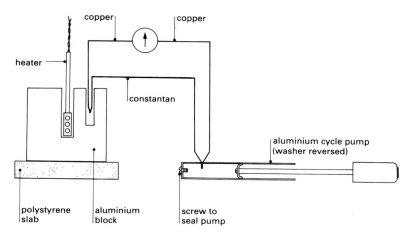

Figure K38
Gas energy transfer.

polystyrene slab | aluminium block | screw to seal pump

When air in the pump is expanded, the casing keeps it at an almost constant temperature by delivering energy to the gas, and itself cooling slightly. The energy delivered can be found by warming the aluminium block electrically, scaling down the electrical energy to allow for the relative masses of block and pump, and differences in the galvanometer readings.

What is the energy given to the gas? What is the entropy decrease of the casing? What is the ratio V_2/V_1 of the volumes of air before and after expansion? How many molecules N are there in the air in the pump? What is the entropy increase $Nk \ln(V_2/V_1)$ of the gas?

EXPERIMENT
K11 'Hot ice'

sodium sulphate decahydrate, 20 g
boiling-tube
thermometer, − 10 to 110 °C
Bunsen burner
balance, resolution 0.1 g
plastic cup
measuring cylinder, 100 cm³

a Dissolve about 5 g of $Na_2SO_4 \cdot 10H_2O$ in about 50 cm³ of water in a plastic cup. Measure the temperature change of the water.

How much energy $\Delta H_{solution}$ is taken from the water to break bonds in the crystalline solid?

b Gently warm about 10 g of $Na_2SO_4 \cdot 10H_2O$ in a boiling-tube, until the crystals dissolve in their own water of crystallization. Cool slowly to about 25 °C. Drop in a further crystal, and observe the temperature T_{eq} at which crystals and water are in equilibrium. Note the release of energy to the surroundings when the solution crystallizes.

At equilibrium,

$$\Delta S_{crystallizing} + energy\ released/T_{eq} = 0$$

Calculate the energy released from the results of part **a**.

Find $\Delta S_{crystallizing}$, per mole of $Na_2SO_4 \cdot 10H_2O$. Compare the value with $\Delta S_{freezing} = -22\,J\,K^{-1}\,mol^{-1}$ for the freezing of one mole of water. Compare $\Delta H_{solution}$ for one mole of $Na_2SO_4 \cdot 10H_2O$ with the value $6000\,J\,mol^{-1}$ for freezing one mole of water.

Why does $Na_2SO_4 \cdot 10H_2O$, which is mostly water, 'freeze' at a temperature higher than the freezing point of water?

EXPERIMENT
K12 Concentration cell

copper(II) sulphate solution, 1 M
2 beakers
filter paper
potassium nitrate solution
high-impedance voltmeter, 100 mV d.c.
distilled water

Which side of the cell is electrically positive? Which side would be positive if Cu^{2+} ions were removed from solution on that side and produced at the other? For one mole of Cu^{2+} ions taken from the concentrated side and produced at the dilute side, what is the entropy increase $-kL\ln$ (lower concentration/higher concentration)?

What is the work delivered electrically when two moles of electrons pass at the observed cell e.m.f. $\mathscr{E}$? If all this work were taken from the surroundings, what would be the entropy decrease of the surroundings?

How would you expect altering the temperature of the cell to change its e.m.f.?

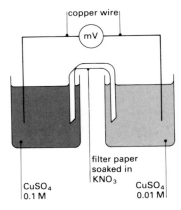

Figure K39
Concentration cell.

QUESTIONS

Entropy and numbers of ways

1(I) Describe, at the molecular level:

a washing drying in a breeze

b ice cubes melting in a glass of water

c milk stirred into tea

d a radiator warming a room

Name some more processes where we observe, or create, a systematic change, but at the molecular level the underlying behaviour is purely chaotic.

2(L) New packs of cards are sold arranged in one particular order. If they are shuffled, they can be arranged in many ways. The first card can be one of 52, the second one of 51, the third one of 50, and so on.

$$W = 52 \times 51 \times 50 \times \ldots \times 2 \times 1 = 52!$$

Use a calculator with the factorial function (!) to find W, $\ln W$, and $k \ln W$. What is the entropy increase when a pack of cards is shuffled?

3(L) When the Mint makes new coins, they are all produced the same way up (say 'heads'). They are arranged in one way. But if everybody in the country put their change down, each coin could show 'heads' or 'tails'.

a Estimate the number N of coins in circulation in Britain.

b Argue that $W = 2^N$ is the number of ways in which the coins could be put down.

c Use a calculator to find $\ln W = \ln 2^N$. Why is it not possible to get 2^N itself on a calculator?

d Calculate the entropy change $\Delta S = k \ln 2^N - k \ln 1$.

4(P) The genetic code has four 'letters', each consisting of a particular organic base. The base molecules are about 10^{-9} m in size.

a The DNA chain molecule carrying the genetic 'message' for a fruit fly is about 10^{-2} m long. What is the number N of 'letters' in the genetic 'message'?

b How many different 'messages' (*i.e.* distinct sequences of 'letters') could be carried by such a chain?

c If a fruit fly DNA molecule is decomposed into its component bases, what is the entropy increase associated with losing its 'message'?

5(P) Figure K40 shows marbles being shaken in a container. The marbles are identical except for their colour. Why can you be sure that the sequence of pictures in (a) must be read from right to left? Why can you not be sure of the order in (b)?

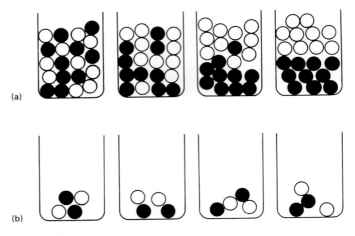

(a)

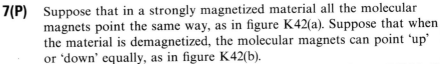

(b)

Figure K40

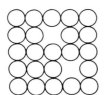

Figure K41

6(L) Crystalline solids can have defects in the crystal lattice. Figure K41 shows a number of atoms, with two empty lattice sites.

a Draw some other pictures with the same number of atoms and vacancies.

b How many different pictures are there with N atoms and *one* vacancy?

7(P) Suppose that in a strongly magnetized material all the molecular magnets point the same way, as in figure K42(a). Suppose that when the material is demagnetized, the molecular magnets can point 'up' or 'down' equally, as in figure K42(b).
i Argue that there are 2^N possible arrangements of figure K42(b), if the direction of one magnet does not affect the others.
ii Calculate the entropy change

$$\Delta S = k \, \Delta \ln W$$

for going from (a) with $W = 1$ to (b) with $W = 2^N$, if $N = L = 6 \times 10^{23}$.

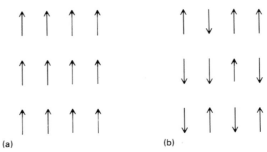

(a)   (b)

Figure K42

Number of ways to multiply

8(I) If a menu has four starters, six main dishes, and five sweets, followed by tea or coffee, how many meals can you order making one selection of starter, main dish, sweet, and drink? Why do the possibilities *multiply*?

9(I) 100 people on holiday are allowed to choose freely between a coach trip or going to the beach. In how many different ways can the people arrange themselves given just two choices? If the organizer loses the list of choices, and makes one at random, how likely is he to pick the original set of choices?

10(P) Plot a graph of $Y = 2^N$ for $N = 1, 2, \ldots, 8$. What would the graph of lg Y against N be like? (lg $Y = \log_{10} Y$.)

Particles spreading out

11(L) Calculate the chance of getting all of 100 particles, moving at random between the two halves of a box, back in one half, as follows:

a Use a calculator to find 2^{100}.

b Check the value, given that lg $2 \approx 0.3$ and that lg $2^{100} = 100$ lg 2, and writing 2^{100} as a power of ten.

c Suppose you look at the box every microsecond. For how many seconds would you have to look on average, before by chance all the particles were in one half?

d The Universe is about 10^{10} years old, and one year is about 3×10^7 seconds. How many Universe lifetimes is your answer to part **c**?

12(L)a About how big is a jar of air (atmospheric pressure and room temperature) which contains 10^{22} molecules?

b Write down lg $2^{10^{22}}$ as a power of 10.

c From the logarithm, to base 10, of a number n we can tell the number of digits in n when n is written out in full up to the decimal point. How many digits are there in $2^{10^{22}}$? If you wrote out $2^{10^{22}}$ with numerals only 1 mm across, how many metres long would it be? How many light years is that? ($c = 3 \times 10^8$ m s^{-1}, 1 year $\approx 3 \times 10^7$ s.) (Can you name a star at that distance?)

13(L) Suppose that, God-like, you are deciding into which of many small parts dV of the volume of a gas every molecule will go. There are N molecules. (See figure K43, page 282.)

a *i* If you do it by throwing a die, why does the die need V/dV sides?
   ii What does the number $W = (V/dV)^N$ represent?

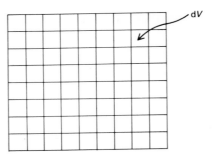

Figure K43

b If the volume is made bigger by dV, the die now needs $(V+dV)/dV$ sides.

    i What does the number $W'=[(V+dV)/dV]^N$ represent?

    ii What does the ratio $W'/W=[(V+dV)/V]^N$ represent?

    iii Express $dS=k\ln(W'/W)$ in terms of V, dV, and N.

14(L) Use a calculator or computer with the natural logarithm function to find $\ln 10$; $\ln 10.5$; $\ln 10.5 - \ln 10$; $0.5/10$.

Compare the last two answers. Try, with any number x, $\ln x$; $\ln(x+dx)$; $\ln(x+dx)-\ln x$; dx/x, where dx is small compared with x.

15(P) What is the entropy change of the gas when, at constant temperature:

a 1 mole of neon expands from a pressure of 1 atmosphere (atm) to $\frac{1}{2}$ atm?

b 1 mole of neon is compressed from $\frac{1}{4}$ atm to $\frac{1}{2}$ atm?

c 1 mole of neon expands from 1 atm to $\frac{1}{4}$ atm?

d 2 moles of neon expands from 4 atm to 1 atm?

e 1 mole of helium contracts from 1 atm to 4 atm?

f 2 moles of helium expands from 16 atm to 1 atm?

16(E) Estimate the entropy increase when a car tyre is punctured.

17(L)a Estimate the volume of a cycle pump, or of a cylinder of a typical car engine.

b Pick any such volume. About how many molecules of ideal gas would there be in it at standard temperature and pressure?

c Use $pV=NkT$ to plot a p–V curve for the gas at $300\,\text{K}$.

d Take any two volumes V_1 and V_2, and find the work involved in going from one to the other, from the area below the curve (figure K44).

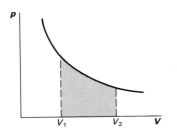

Figure K44

e Find $\ln V_1$ and $\ln V_2$, and calculate

$$\Delta S = Nk(\ln V_2 - \ln V_1) = Nk\ln(V_2/V_1)$$

f Check that the work from **d** is equal to $T\Delta S$.

g Suppose the gas were thermally insulated from its surroundings while the volume changed. What would happen to its temperature, and to its internal energy? Why must there be a thermal exchange of energy with the surroundings if the temperature is to remain constant?

Particles and energy levels

18(I) There are five ways for two particles to share four quanta (assume equally spaced levels). Draw them. Guess how many ways for two particles sharing six quanta.

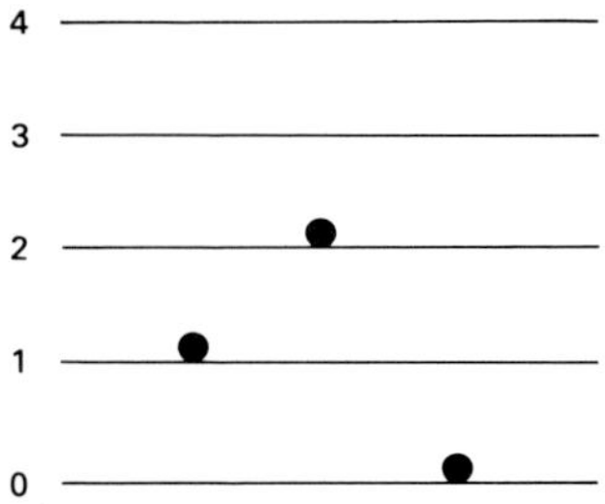

19(I) There are ten ways for three particles to share three quanta. Figure K45 shows one.
Draw some more. Why must there be more than ten ways for three particles to share *four* quanta?

Figure K45

20(I) How many ways are there for N particles to share just one quantum?

K

21(E) Show that the following segment of computer program follows the rule of the energy shuffling game.

```
800  LET N = 100
900  DIM L(100)
1000 LET N1 = RND(N)
1010 LET N2 = RND(N)
1020 IF L(N1) = 0 THEN LET C = 0 ELSE LET C = 1
1030 LET L(N1) = L(N1)−C
1040 LET L(N2) = L(N2)+C
1050 GO TO 1000
```

(RND(N) is a function choosing an integer from 1 to **N** randomly, L(N) is an array storing the level of each of **N** particles.) You could extend the program to give initial levels of particles and keep records of and display the number of particles on each level.

22(P)a Sketch the typical equilibrium pattern of numbers of particles on equally spaced energy levels.

b Show how the pattern would change if the same number of particles shared more energy, and explain why there will now be fewer particles on the very lowest level.

23(P) If there is a fraction $f = 0.5$ as many particles on each level as on the next lower level, and there are 256 particles on the lowest level, calculate the numbers expected on each level up to the eighth. Above what level will it be common to find no particles? How do the answers change if $f = 0.25$, and $f = 0.75$?

24(P) Why does the fact that the number of particles on a given level is a constant fraction of the number on the level below mean that the distribution is correctly called *exponential*? What function of the number of particles on each level would you plot to obtain a *linear* slope of the distribution?

25(R)a Suppose one set X of particles on equally spaced energy levels has f (the Boltzmann factor) equal to 2/3, and another set Y has $f = 1/3$. Which is the hotter?

b Removing a quantum multiplies W by f. Adding a quantum multiplies W by $1/f$. What is the effect on W for the set X of losing one quantum? What is the effect on W for the set Y of gaining one quantum? What is the effect on the product (W for X) × (W for Y)?

26(P) Suppose the Boltzmann factor f for a set of particles distributed on equally spaced levels is 0.5. If the energy level spacing is 10^{-21} J, what is the entropy change if the particles lose:

a 1 quantum

b 100 quanta

c 10^{-18} J

d 1 J

e 1000 J

assuming that there are enough particles for f to remain nearly constant?

Thermal transfer of energy

27(P)a If there are as many quanta as particles, the Boltzmann factor $f = 0.5$ and $\ln f = -0.693$. If the energy level spacing is 10^{-21} J, what is the temperature of such a system?

b What is the factor f for the same level spacing if $T = 300$ K?

c If there are N particles sharing n quanta,

$$f = \frac{n}{n+N}$$

i At 300 K, with level spacing 10^{-21} J, how many quanta are there per particle?
ii About what fraction of those on the lowest level would be on the tenth level?

28(L) When one quantum is added to a system, W is multiplied by $1/f$, and the entropy increases. In the questions below assume that f remains constant.

a f is less than unity. Show that $\Delta S = -k \ln f$ is positive.

b What is the entropy change if *two* quanta are added?

c If energy Q is added, with level spacing ε, how many quanta are added?

d Show that if $\Delta S = -nk\ln f$ for adding n quanta, and $\ln f = -\varepsilon/kT$, adding energy Q increases the entropy by $\Delta S = Q/T$.

29(L)a Complete table K2:

f	$-\ln f$
1	0
0.5	
0.1	
0.01	

Table K2

b When f is *small*, why is the entropy change $\Delta S = -k\ln f$ for adding one quantum *large*?

c As the temperature is made lower, how does the entropy change for adding fixed energy vary?

d If f were 1, the entropy change for adding further energy would be zero. What is the temperature?

e If f were infinitely small, $-\ln f$ would be infinitely big. What would be the temperature?

30(E) Estimate the entropy changes for

a Warming a cupful of water:
   i by one degree at room temperature;
   ii from room temperature to the normal body temperature.

b Cooling an ice-cube's worth of water from room temperature to $0\,^\circ$C.

The Boltzmann factor

31(L)a Use a calculator to complete table K3.

E/kT	$e^{-E/kT}$
1	0.37
2	
5	
10	
20	
50	
100	

Table K3

b What value of E/kT corresponds to a Boltzmann factor of 10^{-6}?

32(P) Obtain the temperatures at which the Boltzmann factor is 1/10 for

a $E = 1.6 \times 10^{-19}\,$J   (1 eV)

b $E = 1.6 \times 10^{-13}$ J (1 MeV)

c $E = 4 \times 10^{-21}$ J (kT at room temperature)

33(P) For energy $E = 1.6 \times 10^{-19}$ J (1 eV), plot a graph of the Boltzmann factor against temperature, over the range 300 K to 350 K. Describe the form of the graph.

Activation processes

34(P) The energy needed to evaporate water is about 2.26 MJ kg^{-1}.

  a How many joules per mole?

  b How many joules per molecule evaporated?

  c When a water molecule evaporates, on average two hydrogen bonds are broken. What is the energy E to break a hydrogen bond?

  d At $T = 300$ K, what is kT? What is E/kT? What is $e^{-E/kT}$?

35(P) $\Delta H/LkT$ for the evaporation of water is about 16 at 300 K, and about 13 at 373 K. Calculate e^{-16} and e^{-13}. Why is the second about 20 times larger than the first? Why does water evaporate more readily at 373 K than at 300 K?

36(P)a If the rate r of an activation process is given by

$$r = Ce^{-E/kT}$$

where C is a constant, show that for temperatures T_1 and T_2

$$\ln\left(\frac{r_2}{r_1}\right) = \frac{E}{k}\left(\frac{1}{T_1} - \frac{1}{T_2}\right)$$

  b *i* What is the activation energy E of a process whose rate is multiplied by 20 when the temperature goes from 300 K to 330 K? *ii* By what factor would the rate be multiplied if the activation energy were half as big?

37(R) (*Hard*) The graphs (figure K46) show the collector current I (logarithmic scale) for an RCA 40389 power transistor, for a range of values of V_{BE}, the base-emitter voltage, at two temperatures. It is expected that

$$I = I_0 e^{eV_{BE}/kT}$$

  a Why do the graphs *i* differ in slope, *ii* but not very much?

  b Estimate the slopes of the two graphs, and hence obtain estimates for $\Delta \ln I/\Delta V_{BE}$ and for e/k.

  c Discuss the experimental difficulties of measuring currents over a range 10^{-10} A to 10^{-3} A.

  d One way to measure such currents is to use an operational amplifier, with resistive feedback, as shown in figure K47. Explain how this system measures small currents.

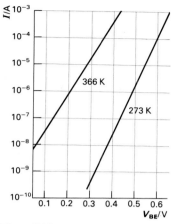

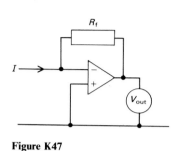

Figure K46

Figure K47

38(R) Power is generated in the Sun by the fusion of protons to form helium nuclei (the process is complex).

a For the process to occur, protons must collide with energy of the order of that needed to bring them to a separation of about 1.5×10^{-15} m, against their electrical repulsion. What is this energy?

b The temperature in the centre of the Sun is about 10^7 K. Is the rate of proton fusion likely to be fast or slow?

c If a star contracts, its central temperature rises. What will happen to the rate of proton fusion?

39(P) The escape of electrons from a hot filament can be thought of as like evaporation, an electron needing energy equal to the work function ϕ to escape, with the electron current being given approximately by

$$I = I_0 e^{-\phi/kT}$$

The graph, figure K48, shows data for platinum. Estimate the work function ϕ for platinum.

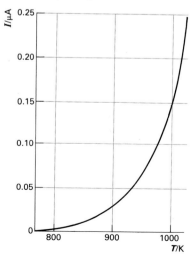

Figure K48
From: CROWTHER, J. A. Ions, electrons, and ionizing radiations. *8th edn.* Edward Arnold, 1949.

Entropy increases

40(P) Explain how each of the following changes involves an increase in entropy:
A ball bouncing on the floor and coming to rest
Mixing a drink
Dissolving sugar in water
A punctured tyre going flat.

41(P) A striking one-way tendency of everyday life is the tendency of moving objects to come to rest, because of friction. How does friction increase entropy?

42(E) A rubber band being stretched is rather like a gas being compressed. Its internal energy does not vary very much when it is stretched, the chains of molecules simply becoming less kinked. When a band is stretched, it becomes warm (feel the temperature change on your lip). The work of stretching is 'dumped' into thermal motion of the molecules (which tends to kink the chains).
  Without any calculation, explain why stretching the band must *decrease* the entropy of arrangement of chains, but *increase* the entropy associated with the energy shared amongst the molecules.

Efficiency of heat engines

43(P) What is the maximum efficiency of a heat engine which

a has a furnace at 2000 K and surroundings at 300 K?

b runs on the 15 K temperature difference between surface ocean water at about 288 K and the deep water at nearly 273 K? Suggest why such an engine might still be a good idea.

44(P) Why, from the point of view of efficiency, is it desirable to run steam turbines with super-heated high pressure steam? Why is super-heated steam necessarily at high pressure?

45(E) Collect data, for example from 'The generation and transmission of electric power' in Unit H, 'Magnetic fields and a.c.' or the Central Electricity Generating Board's *Statistical yearbook*, on the efficiency of various power stations, and of the temperature of the steam used. Estimate their maximum possible efficiencies, and compare with actual efficiencies, looking for a relationship with the age of the plant.

Compression of a gas

46(P) Two moles of argon is at 305 K, pressure 10 atmospheres (1.0 MPa).

a What is its volume?

b The gas is compressed by one per cent, keeping it close to equilibrium, and at constant temperature.
  i How much work is done?
  ii What is the entropy change of the gas?

c What is the relation between **b***i* and **b***ii*?

d How much energy is transferred thermally to the surroundings?

e What is the entropy change of the surroundings?

Equilibrium

47(R) Table K4 shows enthalpies of evaporation (energy needed to evaporate one mole at constant pressure), and the boiling-points at standard pressure, of some liquids.

Liquid	$\Delta H_{evap}/\text{kJ mol}^{-1}$	T/K
carbon disulphide	27.2	319
trichloromethane	29.3	335
hexane	28.8	342
octane	34.9	399
sulphuric acid	50.2	617
water	40.6	373

Table K4

a Calculate the entropy changes $\Delta S_{evap} = \Delta H/T$.

b Guessing roughly that the volume changes by a factor of 1000 on evaporation, estimate $\Delta S_{volume\ change} \approx Nk \ln 1000$ for 1 mole.

c How much of the entropy changes in **a** are explained by **b** (excepting water)? Would the existence of a certain amount of structure in the liquid help explain the difference?

d Water has hydrogen bonds, which give the liquid considerable structure. How does this help explain the value of ΔS_{evap} for water? Methanol also has hydrogen bonds, and has $\Delta H_{evap} = 35.2\,\text{kJ mol}^{-1}$ and $T_{boiling} = 338\,\text{K}$.
Is methanol more like water, or like hexane?

48(R) When steam condenses, water freezes, or a material is magnetized more strongly, energy is given to the surroundings, and also, in each case, the entropy of the substance decreases. In each case, there can be an equilibrium between the two states at a certain temperature.

a Why is energy given to the surroundings, in each case?

b What happens to the entropy of the surroundings?

c What happens to the entropy of the substance?

d What happens to the process as the temperature is raised?

Concentration cells

49(P)   Volumes of 1 M sodium chloride containing 1/10 mole NaCl are
diluted
i to 0.5 M
ii to 0.1 M
iii to 0.01 M

a   How many particles are there in solution?

b   Estimate roughly the entropy changes in each case.

50(R)a   Why is raising the temperature likely to increase the e.m.f. of a
concentration cell?

b   Why, on a simple picture of dilution, would concentration cells made
from pairs 0.1 M and 0.01 M, or 1 M and 0.1 M, have the same
e.m.f.?

c   Why is the e.m.f. of a concentration cell higher for monovalent ions
than for divalent ions, for the same concentration and temperature?

Unit L
WAVES, PARTICLES, AND ATOMS

John Harris
Centre for Science and Mathematics Education, Chelsea College,
University of London

L

SUMMARY OF THE UNIT

INTRODUCTION: THE QUANTUM REVOLUTION

This Unit is about some of the strange and powerful ideas invented by physicists in the first third of the twentieth century. The ideas seem strange because they make us think about apparently familiar and well understood things like light and electrons in a new way. We need these strange ideas because matter on a very small scale – the scale of atoms and electrons – just does not behave in the same way as everyday-sized objects do. The power of these ideas lies in the fact that they help us to explain, for example, the stability and the size of atoms, and the existence of energy levels in atoms. But quantum theory has much wider scope than this: it is essential for our modern understanding of chemical bonds, electrical conductivity, magnetism, the nature of solids, and much more besides. For example, without quantum physics we would have no satisfactory theory of semiconductors and so no transistors, integrated circuits, or microelectronics.

The new quantum ideas truly revolutionized physics, and what may seem at first highly theoretical and abstract ideas affect the lives of people who may know nothing of the ideas that make possible many of the devices they use.

Section L1 ## PHOTONS

What is electromagnetic radiation?

Unit J, 'Electromagnetic waves'

So far in this course electromagnetic radiation has been seen to have two characteristics. It has wave properties, and all wavelengths travel (in a vacuum) at the same speed – very nearly $3 \times 10^8 \, \text{m s}^{-1}$. But different wavelengths have different effects: our eyes are sensitive to visible light but not to radio waves; infra-red doesn't affect normal photographic film, but visible and ultra-violet light do; photosynthesis needs light having wavelengths of about 600 nm and 450 nm; and so on.

DEMONSTRATION L1
Detection of electromagnetic radiation

Long wavelength radiation (radio, television) is detected by aerials which respond to the continuously varying electric and magnetic fields; short wavelength radiation (for example gamma rays) is detected as a series of discrete events in a GM tube. The gamma ray seems more like a stream of particles than a wave.

Waves or particles: the photoelectric effect

Whether light is a wave or a particle is an old question. Isaac Newton in his *Opticks* (1704) wrote of 'very small bodies emitted from shining substances'. In 1803 Thomas Young explained his famous two-source interference experiment, in which light plus light can produce darkness, by comparing light with water waves.

DEMONSTRATION L2
Photoelectric effect

Crucial evidence comes from the photoelectric effect, discovered more or less by chance, when Heinrich Hertz was experimenting with radio waves in 1888. When ultra-violet light falls on a metal surface it can cause electrons to be emitted from the surface. The key facts of the photoelectric effect are:

a If the wavelength is too long, no electrons are emitted however intense the light may be.

b Light of a certain colour produces electrons with a certain maximum energy. Brighter light gives *more* electrons, it does *not* increase the maximum energy.

c If the wavelength is reduced, the maximum energy increases.

READING
The photoelectric effect (page 308)

In 1905 Albert Einstein produced a theory which accounted for these facts. His explanation is summarized in

$$K.E._{max} = hf - \phi$$

DEMONSTRATION L3
Colour of light and energy of photoelectrons

QUESTIONS 1 to 9

heck that J s is the appropriate unit for h

The theory was given support by experiments done by Millikan (1916) and can be tested in the school laboratory.

The theory assumes that light energy comes in packets or quanta (photons); if the frequency of the light is f, the energy, E, of each photon is hf. The constant h has the value 6.6×10^{-34} J s. (It is known as Planck's constant, after the German physicist Max Planck who first introduced the idea that energy is quantized in 1900.)

Light quanta, energy levels, and spectra

The sharp line spectra of gases are evidence that atoms have discrete energy levels. Measuring the frequency of spectral lines, and using $E = hf$ to find the energy of the photon emitted or absorbed and hence the energy change in the atom, is a powerful method of mapping out energy levels. Thus the line at 253 nm in the absorption spectrum of mercury vapour corresponds to a transition from the lowest or ground state of the atom to a level 7.84×10^{-19} J above the ground state. And when an excited mercury atom returns from this level to the ground state it emits radiation of wavelength 253 nm. The other lines in the mercury spectrum correspond to transitions between other pairs of energy levels.

DEMONSTRATION L4
The spectrum of mercury vapour

QUESTIONS 10 to 13

The spectrum and energy levels of the hydrogen atom

EXPERIMENT L5
The hydrogen spectrum

Hydrogen is the simplest element, and its spectrum is easy to interpret. The complete spectrum is conveniently grouped into several families among which the most important are the Lyman series, which is in the ultra-violet; the Balmer series, mostly in the visible (figure L1); and the Paschen series in the infra-red.

Figure L1
Part of the hydrogen spectrum. The scale shows wavelengths in units of 10^{-8} metre.

Table L1 gives the wavelengths and frequencies for many of the lines in the Lyman, Balmer, and Paschen series.

Lyman series		**Balmer series**		**Paschen series**	
wavelength/nm	frequency/10^{14} Hz	wavelength/nm	frequency/10^{14} Hz	wavelength/nm	frequency/10^{14} Hz
121.57	24.659	656.47	4.5665	1875.6	1.5983
102.57	29.226	486.26	6.1649	1282.2	2.3380
97.25	30.824	434.16	6.9044	1094.1	2.7399
94.97	31.564	410.29	7.3064	1005.2	2.9822
93.78	31.966	397.12	7.5487	954.84	3.1395
93.07	32.208	389.01	7.7060		
92.62	32.365				
....	....				
....	....				
Limit	32.881×10^{14} Hz				

Table L1
The hydrogen spectrum.

QUESTION 14

Each series follows the pattern of figure L1: the lines converge at higher frequencies. Each series has a limit: for the Lyman series it is 32.881×10^{14} Hz.

The frequency of a line in the Balmer series turns out to be equal to the *difference* in frequency between two lines in the Lyman series.

The three series are accounted for by a scheme of energy levels like that shown in figure L2.

The Lyman series arises from transitions to the lowest level; the Balmer from transitions to level 2; the Paschen from transitions to level 3.

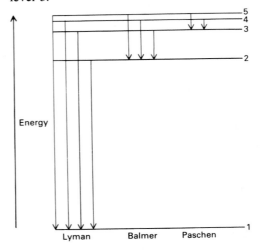

QUESTIONS 15 to 17 **Figure L2**
Some energy levels of a hydrogen atom. The higher energy levels get more and more closely spaced.

Why energy levels are negative

$E = hf$

$h = 6.63 \times 10^{-34}$ J s

The limit of the Lyman series (32.88×10^{14} Hz) corresponds to an energy of 2.18×10^{-18} J. This is equivalent to 13.6 electronvolts, the ionization energy of hydrogen, the energy needed to remove the electron completely from the hydrogen atom. By convention we call the energy zero when two charges are very far apart. Since there is a *decrease* in potential energy when an electron and a proton approach, the energy of the hydrogen atom, or any system where unlike charges are bound together, is *negative*. In particular, the energy of the lowest state of the hydrogen atom (level 1 in figure L2) is -2.18×10^{-18} J. The next level (level 2) is 1.63×10^{-18} J above this, that is, at $(-2.18 + 1.63) \times 10^{-18}$ J $= -0.55 \times 10^{-18}$ J. The next one is at $(-2.18 + 1.935) \times 10^{-18}$ J $= -0.242 \times 10^{-18}$ J, and so on. If the other levels are worked out in this way they form a regular sequence, see table L2.

Energy level/10^{-18} J	Number, n
-2.18	1
-0.55	2
-0.242	3
-0.136	4

Table L2

There is a simple rule here: the energy of a level n is

$$\frac{-2.18 \times 10^{-18}}{n^2} \text{ J}$$

Explaining how a hydrogen atom has stable states with these energies – and no others – is one of the success stories of twentieth century physics. And it depends on a new way of thinking about the electron – as a wave.

Light: waves or particles – or both?

The particle model of light is needed to explain the photoelectric effect, and to make sense of spectra and the energy levels of atoms. But one of the instruments used to analyse spectra – the diffraction grating – depends on the wave behaviour of light.

Even when the light level is so low that there can only be one photon in the apparatus at any given time, diffraction and interference effects persist. So any theory based on photons interacting with each other as they go through a grating fails in this case.

Both models are needed and are inextricably bound together. To find the energy of a photon, which we think of as a *particle*, we need to know the frequency, which we probably get from measuring the length of a *wave* in a superposition experiment. And we can only explain these experiments in terms of light's wave-like behaviour.

Relating the particle and wave model

On the particle model one photon carries energy hf. So the intensity of light at any point depends on the number of photons arriving there each second. But photons do not arrive at a steady rate: at very low intensities the random rate of arrival becomes quite apparent (figure L3). There is a higher chance of a photon arriving (in any short time interval) at a place where the intensity is high, than where the intensity is low.

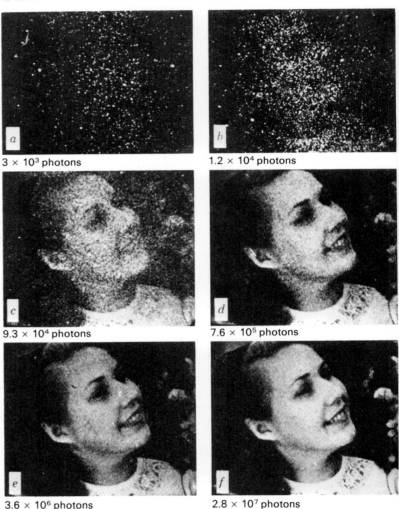

a. 3×10^3 photons

b. 1.2×10^4 photons

c. 9.3×10^4 photons

d. 7.6×10^5 photons

e. 3.6×10^6 photons

f. 2.8×10^7 photons

Figure L3
Series of photographs showing the quality of picture obtainable from various numbers of photons. In very dim light the picture breaks up into a number of randomly spaced dots, just as if a number of lumps of light energy had been delivered to particular places.
ROSE, A. Advances in biological and medical physics, **5**, *211, 1957*.

For an oscillator energy $\propto$ (amplitude)^2

On the wave model intensity depends on (wave amplitude)^2. If the two models are to agree it must be the case that

chance of photon arriving $\propto$ (wave amplitude)^2

The relationship of probability to (amplitude)^2 is an important part of quantum theory's picture of electrons in atoms.

So what *is* light?

READING
'What *is* light?' (page 308)

QUESTION 22

In some experiments (for instance diffraction grating) light behaves like a wave; in others (for example photoelectric effect) it behaves like particles. Neither the wave, nor the particle model on its own gives a complete and satisfactory explanation of light.

Section L2   ELECTRONS

Electrons: particles or waves?

An electron is a small particle with mass 9.1×10^{-31} kg and charge -1.6×10^{-19} C. But figures L4, L5, and L6 show that electrons, like X-rays, can produce diffraction effects. And diffraction is a characteristic of a wave.

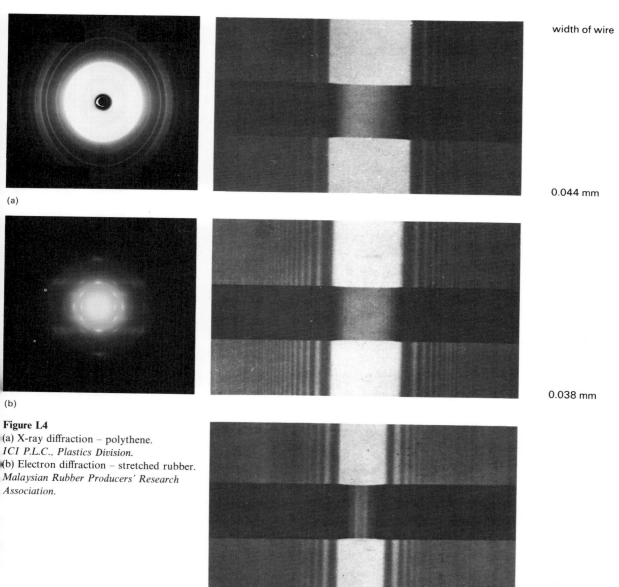

width of wire

0.044 mm

0.038 mm

0.019 mm

(a)

(b)

Figure L4
(a) X-ray diffraction – polythene.
ICI P.L.C., Plastics Division.
(b) Electron diffraction – stretched rubber.
Malaysian Rubber Producers' Research Association.

Figure L5
Diffraction of X-rays produced by narrow wires.
KELLSTROM, G. Nova Acta Regiae Societatis Scientiarum Upsaliensis. *Series* **IV**, *8, 5, 1932.*

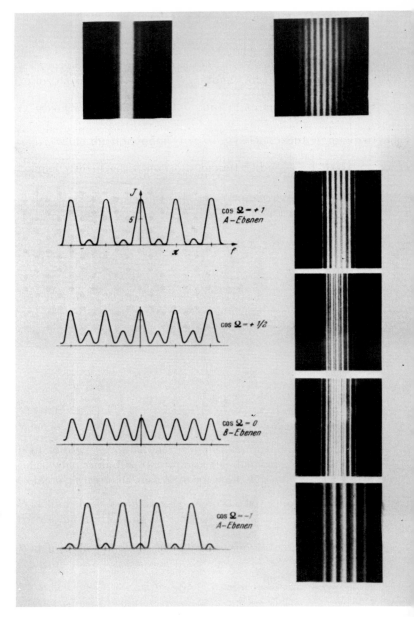

Figure L6
Diffraction of electrons at narrow slits. The top two photographs show electron diffraction at single and double slits. The pictures below show diffraction at three slits and the theoretical intensity curves.
JONSSON, C. Zeitschrift für Physik, **161,** 1961.

DEMONSTRATION L7
Electron diffraction by graphite

QUESTIONS 23, 24

When a beam of electrons, accelerated to a few kilovolts, passes through a thin film of graphite, the electrons are diffracted to form a pattern of rings on the fluorescent screen (figure L7).

The diameter of the rings can be measured and the angle of diffraction can be calculated from the geometry of the tube. If the electrons are given more energy – by being accelerated through a higher potential difference – the diffraction angle decreases.

The rings are formed because the layers of graphite in the film all act as diffraction gratings.

Figure L8 shows an idealized diagram of the hexagonal arrangement of carbon atoms in a graphite layer.

Figure L7
Electron diffraction tube.
Teltron Ltd.

Figure L8
Arrangement of carbon atoms in a graphite layer. (Atoms in the target of the electron diffraction tube are arranged rather less perfectly.)

QUESTIONS 25, 26, 27

If you hold figure L8 up to eye level and look along the page you will see that the atoms are arranged in rows. It is these rows of atoms, acting rather like the lines of a diffraction grating, that give rise to the rings. The spacing between lines of carbon atoms is fixed by the hexagonal structure, but the orientation of these lines of atoms varies from one part of the target to the next, and between the atomic layers of graphite.

EXPERIMENT L8
Optical analogue of electron diffraction

A similar effect can be seen if you rotate a fine diffraction grating held in front of your eye while you look through it at a point source of light with a colour filter in front of it.

QUESTIONS 28, 29

The diffraction of an electron beam by graphite gives *two* rings because there are two characteristic spacings between rows of atoms in the graphite layers.

Wavelength, energy, and momentum of electrons

Unit J, 'Electromagnetic waves'

The interatomic spacing of the carbon atoms in graphite is known from X-ray work, and one can work out the spacings between the two sets of rows of graphite atoms which give rise to the diffraction rings. Then we can use the diffraction grating formula $\lambda = s \sin \theta$ to work out the wavelength λ. More energetic electrons, accelerated through greater p.d.s., give smaller diffraction rings, so they must have smaller wavelengths. But it turns out to be the *momentum*, not the kinetic energy, which is the key to the wavelength. The electron diffraction experiment can be used to check the prediction

$$mv = h/\lambda$$

QUESTIONS 30 to 33

This relationship was proposed in 1923 by the French physicist Louis de Broglie. Within a few years diffraction experiments in the U.S.A. and the U.K. had confirmed the existence of electron waves.

The constant h, which appears here in a relationship between momentum and wavelength, is the same constant that relates energy to frequency for photons in the equation $E = hf$.

What are the units for $h = mv\lambda$? And for $h = E/f$?

Since $Ve = \frac{1}{2}mv^2$

$$mv = \sqrt{2meV}$$

and $\quad \lambda = h/\sqrt{2meV}$

QUESTIONS 34 to 36

All particles, not just electrons, have wave properties and $\lambda = h/mv$ gives the wavelength. Gas molecules have been successfully diffracted, but for heavier particles the wavelength is so small that wave properties are not noticeable.

What *are* the electron waves?

Electrons are not waves – but they do have wave-like properties. The wave associated with an electron tells us where we are likely to find it. The chance of finding an electron at a particular point depends on the amplitude of the wave at that point. If superposition effects are involved – as in a diffraction experiment – the amplitudes of the waves must be added, paying attention to the phase of each. Then the chance of finding an electron at a particular point is proportional to the square of the resultant amplitude at that point:

chance of finding electron $\propto$ (amplitude)^2

This of course parallels the interpretation of amplitude for light waves:

chance of finding photon $\propto$ (amplitude)^2

READING
'Waves and particles' (page 309)

QUESTIONS 37 to 40

The whole notion of particles having wave properties, introduced by de Broglie in 1923, is fundamental to our modern understanding of molecules, of atoms and their constituents, of semiconductors, of low-temperature physics, and much more. In fact it is probably true to say that there is scarcely a branch of physics studied today for which the ideas of 'wave mechanics' aren't an essential part of the physicist's thinking.

Section L3   ELECTRON WAVES IN ATOMS

DEMONSTRATION L7
Electron diffraction by graphite

The evidence that electrons have wave-like properties comes from electron diffraction, in which beams of free electrons pass through or are reflected from a target with a regular atomic structure. By applying this evidence that electrons have wave-like properties to electrons *within atoms* we can understand a lot about the nature and behaviour of atoms themselves. Here are some of the facts about atoms that the electron-wave idea can explain:

QUESTION 41

a   Atoms of an element are all alike and stay alike, displaying remarkable stability.

b   It takes a lot of energy to remove a single electron from an atom, and very much more to change the nucleus.

c   The sizes of atoms.

d   Atoms of each element have their own characteristic set of energy levels.

Standing waves

If an electron in an atom is to be represented as a wave it must be a standing wave, otherwise the electron won't be confined within the atom. Experiments with standing waves on cords show that when a standing wave is formed it always has 1, 2, 3, ..., or any whole number of loops. Each loop is half a wavelength long. If there is one loop on a cord of length l, then the wavelength $\lambda = 2l$, and this is the longest wavelength standing wave that can be set up.

DEMONSTRATION L9
Standing waves

QUESTION 42

Unit D, 'Oscillations and waves'

Standing waves in two dimensions can be demonstrated on a membrane; three-dimensional standing waves also exist, though they are more difficult to show.

Facts about the hydrogen atom

Size: about 10^{-10} m

Ionization energy: 13.6 eV or 2.18×10^{-18} J

Energy levels: $\dfrac{-2.18 \times 10^{-18}}{n^2}$ J

Fact about electron waves

momentum $= h/\lambda$

From these facts it follows that if we imagine a hydrogen atom to be a spherical box the longest wavelength standing wave (one loop) that would fit inside a hydrogen atom has a wavelength of about 4×10^{-10} m, as shown in figure L9.

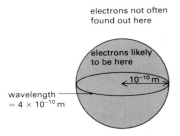

Figure L9
An electron wave in a hydrogen atom 'box'.

QUESTION 43

The momentum can be calculated (h/λ), and from it the electron's kinetic energy. The kinetic energy turns out to be about 1.4×10^{-18} J.

So we imagine an electron with this kinetic energy rattling around in an atom-sized box. Clearly some force is needed to keep the electron confined within this space. This is the electrical force of attraction between it and the proton. The energy needed to separate the electron from the proton when they are 10^{-10} m apart can be calculated from

Unit E, 'Field and potential' $e^2/4\pi\varepsilon_0 r$. It turns out to be 2.3×10^{-18} J. So the electron, with kinetic energy 1.4×10^{-18} J does not have enough energy to get away from the proton. It would need at least 2.3×10^{-18} J to escape.

Similar calculations for different sizes of box show that the *total* energy (K.E. + P.E.) is a minimum for a particular size of box. If the box

QUESTIONS 44, 45 were smaller, the electron would have a smaller wavelength and more momentum, and the K.E. would rise more than the P.E. falls. If the box were made bigger, the P.E. would rise more than the K.E. falls.

QUESTION 46 A more systematic attack on the problem is to write an expression for the total energy of the atom, E, in terms of its radius, r, and find the value of r for which E is a minimum by differentiation.

Some successes for the theory

The crude wave-in-a-box theory explains more than why atoms are the size they are.

It tells why solids are very hard to compress: making each atom smaller means increasing the kinetic energy of the electrons. Doing this to every atom for even a small compression takes a lot of energy.

QUESTION 47 It also tells us why there can not be electrons in the nucleus. Nuclei are about 10^{-14} m across; the kinetic energy of an electron confined in such a small space is of the order of 10^{-9} J or 10^{10} eV. There is no known force that could hold down electrons with such big energies.

We can use the same wave-in-a-box idea to calculate what momentum and hence kinetic energy a nuclear particle (proton or neutron) must have in its nuclear-sized box. The answer turns out to be of the order of 10 MeV. So the potential energy with which nuclear forces bind the particles together must be enough to overcome this. In fact, nuclear binding energies do turn out to be of about this magnitude.

A better model for the hydrogen atom

The wave-in-a-box model is a very crude one. The 'box' which holds the electron near the nucleus is really the potential energy, and the box model takes no account of how the potential energy of the atom varies with the electron's distance from the proton.

Figure L10 shows how the potential energy of the atom varies with distance between proton and electron $\left(E_\mathrm{p} = -\dfrac{1}{4\pi\varepsilon_0}\dfrac{e^2}{r} \right)$.

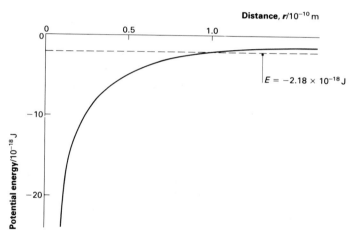

Figure L10
Variation of potential energy with distance for an electron near a proton.

Figure L11 is a representation of two 'potential wells'. One corresponds to the box model; the other suggests, in three dimensions, the way in which the potential energy of an electron actually varies with distance from the nucleus.

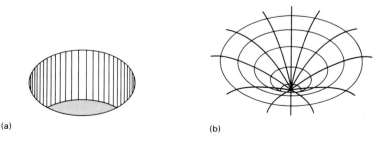

(a)   (b)

Figure L11

The lowest energy level, the ground state, is at $E = -2.18 \times 10^{-18}$ J. This is the *total energy* E. Figure L12 shows how the total energy, the potential energy, E_p, and the kinetic energy, E_k, of the electron are related:

$$E_k = E - E_p$$

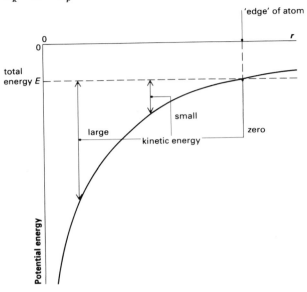

Figure L12
Kinetic energy decreases as electron's distance from proton increases.

DEMONSTRATION L10
Standing waves with variable
wavelength

QUESTIONS 49 to 51

Varying kinetic energy means varying momentum, and hence varying wavelength. Standing waves with varying wavelength can be demonstrated. (The frequency must be the same everywhere – the wavelength varies because the wave speed is different in different parts of the system.)

But an atom is a three-dimensional object, so we have to imagine standing waves of varying wavelength in three dimensions. For simplicity we consider the case where the waves have spherical symmetry: there is a mathematical theorem which allows us to relate spherically symmetrical standing waves to the much simpler one-dimensional standing waves along a line (figure L13).

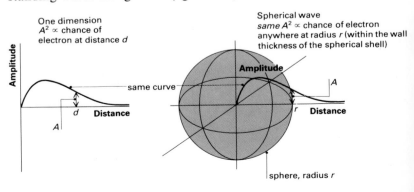

Figure L13

If a one-dimensional standing wave has amplitude A at some point the chance of finding an electron *near that point* depends on A^2. For the spherically symmetrical case we are considering, A^2 at any radius gives the chance of finding the electron *near that radius, in any direction. A^2* is the chance of finding the electron in a spherical shell of constant thickness at radius r. Since the volume of such a shell approaches zero as r becomes very small, so does the wave amplitude A.

Volume of shell $= 4\pi r^2 \, dr$

$A \to 0$ as $r \to 0$

The value of A at any point is given by Schrödinger's equation, which in simple form for a spherical atom is:

$$\frac{d^2 A}{dr^2} = -\left(\frac{2\pi}{\lambda}\right)^2 A$$

(Many treatments of three-dimensional standing waves plot a function ψ – Greek 'psi' – rather than A. $\psi^2 \, dV$ represents the chance of finding the electron in a small volume dV. A and ψ are related by $A = \psi r$, so although A is zero when $r = 0$, ψ is not. In general the shapes of graphs A and ψ against r are different.)

A computer can be used to calculate the wave amplitude, A, as a function of radial distance, r. The facts that go into the program are:

a Total energy E is constant, in this case -2.18×10^{-18} J.

b Potential energy E_p varies as $-1/r$.

c $E_k = E - E_p$.

d Wavelength depends on momentum, and hence on kinetic energy.

e Amplitude of wave is zero at $r = 0$.

Figure L14 shows the result.

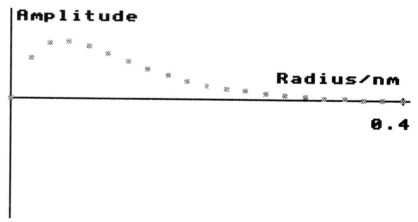

Figure L14
Computer-drawn wave function for hydrogen in its lowest energy level, $n = 1$.
$E = -2.18 \times 10^{-18}$ J.

Such a computer program can be used for other values of total energy E. For most values that are tried the wave amplitude A shoots off towards infinitely high or low values: there are no closed loops, no standing waves and so an electron cannot be bound to an atom for these

QUESTIONS 52, 53

values of E (figure L15). But when $E = -2.18 \times 10^{-18}/n^2$ J, closed loops are formed: the wave mechanics interpretation of the electron in the atom successfully predicts Balmer's $1/n^2$ rule for the hydrogen atom (figures L16, L17).

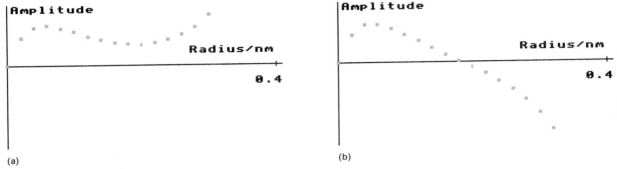

Figure L15
Computer-drawn wave functions for hydrogen. (a) $E = -2.3 \times 10^{-18}$ J. (b) $E = -2.0 \times 10^{-18}$ J.

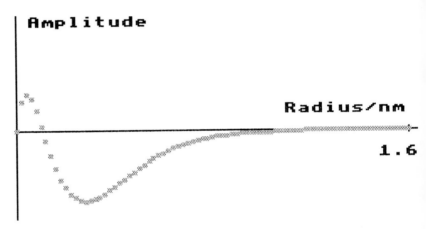

Figure L16
Computer-drawn wave function for hydrogen, at the energy of the level $n = 2$.
$E = -0.546 \times 10^{-18}$ J.

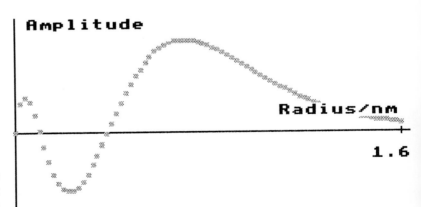

Figure L17
Computer-drawn wave function for hydrogen, at the energy of the level $n = 3$.
$E = -0.243 \times 10^{-18}$ J.

The first closed solution ($E = -2.18 \times 10^{-18}$ J) has one loop, the second ($E = -2.18 \times 10^{-18}/2^2$ J) has two loops, and so on. As the energy level increases so does the size of the atom.

QUESTION 54

A crude, but fairly simple algebraic argument can be used to predict that the energy levels are given by $E \propto -1/n^2$.

An end and a beginning

Figure L18
Erwin Schrödinger (1887–1961), one of the founders of wave mechanics.
Mary Evans Picture Library.

The explanation of the size, stability, and energy levels of the hydrogen atom brings together 'classical' ideas including standing waves, field and potential, kinetic and potential energy, and momentum, and also the 'new' idea that associated with a particle there is a wave with wavelength $\lambda = h/mv$. While this is the end of this Course, it is, in a very real sense, the beginning of today's physics, for the ideas of wave mechanics now pervade nearly every part of the subject. The hydrogen atom – one proton and one electron – is the simplest example. To predict the size and energy levels of the helium ion He$^+$ – a single electron in the potential well of a nucleus containing two protons – uses exactly the same ideas. Other examples that require only a little extension of the ideas used in this Unit include the 2, 8, 18, ... pattern in the Periodic Table of the elements, and the escape of an alpha particle from a radioactive nucleus.

The ideas of wave mechanics were first developed in the 1920s. Today they find application at all levels from the sub-atomic through chemical bonding and the electrical, thermal, optical, and mechanical properties of matter in bulk, to cosmology. For example, fundamental research in semiconductors, essential for today's and tomorrow's microelectronics, would be impossible without quantum mechanics. Quantum mechanics helps our understanding of the hydrogen bond, which plays such a vital role in biology. We are used to thinking of quantum physics as being relevant to the very small, but it also has a role in quite a different realm: models which scientists are developing for events in the first fractions of a second of the Universe after the Big Bang also depend on quantum physics. Here the world of sub-atomic particles becomes the clue to the history of the Universe itself. In the seventeenth century the theories of Newton showed how motion on Earth and motion in the heavens obey the same laws.

'The particles and forces of nature' and 'Our nuclear history' in the Reader *Particles, imaging, and nuclei*

Today quantum theory continues this grand design, digging deeper into the microscopic world in laboratories and expanding ever more widely our attempts to make a single unified picture of the history and structure of matter.

L

READINGS

THE PHOTOELECTRIC EFFECT

Einstein, who first proposed using the quantum picture to explain the photoelectric effect, explains it as clearly as anybody:

'According to the concept that the incident light consists of energy quanta of magnitude hf, however, one can conceive of the ejection of electrons by light in the following way. Energy quanta (photons) penetrate into the surface layer of the body, and their energy is transformed, at least in part, into kinetic energy of electrons. The simplest way to imagine this is that a light quantum delivers its entire energy to a single electron; we shall assume that this is what happens ... An electron to which kinetic energy has been imparted within the body will have lost some of this energy by the time it reaches the surface. Furthermore, we shall assume that in leaving the surface of the body each electron must perform an amount of work, ϕ, characteristic of the substance of which the body is composed. The ejected electrons leaving the body with the largest normal velocity will be those that were directly at the surface. The kinetic energy of such electrons is given by $K.E._{max} = hf - \phi$.

'If the emitting body is charged to a positive potential difference relative to a neighbouring conductor, and if V represents the potential difference which just stops the photoelectric current ... [then]

$$eV = hf - \phi$$

where e denotes the electronic charge.

'If the deduced formula is correct, a graph of V versus the frequency of the incident light must be a straight line with a slope that is independent of the nature of the emitting substance ... .'

From EINSTEIN, A. *Annalen der Physik*, **17**, 132, 1905, as reproduced in translation, in ARONS, A. B. *Development of concepts of physics*, Addison-Wesley, 1965. (Einstein's symbols have been modified.)

Questions
You should be able to answer questions **2**, **3**, and **4**, on page 324, after reading this passage.

WHAT *IS* LIGHT?

Richard Feynman is one of the present-day research physicists who have learned to live with the problem. He works in theoretical quantum mechanics, and accepting the conflict is the only way he and others have found to make progress.

In the Feynman lectures on physics *Volume 1*, Chapter 37, he says:

'Things on a very small scale behave like nothing that you have any direct experience about. They do not behave like waves, they do not behave like particles, they do not behave like clouds, or billiard balls, or weights on springs, or like anything that you have ever seen.

'Newton thought that light was made up of particles, but then it was discovered ... that it behaves like a wave. Later, however, ... Now we have given up. We say, "It is like *neither*".

'Because atomic behaviour is so unlike ordinary experience, it is very difficult to get used to and it appears peculiar and mysterious to everyone, both to the novice and the experienced physicist. Even the experts do not understand it the way they would like to, and it is perfectly reasonable that they should not, because all of direct human experience and of human intuition applies to large objects. We know how large objects will act, but things on a small scale just do not act that way.'

About the idea that photons arrive in large numbers where a wave would have a large amplitude, Feynman says:

'One might still like to ask: "How does it work? What is the machinery behind the law?". No one has found any machinery behind the law. No one can "explain" any more than we have just "explained". No one will give you any deeper representation [model] of the situation.'

Question
This extract may help you answer question **22**, on page 328.

L

WAVES AND PARTICLES

The dual nature of matter – and of radiation – is one of the keys to understanding modern physics. It is also one of the most puzzling aspects of the subject. Much has been written about it. Some recommended passages are listed below, followed by a list of questions. You should read at least one of the passages and while you do so bear in mind the questions.

FEYNMAN, LEIGHTON, and SANDS, The Feynman lectures on physics *Volume 1*, Chapter 37. This is difficult, but worth it. Concentrate on 37–1 to 37–5, without worrying about the algebra in 37–3. Feynman describes beautifully how the quantum world behaves, and you should read the words rather than the mathematics.

PSSC *Physics* 3rd edition, Chapter 33.
PSSC *College physics* 5th edition, Chapters 31, 33, 34.
The chapter from the PSSC course gives information at an appropriate level. It is worth reading carefully. One interesting section compares the photon and the electromagnetic wave models of light. The three *College physics* chapters expand the same material.

ROGERS, *Physics for the inquiring mind*, Chapter 44. This is a long chapter, and although you may like to read it all, the especially relevant parts are pages 723 (about photons) to 727, and pages 737 (particles and waves) to 742. The diagrams on pages 723, 725, 740, and 741 are very useful, as is the table at the top of page 738.

BORN, *The restless Universe*, Chapter III. Max Born was one of the physicists who first explored the quantum world. He first suggested that chance or probability had to be used to describe the behaviour of particles. Pages 106–117 will be revision for most students. But read pages 117–121 about photons. You could skip pages 122–133 on spectra and Bohr's model of the atom; also skip pages 133–139 on the Compton effect and pages 139–151 which introduce electron waves. You should read pages 151–158 carefully. See especially plate III(b). The final pages, 159–165, are interesting, but could be missed.

TOULMIN and GOODFIELD, *The architecture of matter*, Chapter 12. This is a fairly condensed historical account of the development of quantum ideas. Concentrate most on the section, 'Radiation is atomized'. You could stop at the point where Rutherford's nuclear model of the atom is discussed.

ROTHMAN, *The laws of physics*, Chapter 10. This is also historical, but less condensed than Toulmin and Goodfield. It is worth following up to page 180, but the final part ('The uncertainty principle') could be omitted. (Energy is measured on page 169 in ergs. 1 erg is equal to 10^{-7} joule.) If you have little time, omit pages 172–178 ('The size of a photon').

PROJECT PHYSICS Reader *Unit 5*. This contains a good chapter by Banesh Hoffman.

CARO, MCDONELL, and SPICER, *Modern physics*, Chapter 3. This chapter concerns the photoelectric effect, and the behaviour of photons. It is useful as a guide to which ideas come from experiment and which from theory. Part of Chapter 9 deals with matter waves.

TOLANSKY, *Revolution in optics*, Chapter 2. Do not bother with pages 33–37 on 'black body' radiation. Concentrate on pages 37 ('The photon') to 43. The remaining pages, 43–50, link up usefully with other parts of our work, but are less essential.

PROJECT PHYSICS Text *Unit 5*, Chapter 18. Section 18.4 discusses the photoelectric effect, and its interpretation is considered in 18.5. Section 18.6, on X-rays, is useful but less necessary. Chapter 20, sections 20.2 and 20.3, gives a good outline of the wave and particle behaviour of photons and electrons. (You will have to accept one formula from relativity.) Section 20.4 outlines the developments in quantum theory that will form most of the remaining work in our course.

HOFFMANN, *The strange story of the quantum*. Chapter 8 discusses the idea of de Broglie and the Davisson–Germer electron diffraction experiment. Electrons as waves and particles are discussed on pages 166–173. Chapter 3 discusses the photoelectric effect.

OPEN UNIVERSITY, Science Foundation Course S101, Unit 9 *Light: waves or particles?* Section 6 (The photoelectric effect) and Section 7 (Waves and particles) are particularly relevant. Units 10 and 11 are called *Atomic structure*: section 5 deals with spectra and energy levels. (Other parts of Units 10 and 11 such as Section 3 'Atomic structure – the nuclear model', and section 4 'Radioactivity and nuclear reactions' are relevant to other parts of this course.)

BOLTON, *Patterns in physics*. Chapter 7 deals briefly with spectra, the photoelectric effect, energy levels, and the wave properties of electrons. You may find the section on 'The energy necessary for sight', and the part dealing with lasers interesting though they are not necessary for this course.

DUNCAN, *Advanced physics: fields, waves, and atoms*, or *Physics: a textbook for advanced level students*. The sections relevant to this work are 'Photoelectric emission', 'Quantum theory', 'Energy levels in atoms', 'Evidence of energy levels', 'Wave particle duality of matter'.

AKRILL, BENNET, and MILLAR, *Physics*. Parts of Chapter 18 (especially 18.3 The photoelectric effect, 18.4 Energy levels) are useful.

BENNET, *Electricity and modern physics*. Section 13.4 on the photo-electric effect. (Note that the selenium photovoltaic cell is quite different from the photocells used to test Einstein's relation.) Section 13.5 briefly deals with quantum theory, wave – particle duality, spectra and wave mechanics.

WENHAM, DORLING, SNELL, and TAYLOR, *Physics: concepts and models*. 'Electricity, matter and light' deals with photoelectricity, energy levels, and spectra; 'The atom and its electrons' deals with the wave nature of electrons. (In the second edition of this book this work appears in the Section 'The atom, electrons and radiation'.)

L

Questions

Now here are some questions to ask yourself as you read:

a Does the author say that $E = hf$ comes from experiment, from theory, from both, or from elsewhere?

b Does the author say that $mv = h/\lambda$ comes from experiment, theory, both, or neither? Are the answers for photons the same as for electrons, or not?

c Does the author say that the behaviour of electrons and photons can be deduced from deeper ideas?

d What does the author say about why the description of the quantum world is widely accepted?

f Does the author mention 'probability'? What is said to be probable or not probable?

g What is said to be random, unpredictable?

h What is said to be predictable?

i Does the author explain why random effects are not seen on the large scale, for photons, or for electrons?

j Does the author say whether photons can vanish, unlike electrons? (Watch out for words like 'absorbed'.)

k Are photons said to have mass as well as momentum?

l Do you have the impression that in the development of these ideas, experiment led theory, theory led experiment, or a bit of both happened?

m Does the author talk about 'models' or 'analogues' or 'pictures' (or some similar word) of photons or electrons?

n Does the author say we have no adequate model of photons and electrons, or that we have two good models, or that we have a complicated model, or that we shouldn't expect to have a model? What do you think about these questions?

Questions **38**, **39**, and **40** on pages 333 to 334 give an opportunity to write about these ideas yourself.

POSTSCRIPT

Sir Nevill Mott began research in physics soon after Schrödinger and Heisenberg laid the foundations of modern quantum theory in 1925. He shared the 1977 Nobel prize for physics for work which involved the applications of quantum ideas to disordered structures.

A personal note on the origin and future of quantum mechanics by Professor Sir Nevill Mott.

The organizers of the Revised Advanced Physics Project have asked me to write a few words about quantum mechanics, both as it looked in the mid 1920s when I started research and as it looks now. Then Bohr's theory of the atom held the field. We were brought up on it, our text books and lectures contained beautiful pictures of elliptical orbits, and I think we students really believed they existed. They explained so much: the Balmer series in the spectrum of hydrogen, X-ray spectra, and a lot more besides.

I believe that the leaders of physics at that time were divided into those who were trying to make the Bohr theory better and better and those – many fewer – who felt it would in the end have to be replaced by something quite different. Among the latter was the German physicist Heisenberg, and he and others produced the first breakthrough, the so-called 'matrix mechanics' which did promise to be quite general. It promised to be a form of mechanics replacing Newtonian mechanics, capable of answering any question that Newtonian mechanics could answer, but of giving different answers at any rate for problems about atoms. The mathematics promised to be difficult; physicists who were good at mathematics thought they would have a lot of fun.

Schrödinger's equation was a bit of a bombshell. Schrödinger used 'easy' mathematics, differential equations, which are part of any university course. I remember a talented mathematical contemporary saying to me, 'All the fun has gone out of quantum theory, I'm going to study Law' – and he did. He was wrong; the later developments of quantum mechanics are difficult enough in all conscience. But what I remember most vividly about this equation was that Schrödinger himself did not know what it meant! He thought his 'wave intensity' must be interpreted as density of charge. We know now that this is only true in a statistical sense, and that the amplitude gives the *probability* that a particle will be found somewhere. This was first clearly stated by Max Born, a German physicist who moved to England in 1933.

To start research just after Schrödinger's equation was – perhaps – like being an explorer just after Columbus. The facts of physics and chemistry were wide open. In a very few years Schrödinger's equation was used to explain why atoms form molecules, why some solids conduct electricity and others do not, how radioactive decay occurs, and the details of the spectra of helium and most other atoms. It did everything that Bohr's theory could do and a lot more. Most convincing of all, it made predictions. For instance, it showed that the Rutherford scattering formula – really the basis of all of nuclear physics – did not work if an alpha particle hit a nucleus, namely of helium, of just the same kind as itself. When this prediction was made, the Cavendish Laboratory quickly mounted the experiments which showed that it was so. And even more important, quantum mechanics predicted that moving protons, quite slow by the standards of nuclear physics, could penetrate into an atomic nucleus of a light element, and so encouraged Cockcroft and Walton to make their famous first disintegration of the nucleus with artificially accelerated particles. What quantum mechanics did *not* do was to predict the neutron! And if one looks at quantum mechanics as it is today, it is in nuclear or particle physics that it is still in a state of flux. At the time of writing there is considerable disagreement between experts about the nature of the solutions of Schrödinger's equation for this case. Here it is just like Bohr's theory was, brilliantly successful sometimes, failing at others, constantly being modified, and calling on all the techniques of advanced mathematics. No-one would pretend that here it was the last word.

But outside the nucleus, the least one can say is that no one has proved it wrong. In the theory of molecules the theoretical chemists use all the resources of modern computers to calculate the properties of molecules and achieve greater and greater success. Schrödinger's equation gets more and more complicated as the number of electrons in a molecule increases, so the computer comes into its own here. In solids, particularly metals, there are problems of real mathematical difficulty. Superconductivity is one, understood in principle but not in detail. Our whole thinking about semiconductors and transistors is based on quantum mechanics and has become a very exact branch of science. At the time of writing there is a great deal of interest in non-crystalline semiconductors, which present a more difficult problem – how does the electron find its way among a jumble of molecules put together without pattern? But no-one doubts that quantum mechanics is competent to give the answer, and will in the not too distant future.

What of the more distant future? I see quantum mechanics applied to more and more complicated systems – the molecules of biology, technically useful alloys, conducting glasses, and polymers. Quantum mechanics, I dare guess, will not change, but the methods of using it will change, as they have already in the last few decades. And in the nucleus and in stellar interiors? It would be arrogant to guess. Will a billion dollar accelerator give us the final understanding of the nuclear particles, or will some brilliant insight in theory? Only the future can show.

LABORATORY NOTES

DEMONSTRATION
L1   Detection of electromagnetic radiation

L1a   Radio waves

portable radio

Tune the radio to a broadcast. You should be able to show that the radio is responding to electrical or magnetic waves. (Try pointing the aerial or ferrite rod in different directions; try screening the radio with a metal sheet (*e.g.* aluminium foil) or grid.)

L1b   Gamma rays

gamma GM tube
GM tube holder
scaler
pure gamma source
source holder

Show that this detector responds as if electromagnetic radiation consists of discrete quanta.

DEMONSTRATION
L2   Photoelectric effect

L2a   Demonstration of photoelectric effect with zinc plate and gold-leaf electroscope

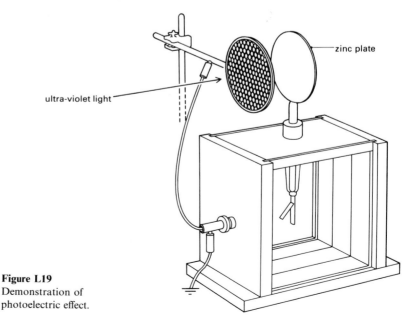

ultra-violet light

zinc plate

Figure L19
Demonstration of
photoelectric effect.

gold-leaf electroscope
zinc plate attachment
wire mesh about 5 cm diameter
e.h.t. power supply
piece of fine emery cloth
glass plate about 25 cm square
ultra-violet lamp
retort stand base, rod, boss, and clamp
leads

Safety note: Take care not to look directly at the ultra-violet lamp.

The surface of the zinc plate must be cleaned with the emery cloth. The electroscope case and the wire mesh are earthed.

Give the zinc plate a negative charge (from the e.h.t. supply), and then shine ultra-violet light on the zinc plate. There should be evidence of some movement of charge from the electroscope. What sign has that charge?

Repeat the experiment with a sheet of glass between the ultra-violet lamp and the zinc plate.

Repeat the experiment starting with positive charge on the zinc plate.

Explain the effects.

L2b Simple photoelectric cell using magnesium ribbon

picoammeter
cell holder with four cells
ultra-violet lamp
magnesium ribbon 100 mm long
glass plate about 25 cm square
wire gauze, 70 mm × 60 mm, *e.g.* 20 mesh copper
retort stand base, rod, boss, and clamp
crocodile clip
razor blade
leads

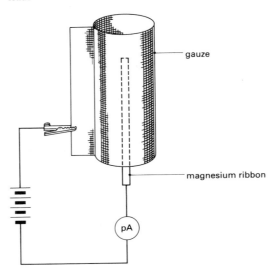

Figure L20
Simple photoelectric cell.

Safety note: Take care not to look directly at the ultra-violet lamp.

The magnesium ribbon must be scraped clean with the razor blade before one end of it is put into the meter's input socket. The gauze is used to make a cylinder around, *but not touching* the ribbon.

You should be able to show that a current flows between the ribbon and the gauze when ultra-violet light falls on the clean magnesium surface. If the current is due to movement of negatively charged electrons which way are they travelling?

What happens if you put a sheet of glass between the lamp and the 'photocell'? Explain the effect.

You may be able to experiment with other metals in place of magnesium.

DEMONSTRATION
L3 Colour of light and energy of photoelectrons

parallel beam projector
l.t. variable voltage supply
high-dispersion prism
photoelectric cell
high-impedance voltmeter
cell holder with one cell
card with slit
set of stops
leads

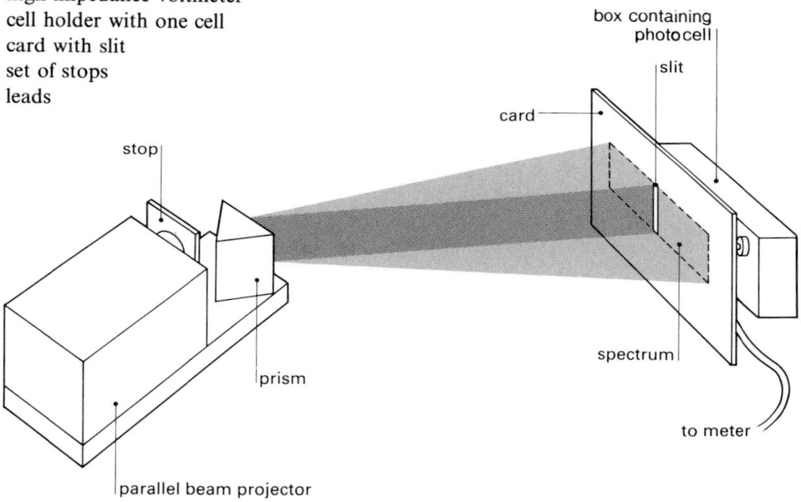

Figure L21
Projection of a spectrum on a photocell.

The apparatus is set up to allow a narrow beam of light of one colour to fall on the emitting surface of the photocell. A high-impedance voltmeter is connected across the photocell.

Variation with colour How does the p.d. developed across the photocell vary as the spectrum is slowly swept from red to blue across the slit?

Estimate the wavelength (and hence frequency) of the light and try to obtain a value for *h* by using the equation

$$\text{K.E.}_{\text{max}} = hf - \phi$$

(ϕ is a constant; the p.d. developed across the photocell is proportional to K.E.$_{\text{max}}$. The visible spectrum extends from about 700 nm to 400 nm.)

Variation with intensity When blue light is falling on the slit try reducing the intensity by placing stops over the lens of the projector. Does the p.d. change as much as the light intensity?

DEMONSTRATION
L4 The spectrum of mercury vapour

mercury discharge lamp
concave reflection grating
screen with slit (see below)
strip of green fluorescent paper, 20 mm wide, 0.5 m long
retort stand base, rod, boss, and clamp
a little mercury in a polythene bottle
microscope slide
fine diffraction grating

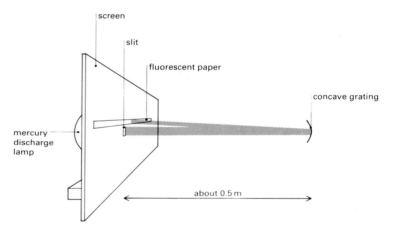

Figure L22
Production of mercury spectrum using a reflection grating.

Safety note: This experiment involves ultra-violet light and mercury vapour: both are potentially dangerous.

Do not look directly at the lamp. Take care when using mercury and make sure that none spills.

This demonstration must be done in a well-darkened room.

Light from the mercury lamp falls on the concave reflection grating and is reflected back to the screen where a spectrum is formed. You should see two ultra-violet lines (on the fluorescent paper only, figure L23). They are in fact the first and second order lines due to light of the same wavelength. What happens to the spectrum when light from the mercury lamp passes through glass, *e.g.* a microscope slide?

The green line in the mercury spectrum is at 546 nm (546×10^{-9} m). Use this to estimate the wavelength of the ultra-violet line.

If a polythene bottle containing *a few drops* of mercury is held just below the grating and squeezed *gently*, light from the mercury lamp passes through vapour containing cold mercury atoms. What effect does this have on the spectrum?

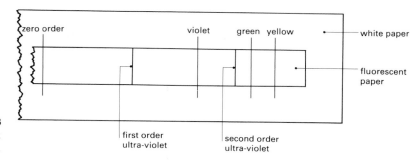

Figure L23
Spectrum of mercury using fluorescent paper to detect ultra-violet lines.

zero order

violet   green yellow   ● → white paper

first order
ultra-violet

second order
ultra-violet

fluorescent
paper

OPTIONAL EXPERIMENT
L5   The hydrogen spectrum

fine diffraction grating (or direct vision spectroscope)
hydrogen spectrum tube
holder for spectrum tube
e.h.t. power supply
leads

Run the hydrogen spectrum tube from the e.h.t. power supply. Look at it through the grating held close to your eye, or through the spectroscope.

If the tube contains atomic hydrogen you should see the regular arrangement of spectral lines which are the visible part of the Balmer spectrum.

Use the grating to look at the spectra of street lights, advertising signs, etc.

EXPERIMENT
L6   Interference of single photons

m.e.s. lamp, 1.25 V, 0.25 A
Worcester circuit board
spring connector with lampholder
cell
fogged photographic film
35 mm slide mounts
coarse grating
photographic exposure meter
slide projector

Look at the lamp through the diffraction grating and observe the spectrum. Put filters in front of the lamp – in a darkened room the spectrum should still be visible if you stand about 0.5 m from the lamp.

The amount of light transmitted by the filters can be estimated by using the exposure meter and slide projector.

Question **21** (page 328) shows how you can estimate the number of photons entering your eye each second. From this, and the fact that they travel at $3 \times 10^8 \, \text{m s}^{-1}$ you can calculate how 'far apart' they are.

Do you still see the diffraction spectrum with the filters in place, when comparatively few, well spaced photons enter your eye each second?

L7 Electron diffraction by graphite

electron diffraction tube
e.h.t. power supply
transformer
cylindrical magnet
ruler
leads

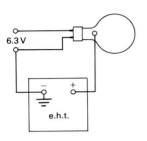

6.3 V

e.h.t.

Figure L24
Circuit for electron diffraction tube.

Earth the negative terminal of the e.h.t. supply, and connect it to one of the terminals in the tube base. Connect the positive e.h.t. terminal to the anode, not using the 50 MΩ resistor.

You should see a pattern of rings on the fluorescent screen.

What happens to the pattern as you vary the anode voltage? Measure the diameter of the rings at several voltages.

What happens if you put a magnet near the neck of the tube?

OPTIONAL EXPERIMENT

L8 Optical analogue of electron diffraction

either
compact light source
transformer
or
m.e.s. lamp, 2.5 V, 0.3 A, in holder
cell holder with 2 cells

fine diffraction gratings
colour filter (*e.g.* green)
leads

Put the filter in front of the light source. Stand about 3 m away, hold the diffraction grating in front of your eye, and look at the lamp.

How does the position of the diffracted spots of light depend on the orientation of the grating?

Use this to suggest why the electron diffraction experiment shows rings, not spots.

DEMONSTRATION

L9 Standing waves

L9a Standing waves on a rubber cord

signal generator
vibrator
xenon flasher
rubber cord, (0.5 m long, 3 mm square cross-section)
retort stand base, rod, boss, and clamp
2 small wooden blocks (to clamp rubber)
2 small G-clamps
leads

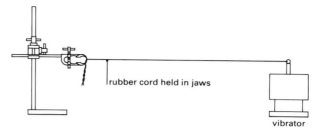

Figure L25

The vibrator is driven by the signal generator.

Does the cord vibrate when driven at any frequency, or only at certain frequencies?

What is the lowest frequency at which the cord will vibrate?

How many 'loops' are seen when it is vibrating at its lowest frequency?

What is the relationship between the wavelength of this one-loop standing wave and the length of the cord?

L9b   Vibrations in a rubber sheet

signal generator
large loudspeaker
xenon flasher
sheet of rubber
3 retort stand bases and rods
boss and clamp
large aluminium ring
rubber band
leads

Start with the loudspeaker under the centre of the rubber sheet, and slowly increase the frequency from about 10 Hz.

What is the lowest frequency that will excite standing waves? At this frequency does the wavelength have its lowest or highest value?

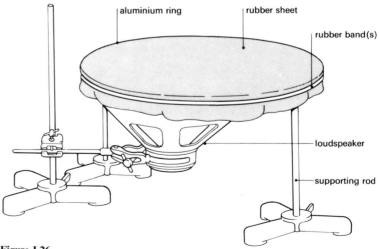

Figure L26
Standing wave experiments.

Look for different patterns of vibration at higher frequency, and try moving the loudspeaker off centre (as shown in figure L26) to see more complicated patterns.

DEMONSTRATION

L10 Standing waves with varying wavelength

You can set up standing waves with varying wavelength in different systems.

L10a Rubber cords of different thickness

signal generator
vibrator
rubber cord, 0.5 m long, 3 mm square cross-section
light rubber cord, 0.5 m long (*e.g.* dress-making elastic)
leads

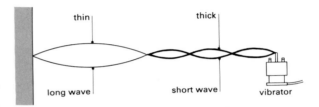

Figure L27
Oscillating rubber cords.

Tie the two cords together.

Adjust the frequency of the signal generator until you get standing waves of large amplitude.

Do both cords vibrate with the same frequency?

In which cord is the wavelength shorter?

In which cord does the wave travel more slowly? How do you know? Explain why the wave travels more slowly in that cord.

L10b A hanging chain

length of light chain (*e.g.* from bath plug)

Hold the chain at the top, and shake it to set up standing waves.

It may help to swing the top of the chain around in a small circle.

Where is the wavelength large, and where small? Where is the curvature of the chain large and where small, *i.e.*, where does it change direction quickly, and where is it more nearly straight?

Where does the wave travel quickly, and where more slowly? How do you know?

Explain *why* the wave speed varies.

Figure L28
Oscillating hanging chain.

L10c   Rubber strip of varying width

signal generator
vibrator
xenon flasher
V-shaped strip of rubber
leads

wood jaws

vibrator

Figure L29
An oscillating V-shaped rubber strip.

Adjust the frequency of the signal generator until large-amplitude standing waves are formed.

Is the wavelength of the standing waves constant? If not where is it larger and where smaller?

Adjust the frequency to obtain a single loop (figure L30).

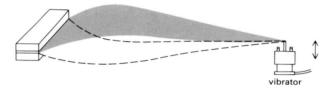

vibrator

Figure L30
Lowest mode of V-shaped rubber strip.

Is the peak in the middle?

Where is the rubber curved more sharply, and where less so?

The mass per unit length of the rubber strip varies along its length. At which end will the wave speed be least?

Which are curved more sharply – waves of short or long wavelength?

You should be able to relate the changing curvature to the variation in wave speed along the strip.

QUESTIONS

The photoelectric effect; $E = hf$

1(I) The energy of a light photon, or of an electron, may be expressed in joules or in electronvolts. (One electronvolt is the energy gained by an electron when it is accelerated by a potential difference of one volt.)

What is the value of one electronvolt (1 eV) in joules?

You should read Einstein's own explanation of the photoelectric effect reprinted on page 308, before answering questions **2** to **4**.

2(P) What is the minimum frequency of light needed to ionize a helium atom, whose ionization energy is about 24 eV?

3(P) Light of frequency 8×10^{14} Hz releases electrons from sodium metal.

a What is the wavelength of this light?

b What region of the spectrum is it in – infra-red, visible, or ultra-violet?

c According to Einstein's theory, will light of *shorter* wavelength than this eject more energetic or less energetic electrons?

4(L) In an experiment with a simple photocell it was found that red light ($f = 4.5 \times 10^{14}$ Hz) ejected electrons with a maximum energy of about 0.2 eV, while violet light ($f = 7.5 \times 10^{14}$ Hz) gave electrons of 1.4 eV. Use Einstein's relationship to obtain a value for Planck's constant, h.

5(R) Light falls on a metal surface. Electrons ejected from the metal surface are collected by a collector, which is connected via a battery and a meter to the metal, as shown in figure L31.

Which one of the following statements about the photoelectric effect in such an experiment is true?

A The number of electrons ejected per second from the metal is proportional to the potential difference between the metal and the collector.

B The number of photoelectrons produced per second is proportional to the frequency of the light.

C The maximum energy of the photoelectrons is proportional to the intensity of the light.

D The maximum energy of the photoelectrons is dependent on the frequency of the light.

E The maximum energy of the photoelectrons is independent of the particular metal used.

(Coded answer paper, 1979)

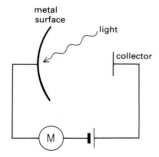

Figure L31

6(P)   Use $E = hf$ and $c = f\lambda$ to complete the blanks in table L3.

	BBC Radio 4	**Microwaves**	**Visible light**	**Gamma rays**
λ	1500 m	3×10^{-2} m		
f			5×10^{14} Hz	
E				10^6 eV

Table L3

Calculate E in both joules and electronvolts.

7(P)   Nuclei, like atoms, can also absorb and emit electromagnetic radiation. It takes 2.2 MeV to break apart a deuteron (a neutron plus proton). What wavelength of radiation is needed to do this? Is your answer the smallest or the largest wavelength that will do?

8(P)   The school microwave apparatus ($\lambda \approx 3$ cm) has a power of about 10^{-3} watt. About how many photons does it emit each second? In each cycle of oscillation?

9(P)   Your answer to question **8** may be about 10^{20} photons per second. How much power would a gamma ray source deliver if it emitted 10^{20} photons each second?

A school gamma ray source does not burn a hole in its box, despite this calculation. How do you explain this?

Light quanta, energy levels, and spectra

10(I)   What is the energy, in J and in eV, of a photon of light of wavelength 253 nm?

11(L)   Table L4 shows the energy levels of a mercury atom, measured from the lowest level, A.

a   Identify the origin of the line at wavelength 253 nm in the mercury spectrum, *i.e.*, say which are the energy levels involved.

b   What is the wavelength associated with a jump between the levels marked D and F?

c   Will light be emitted or absorbed if the transition is *from* F *to* D?

Energy/J	Energy/eV	
1.41×10^{-18}	8.84	F
1.24×10^{-18}	7.73	E
1.07×10^{-18}	6.70	D
0.875×10^{-18}	5.46	C
0.784×10^{-18}	4.90	B
0	0	A

Table L4

12(R) Suppose that a certain atom had only four possible energy levels. What would be the maximum number of different frequencies there could be in the spectrum of the radiation it could emit?

A 3   B 4   C 5   D 6   E 8

(Coded answer paper, 1978)

13(R) When electrons of energy 4.9 eV bombard mercury atoms in mercury vapour, some atoms in the lowest energy level (ground state) are excited to an energy 4.9 eV above the ground state, after which they return to the ground state, emitting a photon of ultraviolet radiation.

If the number of bombarding electrons is reduced, but their energy is still 4.9 eV, which of the following correctly describe(s) changes to the radiation emitted?

1 The intensity (brightness) of the radiation is reduced.
2 The wavelength of the radiation is reduced.
3 The energy of each photon of the radiation is reduced.

A 1 only   B 2 only   C 1 and 3 only
D 2 and 3 only   E 1, 2, and 3

(Coded answer paper, 1979)

The spectrum and energy levels of hydrogen

14(I)a Calculate the energy of a photon whose frequency is 32.881×10^{14} Hz. (Use $h = 6.63 \times 10^{-34}$ J s.)

b Look up the ionization energy for hydrogen. Compare with your answer to **a**.

15(I) See figure L32.

The transitions marked A, B, C, and D give rise to four members of the Lyman series. Will the transition A be the longest or the shortest wavelength line in the series?

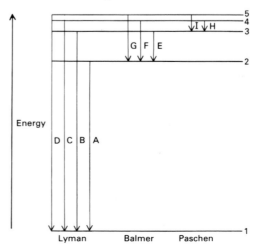

Figure L32
Some energy levels of a hydrogen atom.

16(L)   See figure L32.

The frequencies corresponding to the transitions marked A and B are 24.659×10^{14} Hz and 29.226×10^{14} Hz respectively.

a   What frequency will be emitted by the transition marked E?

b   The third line in the Balmer series (corresponding to the transition marked G) has a frequency of 6.9044×10^{14} Hz. Calculate the energy difference between levels 2 and 5.

17(L)   The frequencies of the first four lines in the Lyman series, (corresponding to the transitions marked A, B, C, and D in figure L32) are given in table L5.

Frequency/10^{14} Hz	Transition
24.659	A
29.226	B
30.824	C
31.564	D

Table L5

Calculate the corresponding photon energies in joules. (Use $h = 6.63 \times 10^{-34}$ J s.)

18(L)   This question asks you to calculate the total energy per kilogram of the Earth in its orbit around the Sun. You should answer in terms of the gravitational constant, G, the mass of the Sun, m, and the mean radius of the Earth's orbit, r.

a   What is the potential (gravitational potential energy per kilogram) of the Earth in its orbit round the Sun?

b   Use the gravitational force on the Earth and the centripetal force needed to keep it in orbit at distance r from the Sun to obtain an expression for v, the speed of the Earth in its orbit, assumed circular.

c   What is the kinetic energy per kilogram of the Earth?

d   What is the total energy per kilogram of the Earth?

Your answer to **d** should be a negative quantity. If the Earth had so much kinetic energy that the total energy were positive, then the gravitational attraction of the Sun would not be enough to hold it in orbit. In any bound system, including the hydrogen atom (an electron bound to a proton), the total energy is negative.

19(L) To answer this question you need to know the photon energies (in J) of the first four lines in the Lyman series (see question **17**). Level 1 in figure L32 is the ground state of the hydrogen atom. The ionization energy of hydrogen is 13.6 eV (2.18×10^{-18} J).

a At what energy is level 1?

b Work out the energies (in J) of levels 2, 3, 4, and 5.

20(L)a Check that the expression $-2.18 \times 10^{-18}/n^2$ J correctly predicts the energy levels calculated in question **19**.

b Calculate the 8th energy level.

Light: waves or particles – or both?

21(L) A small lamp passes 0.2 A when the p.d. across it is 1.5 V.

a What is the total power transformed?

b Perhaps 3% of this is visible light. About how many visible photons are emitted each second?
(Take $f = 6 \times 10^{14}$ Hz.)

c Suppose your eye is about 0.3 m from the lamp. About what fraction of these photons will enter your eye?

d From the number of photons entering your eye each second work out the average time interval between the arrival of photons at the eye.

e If these photons are travelling at 3×10^8 m s^{-1} about how far behind is the next photon when one enters your eye?

f Suppose the intensity of light is reduced by a factor of 10^4 (e.g. by grey filters). How 'far apart' are the photons that now enter your eye?

22(E) Summarize what is known about the *behaviour* of light, and the *models* of light that are used to explain the phenomena. Say which model(s) is(are) useful in explaining different phenomena. *Why* do we seem to need two quite different models?

Electron diffraction

23(I) In optical diffraction by a grating, is red light diffracted more or less – i.e., through larger or smaller angles – than blue light?

24(I) In the electron diffraction experiment the diffraction angle decreases if the electrons have higher energy. Thinking about the wave-like behaviour of electrons, does higher energy mean longer or shorter wavelength?

25(L) Suppose that the two rings formed at angles θ_1 and θ_2 in the electron diffraction experiment with graphite come from rows of atoms with spacings s_1 and s_2. Use the grating formula $\lambda = s \sin \theta$ to get an expression comparing the sines of the angles θ_1 and θ_2. Does the expression depend on wavelength, λ?

26(I) Figure L33 shows the geometry of the electron diffraction tube.

a What is the value of θ, in radians?

b What is $\sin \theta$, approximately?

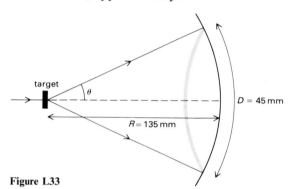

Figure L33

27(L) Table L6 shows the diameter of the two rings formed at different accelerating voltages in an electron diffraction experiment with graphite.

Electron gun p.d./V	D_1/mm	D_2/mm
5000	26	45
4000	28.5	49.5
3000	34	56

Table L6
Diffraction ring diameters

a Calculate D_2/D_1 for each voltage, and the average value of D_2/D_1.

Because the diffraction angle θ is small (see question **26**) the ring diameter is approximately proportional to $\sin \theta$.

b Use your value of D_2/D_1 ($\approx \sin \theta_2/\sin \theta_1$) to calculate the relative spacings of the rows of atoms responsible for these rings.

c Does the wider ring (diameter D_2) come from rows of atoms with larger or smaller spacing than the rows that give the ring with diameter D_1?

d Does the angle of diffraction increase or decrease as the accelerating voltage is increased? What does this suggest happens to the wavelength associated with the electrons as the energy of the electrons is increased?

28(L) This question is about the spacings between different rows of carbon atoms in the hexagonal arrangement of graphite.

In figure L34 two sets of rows are marked which could be responsible for the two diffraction rings. The hexagons of carbon atoms have sides 1.42×10^{-10} m long – distance marked a in figure L34(b). The vertical lines show rows of atoms $\dfrac{\sqrt{3}}{2} \times (1.42 \times 10^{-10}\,\text{m})$ apart, while the horizontal rows are $\dfrac{3}{2} \times (1.42 \times 10^{-10}\,\text{m})$ apart. The geometry involved is shown in figure L34(b).

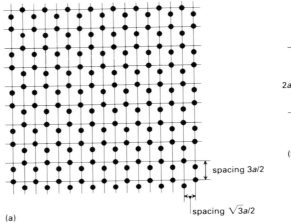

(b)

spacing $3a/2$

spacing $\sqrt{3}a/2$

Figure L34
(a) Two row spacings in a graphite layer.
(b) Geometry of row spacings.   (a)

a What is the ratio of the spacing of these two sets of rows?

b If these rows were the ones responsible for the electron diffraction rings, what would be the ratio of the diameters of the rings? Compare with your answer to question **27a**.

c Which of the rows marked in figure L34(a) – horizontal or vertical – correspond to the rings labelled D_1 in question **27**, and which to D_2?

29(R) Which of the following facts directly support(s) the view that electrons have wave properties?

1 When light of short wavelength falls on a suitable metal, electrons are emitted from the metal.
2 A beam of electrons can be diffracted by a suitable crystalline material.
3 There is an oscillatory force on an electron placed in a beam of radio waves.

A 1 only   **B** 2 only   **C** 1 and 3 only
D 2 and 3 only   **E** 1, 2, and 3.

(Coded answer paper, 1979)

Wavelength, energy, and momentum of electrons

30(L) In 1923 the Frenchman Louis de Broglie suggested that waves might be associated with particles. He predicted that momentum multiplied by wavelength would be constant

$$mv \propto 1/\lambda$$

a If the accelerating p.d. is V, will the velocity v of the electrons be proportional to V, $1/V$, $1/\sqrt{V}$, or $\sqrt{V}$?

b In an electron diffraction experiment how does the diameter of the ring, D, depend on the wavelength, λ?

31(L) Table L7 gives some results from a paper on electron diffraction by G. P. Thomson in 1928. He used an aluminium target.

Date	V/volt	D/cm
October 7	17 500	3.10
October 10	30 500	2.45
October 7	31 800	2.32
October 7	40 000	2.12
October 7	44 000	2.08
October 7	48 600	1.90
October 11	48 600	1.98
October 12	56 500	1.83
October 12	56 500	1.80

Table L7

From THOMSON, G. P. *'Experiments on the diffraction of cathode rays'.* Proceedings of the Royal Society, A. *117, 1928.*

Use your answers to question **30** to predict some function of D and V (such as $D \times V$, $D\sqrt{V}$, V/D, ...) which you would expect to be constant. Then check whether this function *is* constant for these results.

32(L) In an electron diffraction experiment using graphite the larger ring, formed by rows of carbon atoms 1.23×10^{-10} m apart, was formed at an angle of 0.167 radian.

a What is the wavelength?

b Write an expression for the kinetic energy of an electron ($\frac{1}{2}mv^2$) in terms of its charge, e, and the accelerating voltage, V.

c Obtain an expression for momentum, mv, in terms of e, V, and m.

The accelerating voltage was 5000 V.

d Work out the constant h in $mv = h/\lambda$.

e Are the units of this constant (momentum × wavelength) the same as those of the constant in $E = hf$?

33(L) Figure L35 is a graph prepared by Davisson in 1928 collecting several people's results together. Wavelength λ is plotted against $1/\sqrt{V}$ (V is accelerating p.d.).

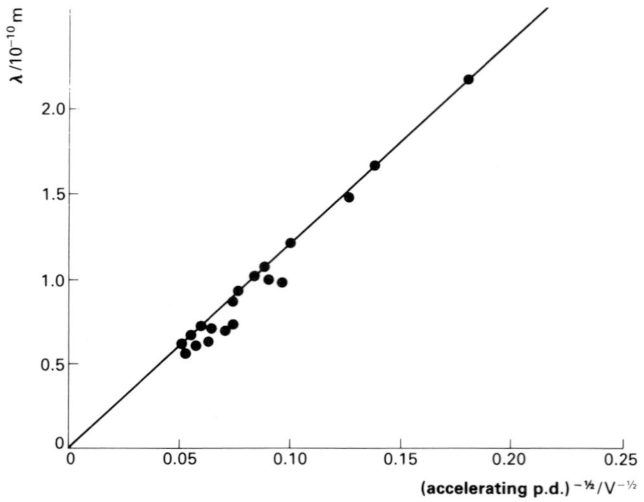

Figure L35
Wavelength of electrons plotted against reciprocal of the square root of the accelerating voltage.
Davisson, Clinton J. 'Are electrons waves?'
Journal of the Franklin Institute, **205**,
1928.

In your answer to question **32c** you should have found

$$mv = \sqrt{2meV}$$

a Show that the slope of the graph is $h/\sqrt{2me}$.

b Find h from the slope. (V was measured in volts, λ in units of 10^{-10} m.)

Matter waves

34(P) How much more slowly will a neutron have to travel than an electron if they are to have the same wavelength?

35(E) An electron has a wavelength of about 10^{-10} m when its velocity is of the order of 10^7 m s^{-1}. Estimate the wavelength associated with a ball in a game of tennis.

36(R) What happens to a diffraction pattern as the wavelength gets smaller and smaller? What happens as the wavelength is made larger? Why are X-rays and not visible light used to study crystal structures by diffraction methods? Why are diffraction effects with tennis balls never seen?

37(L) When light waves are diffracted by a spherical object of diameter b the first minimum of intensity occurs at an angle θ, given by $\sin\theta = 1.22\lambda/b$. If the wavelength is known, the size of the object can be estimated from the diffraction pattern.
  When high-energy electrons are scattered by nuclei, the nuclear size can be estimated from the scattering pattern. Figure L35 shows how the scattering probability for electrons varies with angle for several nuclei, and different electron energies. The scattering probability determines the light intensity in a diffraction pattern.
  For these very energetic electrons the momentum, p, and energy, E, are connected by the relativistic formula $p = E/c$.

a Calculate the momentum and hence (from $\lambda = h/p$) the wavelength of 420 MeV and 183 MeV electrons.

b Use the information in figure L36, and $\sin \theta = 1.22\lambda/b$ to estimate the size of the nuclei of carbon, oxygen, and vanadium.

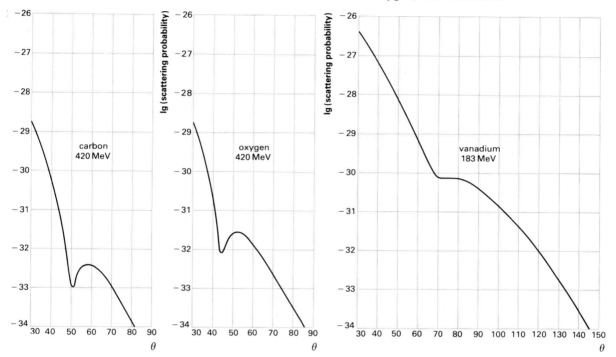

Figure L36
From: Physics (Advanced) Notes for the guidance of teachers on the nuclear physics option. *JMB, 1981.*

38(R) Write an account of the evidence for the existence of

either **a** discrete energy levels within the atom

or **b** wave properties associated with the electron.

(Special paper, 1979)

39(R) The passage below was written by someone who knows something of the ideas involved, but is confused and puzzled about them.

'The idea of matter as like waves is really a very silly invention. It's fairly easy to think of electrons as very tiny billiard balls – and that used to be all right. But to say that when you go to very tiny things they start behaving like waves instead, then it's almost an insult to one's intelligence. Let's hope they can think of a better idea some day.'

Write a short explanation of the passage. Your explanation should first point out any mistakes or ambiguities and then make a more accurate and complete statement to help the author to understand.

(Part question, Long answer paper, 1978)

40(E) Write an explanation of 'wave – particle duality' for an intelligent non-scientist of your own age.

Electron waves in a hydrogen atom box

41(I) Review the evidence for :

a The stability of atoms.

b The size of atoms.

c The energy levels of atoms.

42(I)a What is the wavelength of a one-loop standing wave on a cord length l?

b Is this the longest or the shortest wavelength standing wave that can fit in this length?

43(L) Figure L37 shows a crude representation of an electron inside a hydrogen atom 'box'.

a What is the wavelength of the one-loop standing wave shown?

b Is this the largest or smallest wavelength standing wave that would fit into this space?

c Calculate the momentum associated with the wavelength you calculated in **a**.

d May the electron have less than this momentum, in these circumstances?

e Calculate the kinetic energy of the electron.

f Is this the maximum or minimum possible kinetic energy for the electron?

g What prevents the electron, with this kinetic energy, flying away from its proton?

h Calculate the energy that must be transferred to electrical potential energy to move an electron from 1.0×10^{-10} m to a long distance from a proton, that is, to free the electron.

i Has an electron with the kinetic energy you calculated in **e** enough energy to escape from a distance of 1.0×10^{-10} m from a proton?

44(L) Suppose an electron were confined to a space ten times smaller, 0.1×10^{-10} m.

a By what factors will the wavelength, momentum, and kinetic energy differ from those calculated in question **43**? For each quantity say whether it is larger or smaller.

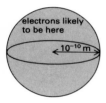

electrons not often found out here

electrons likely to be here

10^{-10} m

Figure L37

b How much energy must be transferred to electrical potential energy to remove an electron from a distance 0.1×10^{-10} m from a proton?

c Compare your answer to **b** with the kinetic energy of an electron in this space. Would the electrical attraction be enough to keep an electron in this space?

45(L)a Imagine an atom ten times larger, *i.e.*, with radius 10×10^{-10} m. By what factors will the electron's kinetic energy and the electrical potential energy change? Apply these factors to the values calculated for 1.0×10^{-10} m. Remembering that the electrical potential energy is *negative*, calculate the total energy at 10×10^{-10} m.

Since the tendency is to the lowest energy you should be able to say what would happen to a 10×10^{-10} m atom.

b Apply the same line of reasoning to a ten times smaller atom, 0.1×10^{-10} m. You should find that the total energy at this size is greater than at 1.0×10^{-10} m.

In fact these calculations, though crude, suggest that the atom has minimum energy when its size is about 1.0×10^{-10} m.

46(L) This question presents an alternative argument, based on calculus, for the size of an atom.

If one loop of an electron standing wave fits into an atom of radius r, then the wavelength $\lambda = 4r$.

a What is the momentum of this electron?

b What is its kinetic energy?

c What is the potential energy when the electron is at distance r from a proton?

d What is the total energy, E, of the atom?

e The total energy will be a minimum when $dE/dr = 0$. Work out dE/dr.

f Calculate the value of r for which $dE/dr = 0$.

Particles in the nucleus?

47(L) An atomic nucleus is about 10^{-14} m in size.

a Calculate the kinetic energy of an electron with $\lambda \approx 10^{-14}$ m.

b Calculate the electrical potential energy for a proton and electron 10^{-14} m apart.

c Is the electrical attraction sufficient to keep the electron within the nucleus?

48(L)a Find the least kinetic energy that a neutron or proton must have if it is to be contained in a space such that $\lambda \approx 10^{-14}$ m.

b Protons and neutrons are bound together within the nucleus by the 'strong' nuclear force. Because this force only operates over very short distances, it is not so well understood as the electrical force. But what can you say about the potential energy due to this force, from your calculation of the nuclear particle's kinetic energy?

A better model for the hydrogen atom

49(P) Figure L38 shows two cords, one heavy and one light tied end to end. One end is fixed, the other is vibrated.

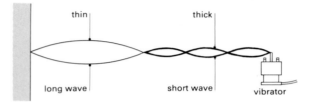

Figure L38

a Do both cords vibrate with the same frequency?

b On which cord does the wave travel more slowly?

c Why does it travel more slowly on this part of the cord?

50(R)a Figure L39 shows a standing wave in a long narrow spring which is vibrating from side to side on a smooth horizontal surface.
  What factors together determine the frequency of the vibrations?

Figure L39

b Figure L40 shows a standing wave in the same spring when it is arranged vertically between two supports; the speed of propagation of the wave, and hence the wavelength, is now decreasing towards the lower end. Why does the speed decrease towards the lower end?

c Suggest one similarity and one difference between the standing waves shown in figure L40 and electron standing waves in an atom.

(Short answer paper, 1979)

Figure L40

51(L) Parts (a)–(d) in figure L41 show some possible waves of varying wavelength 'fitted into' the space between $r = 0$ and the 'edge' of the atom. Which of the waves shown in (a)–(d) have the right kind of variation of wavelength with radius?
  (Remember how kinetic energy varies with distance from the centre of the atom, and how wavelength depends on kinetic energy.)

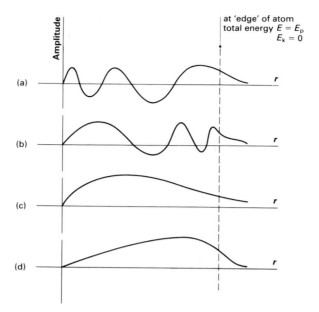

at 'edge' of atom
total energy $E = E_p$
$E_k = 0$

(a)

(b)

(c)

(d)

Figure L41

52(R) Which of the following sets of ideas are needed to provide a theory which can account for the size and energy of a hydrogen atom?

1 The electrical energy due to forces between charged particles.
2 The wavelength associated with moving particles (de Broglie waves).
3 The mechanics of the motion of massive particles (*e.g.* momentum, kinetic energy).

A 1 only   B 1 and 2 only   C 2 and 3 only
D 1 and 3 only   E 1, 2, and 3.

(Coded answer paper, 1978)

53(R) This question is about the ideas and evidence in the wave theory of atoms.

The passage below consists of numbered statements *i* to *v*. For each of these you are asked to give arguments which *explain* and *support* them.

The arguments that you use may be of many kinds and you should indicate what kind they are – for example theories, models, calculations, evidence, etc.

Passage
i It can be shown that electrons have wave properties, having a wavelength λ related to their momentum by $mv = h/\lambda$.

ii If a wave-like electron is confined in a 'box' of size 10^{-10} m, its momentum can't be less than a certain size, and so its kinetic energy has a lower limit too. The smaller the box, the bigger the kinetic energy of the electrons.

iii If the atom is to be stable, the sum of potential and kinetic energy of the electron must be negative. We know that the electrical potential energy of an electron is $-10\,eV$ when it is about $10^{-10}\,m$ from a proton. All this leads to an explanation of why atoms cannot be much smaller than about $10^{-10}\,m$.

iv Consideration of its spectrum shows that a hydrogen atom has a whole series of energy levels with energies given by c/n^2, where c is a constant and n has values 0, 1, 2, 3, ..., etc.

v The simplest idea is that electrons in hydrogen behave like standing waves on a string of length r (figure L42).
This would explain why there are discrete values of kinetic energy associated with integers n but it would give the wrong rule for the way the energy depends on n.

(Long answer paper, 1980)

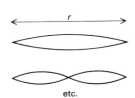

Figure L42

54(L) Figure L43 shows the potential energy curve for an electron near a proton.

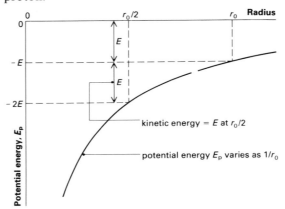

Figure L43

The total energy, E, of the atom is constant and is a negative quantity. It is the sum of potential and kinetic energies. At the edge of the atom, r_0, the kinetic energy is zero, and the potential energy $E_p = -E$. At $r_0/2$ E_p is $-2E$ (from the $1/r$ rule). For the total energy to be constant kinetic energy $= E - E_p = -E + 2E = E$. We will use this value of the kinetic energy at $r_0/2$ as the average value of kinetic energy between 0 and r_0.

a Average kinetic energy $\propto E$. How does average momentum depend on E?

b How does average wavelength depend on E?

c How does total energy E depend on the size of the atom, r_0? (Remember that at the 'edge' of the atom E is the potential energy E_p, at that radius, and $E_p \propto -1/r$.)

d Suppose n loops of mean wavelength λ fit into an atom of radius r_0. How does n depend on λ and r?

e Use your answer to **b** and **c** in **d** to find a relationship between E and n.

ANSWERS TO SELECTED QUESTIONS

UNIT H
Magnetic fields and a.c.

1a Perpendicular to both x and y axes.
b A brick, a box, a die, a lump of sugar.

3a 0.04 T
b 0.002 N
c The force is T newtons per metre.

4a 0.004 N m
b 0.004 N m
c 0 (the forces are in the plane of the coil and tend to push the sides in or out, not to turn the coil).

5a 1300 A
b This is an enormous current. It would melt the wire. A thicker wire would need a greater current and would get hotter. An aluminium wire (lower density) would need less current. Note that the current would have to flow at all times, and because the Earth's magnetic field has a vertical component there would also be a horizontal force on the wire.

7a Ne
b Ne/t
c vt
d $F = BNev$
e Bev
f BQv

9a BQv
b Towards the front edge.
c The moving charge carriers are pushed towards the front edge, so the density there will build up. It will continue to increase until there is an equally strong electrical force in the opposite direction, i.e., from front to back.
d The electric force (EQ) must be equal in magnitude to the magnetic force, BQv. So the electric field $E = Bv$.
e Front edge negative, rear edge positive.
f $V = Ed = Bvd$
g bd
h $n = BI/VbQ$

11a eV
b $v = \sqrt{2eV/m}$
c $F = Bev$; at right angles to v and B.
d $a = Bev/m$
e No
f $e/m = 2V/B^2 r^2$

13a See figure Q1(a).
b See figure Q1(b).

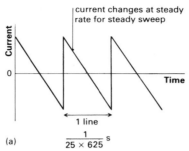

(a)

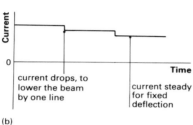

(b)

Figure Q1
(a) Current in coils for horizontal deflection.
(b) Current in coils for vertical deflection.

The field giving horizontal deflection must vary at a steady rate as the spot sweeps across the screen at a steady speed. If the middle of the screen corresponds to zero deflection and zero field, the current must vary in sign. The steps shown in the vertical deflection current are there to keep the spot at a fixed height for the whole of each line, dropping this height by one line spacing every time a line is completed. In practice, a very slowly changing current is used. Each line on the screen is tilted by an angle of about 1/625 radian. Such a steadily changing current would be much easier to produce than a series of small sharp steps.

17a The field is $k\,\mathrm{N\,A^{-1}\,m^{-1}}$
b z
c The force is k newtons
d x
e $2 \times 10^{-7}\,\mathrm{N\,A^{-2}}$
f $4\pi \times 10^{-7}\,\mathrm{N\,A^{-2}}$

19a $1.5 \times 10^{-3}\,\mathrm{T}$
b $0.75 \times 10^{-3}\,\mathrm{T}$

21 *Some* of the points to be made in an answer include:
a Need to know or estimate the mass and charge of an electron; the p.d. of the electron gun; the acceleration due to gravity; the distance from gun to screen.
b The current in the wire; the formula for magnetic field strength (near a straight wire, a solenoid?); the value of μ_0.

23a A force BQv parallel to the length of the rod.
b A current will flow.
c $E = \mathscr{E}/l$
d $Q\mathscr{E}/l$
e $\mathscr{E} = Blv$
f No; Q does not appear in the expression for the e.m.f.
g $I^2 Rt$
h No. The force BIl must act against the motion of the rod. If it helped the motion one would only have to start the rod moving for it to go faster and faster, gaining energy without drawing on any supply.
i vt
j $BIlvt$
k $IR = Blv$. Since IR is the p.d. across the resistor, which must be equal to the induced e.m.f. $\mathscr{E} = Blv$. Notice that the argument of steps **g** to **k**, which was about energy, has given the same result as the argument about force in steps **a** to **e**.
l No. Charges will be pushed to one end of both conductors as they move together through the B-field, but after this initial movement of charge, the rod and wire travel along with one end of the pair positively charged with respect to the other end, but with no current circulating.

26a $I = V/R$
b See figure Q2.

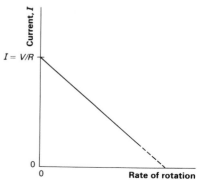

Figure Q2

c The torque will fall as the rate of rotation increases.

d The rate of rotation must fall. If the motor is not producing enough torque to turn the larger load, it will slow down. As it does so, the induced e.m.f. in its rotor falls. The constant supply p.d. can now drive a larger current through the rotor, so the current rises. It rises until the motor has slowed down enough to deliver sufficient torque to turn the load. In this way, an electric motor is a self-adjusting device.

27a As long as the motor is turning, an e.m.f. is induced in the rotor and the current in it is given by $V - \mathscr{E} = IR$. The applied p.d., V, is constant at 5 V, so I is always less than $V/R = 5$ A, the value it would have if the rotor were stationary and $\mathscr{E} = 0$. The faster the rotor turns, the larger $\mathscr{E}$ and the smaller I become.

b The field, B, in which the rotor turns is constant, so the torque is proportional to the rotor current. The larger the load, the larger the current must be. The motor slows down as much as is necessary for this larger current to flow, if that is possible without it stalling.

c Raise the p.d. applied to the rotor, so that it exceeds the induced e.m.f. at 27 revolutions per second (about 4 V) by as much as is needed to drive 3.1 A through 1 Ω (3.1 V). This assumes that the torque required remains the same, and so, since the torque is proportional to the current, that the current will remain 3.1 A.

28a $B = 0.75 \times 10^{-3}$ T; $\Phi = 3.7 \times 10^{-6}$ Wb
b $B = 0.75 \times 10^{-3}$ T; $\Phi = 1.9 \times 10^{-6}$ Wb
c $B = 0.75 \times 10^{-3}$ T; $\Phi = 6.3 \times 10^{-6}$ Wb

31a Resistance = resistivity × length/area.
b Potential difference = current × resistance = current × resistivity × length/area. If current is analogous to flux, potential difference is analogous to current-turns, NI. The current-turns 'drive the flux round the circuit'.
c $\mu_r\mu_0$ is analogous to 1/resistivity; that is, to conductivity.

d
driving force	temperature difference
rate of flow	flow of energy in joules per second
length	thickness of insulation
conductivity	thermal conductivity
area	surface area of hot water tank

e Reluctance corresponds to resistance.

32a About 5×10^7 A^2 m^{-1} N^{-1}
b If l is doubled (keeping the same number of turns per metre), then so is N, the total number of turns. But doubling l also doubles the reluctance. Since both current-turns and reluctance are doubled, the flux stays the same.
c About 6×10^{-6} N m A^{-1} or Wb
d About 1.2×10^{-3} T (or Wb m^{-2})
e A steel retort stand rod might have a diameter of 10 mm, and a cross-sectional area of about 80 mm^2. The cross-section of the solenoid is about 5000 mm^2. If the steel 'conducts' flux 500 times better than the air, the ratio of the fluxes is about $500 \times 80/5000$, or about 8. (This estimate neglects the fact that the solenoid area not occupied by iron is only $(5000 - 80)$ mm^2, not 5000 mm^2.)

36a 0.05 H
b The p.d. across coil B will be very much less. Because of the greater reluctance, the flux produced by the same current will be much less. So the rate of change of flux linkage and hence the e.m.f. induced in coil B will be much less for the same rate of change of current.
c The p.d. across coil B will be doubled: having twice as many turns in A will double the flux for the same current. The rate of change of flux is doubled and so therefore is the induced e.m.f.
d Doubling the number of turns in coil B doubles the flux linkage. The rate of change of flux linkage doubles, and so therefore does the induced e.m.f.
e Because the flux is decreasing the p.d. across B will have the opposite sign. Because the rate of change of current, and therefore of flux and of flux linkage, has half its previous value the magnitude of the p.d. across coil B will be 0.75 V.

37a The p.d. across R is only 0.05 V when the current is 0.5 A, so the p.d. across L is very nearly 2 V. The rate of rise of current is 50 A s^{-1}, so the inductance is 2/50 H, or 0.04 H, approximately.
b By connecting an oscilloscope across R.
c The p.d. across R when the current is 0.5 A is still only 0.1 V, so that the p.d. across L is still not much under 2 V. The rate of rise of current will be much the same.
d The *initial* rate of rise of current will be the same, 50 A s^{-1}. When the current is 0.5 A, the p.d. across R is 1 V, leaving only 1 V across L. The rate of rise of current must now be about half what it

was when there was nearly 2 V across L, being now about 25 A s^{-1}.

43

Number of turns on primary, P	Number of turns on secondary, S	Brightness of lamp, L	Alternating p.d. across S/volts
20	50	normal	2.5
50	20	dim	0.4
20	30	dim	1.5
40	100	normal	2.5
20	80	bright	4.0

Table Q1

Note that, if the coils are wound from fin wire, it may well be that the resistance of coil with many turns is important, and th lamp may then not light as it would if the coil's resistance were negligible.

44a The flux through the secondary coil must be pretty much the same wherever the coil is on the core. The greater proportion of the flux must circle round within the core, with little flux passing through the air.
b The flux has to cross the air gaps. The system behaves for flux as an electric circuit behaves for current. The air gaps correspond to lengths of high-resistivity material inserted into a circuit of thick copper wire. The current then depends more on the high-resistance part of the circuit than on the low-resistance part. Similarly, a small air gap in an iron-filled 'magnetic circuit' reduces the flux in the 'circuit' by a large factor.
c The result **b** suggests that the flux is determined by the whole 'magnetic circuit' If there are air gaps, the flux has a low value right round the circuit. (Similarly, one would have a low current in a thick copper bar if somewhere else in the electr circuit there were a high resistance.)
d The flux links each coil, and each has a e.m.f. induced in it. Current can be drawn from each, a corresponding current flowin in the single primary. That each coil can light a lamp is no stranger than that three times as much current could be drawn from one coil.
e The primary current should be about three times larger.

47 Suggested demonstrations using small laminated C-cores and 120 + 120 turn coil might include:

Connect primary to a d.c. source (*e.g.* 1.5 cell), then to an a.c. source (2 V, 50 Hz) to show that transformers work only for a.c., not for d.c. (Take care that current in primary is not large enough to cause over-heating on d.c.) Use 1.5 V lamp on secondary.

Show effect of turns ratio: for given a.c. input (say 2 V) and about 10 primary turns wound from insulated wire, increase secondary turns until lamp lights.

Show effect of using 2 V, 4 V, 6 V, ..., a.c. input on output voltage with, say, 120-turn coils as primary and secondary, using a.c. voltmeters to measure V_p, V_s; hence establish that $V_s/V_p \approx N_s/N_p$; show use as step-up and step-down transformer.

Measure current in primary and secondary coils (a.c. meter 1 or 5 A) to show that although transformer can be used to step up voltage there is no gain in *power*, and in fact power out is slightly less than power in.

Increase load on secondary (perhaps by starting with no load on secondary, then connecting one lamp, then two or more lamps in parallel) to show that current in primary rises as current in secondary rises.

Show importance of magnetic circuit linking the two coils by making a small, then a large, air gap between two C-cores, and/or show effect of no iron core linking the two coils.

Point out that iron core is laminated – to reduce losses due to eddy currents.

Show that these losses become more important at high frequencies (signal generator, oscilloscope).

48a P/V
b $I^2R = (P/V)^2R$
c Reduce I (*i.e.* increase V); reduce R.
d a.c. can be stepped up and down using transformers; d.c. cannot. Although power should be transmitted at high voltage to reduce losses, generators do not produce such high-voltage a.c., nor do consumers use it.
e 3:1
f 1:9
g Nine times more for the 132 kV system.
h Insulators, *e.g.* between the conductor and the supporting tower, must be larger. Also clearances between conductors and surroundings must be greater.

49ai I^2R
ii $I^2R/2$
iii I^2R

b $I/\sqrt{2}$
c Its square is the average, or mean, of the square of the varying current. So it is the root of the mean of the square of the varying current. The usual abbreviation is r.m.s.
d 1/2
e $I/\sqrt{2}$

Note: It happens that $I_{r.m.s.} = I_{maximum}/\sqrt{2}$ in both **b** and **e**, though for different reasons. This result is *not* generally true for all varying wave forms. In a**iii**, for example, $I_{r.m.s.} = I_{maximum}$ for fairly obvious reasons, even though the current 'alternates'.

51a No; the current is zero.
b No; the p.d. is zero, so the coil is not in a magnetic field.
c The forces are equal in magnitude and opposite in direction as the current is the same size at both times but reverses its direction.
d Zero
e The wattmeter would give a reading. It must, as the lamp would light and would be dissipating energy. If it does, the current and p.d. across the two together can no longer have the phase relationship shown in figure H103, for that phase relationship gives zero average force on the wattmeter coil. In fact, if the lamp is the only component in the circuit, the current and p.d. will be in phase.

53a The same maximum current would have to be attained from zero in half the time, so the rate of change of current would have doubled.
b The time for the change of current has halved; to keep the rate of change constant, the maximum current must have halved, so that half the change happens in half the time, at the same rate.
c The maximum output p.d. is the maximum p.d. across R, which is IR if I is the maximum current. As the latter has halved, so has the output p.d. Of course this only works out so simply if R is very small, so that IR is not an appreciable part of the input p.d. Nevertheless, the output as a fraction of the input always falls as the frequency is raised in this circuit.
d Less of a high frequency input appears across the output, than of a low frequency. The circuit acts as a 'filter' which only passes lower frequency signals to the next stage. The circuit is used to discourage unwanted mains frequency voltages from mixing with steady (zero frequency)

voltages in devices which draw their power from the a.c. mains.

55a The p.d. across the coil is proportional to the rate of change of current, dI/dt. When I has its maximum value dI/dt is zero.
bi OA, BC
ii AB, CD
When the product VI is positive the source is supplying energy; when this product is negative it is receiving energy.
The energy comes from the magnetic field set up by the current in the coil.

56a Stored in the springs.
b Stored in the capacitor.
c The force exerted by the springs and the mass of the trolley.
d The p.d. across the capacitor and the inductance of the coil.
e The velocity is momentarily constant, because there is no net force on the trolley.
f The current is momentarily constant, because there is no p.d. across the coil.
g The springs begin to exert a force, slowing down the trolley.
h A p.d. builds up across the capacitor, and the current decreases.
i The system has as much energy as before, stored in the springs again. If energy is conserved, one could infer that the trolley had energy equal to the total energy, when it was in the centre position, and the undisplaced springs had no energy. This is, of course, the trolley's kinetic energy, $\frac{1}{2}mv^2$.
j The system has as much energy as before, stored in the capacitor again. If energy is conserved, one could infer that the inductor had energy equal to the total energy, when the capacitor was uncharged and had no energy. The energy of an inductor is the electrical analogue of kinetic energy, and is given by $\frac{1}{2}LI^2$.

59 An answer might include the following points, together with fuller explanations than are given here.
1 The current in the inductor I_L lags behind the p.d. between X and Y by a quarter of a cycle ($V \propto dI_L/dt$, so when $V = 0$, $dI_L/dt = 0$; when $V = V_0$, dI_L/dt has its maximum value, *i.e.* $I_L = 0$ ...). But current in the capacitor leads p.d. across it by quarter of a cycle (explanation in terms of Q, V, and $I_C = dQ/dt$ ...). Net effect is phase difference of half a cycle between the two currents. Thus one is positive when the other is negative, and vice versa:

charge circulates around the LC circuit first in one direction then in the other, then ...

2 Values of I_L and I_C depend on values of L, C, and frequency f. $I_C \propto f$; $I_L \propto 1/f$. At resonant frequency $I_L = I_C$ in magnitude. Because these currents are in opposite directions charge circulates around the LC circuit first in one direction, then in the other, without much charge entering or leaving the circuit at X or Y. If frequency is increased I_L decreases, I_C increases: current is then drawn from the supply to 'make up the difference'.

3 When C is fully charged the current in the LC circuit is momentarily zero (at resonant frequency). Energy $(=\frac{1}{2}CV^2)$ is stored in the electric field between capacitor plates (cf. trolley at rest with spring fully compressed). The capacitor discharges through the inductor, current grows (cf. spring pushes trolley which accelerates). Current in the inductor causes a magnetic field around it which can store energy (cf. kinetic energy of moving trolley). The capacitor charges up in the opposite sense ...

UNIT I
Linear electronics, feedback and control

1a $V \times \dfrac{R_2}{R_1 + R_2}$

b $6\frac{2}{3}$ V

c $\frac{2}{3}$ mA

d $6\frac{2}{3}$ V, 0.067 mA

2 1.5 V

3a $V_1 + V_2$

b $\dfrac{R_1}{R_2}$

c a Doubled, **b** the same.

4a 0.2 mA
b 0.2 mA
c 20 V
d X
e Negative.
f Equal resistances.

5a 20 μC
b 100 μC

6a 0.5 mC
b 0.67×10^{-3} F
c Very high resistance voltmeter (e.g.

electrometer), or oscilloscope. (Charge would leak away through a normal voltmeter.)

7a Exponential decay curve.
b Current $\propto$ slope of first graph.
c Linear rise.

13a 20, 26, 32, 38.
b 10^5
c 2×10^5

15a 0 V
b 0.2 V
c 2×10^{-5} A
d 2×10^{-5} A
e -2 V
f Negative
g 2×10^{-6} A
h 2 V

16e $V_{out}/V_{in} = -R_f/R_{in}$

18a -1 mV
b 1001 mV
c 1001 mV
d -1002 mV
e $+2000$ mV
f 500 mV, $+499$ mV.
g Opposite direction.
h Much too large.
i 0.5 mV rise.
j -0.5 mV
k $+1000$ mV; nearly.

19a 0 V
b 3 V
c 3×10^{-5} A
d 5×10^{-5} A
e 8×10^{-5} A
f 8 V
g -8 V
h $V_{out} = -(V_A + V_B)$
i $V_{out} = -(2V_A + V_B)$
j -7 V
k $V_{out} = -2(V_A + V_B)$; $V_{out} = -1.6$ V.
l $V_{out} = -10(V_A + V_B)$; $V_{out} = -8$ V.

21a $R_C = 5R_f$
b $R_B = \frac{5}{2}R_f$
c $R_A = \frac{5}{4}R_f$
d e.g. $R_C = 40$ kΩ, $R_B = 20$ kΩ, $R_A = 10$ kΩ, $R_f = 8$ kΩ
e The required ratios are
$1:\frac{1}{2}:\frac{1}{4}: ... \frac{1}{32}$ (inputs): $\frac{1}{50}$ (feedback).

22a Ramp and analogue negative terminal to comparator 1; ramp and analogue positive terminal to comparator 2;

comparators to bistable inputs A and B respectively; bistable and clock into AND; AND to counter 1 Mz input; comparator to counter input P.
b Display goes to zero at start of each count and begins to count up. If voltage was near level of top of ramp, the reading would be displayed for negligible time. Either add (unspecified) circuitry to 'hold' (latch) the reading until next reading is ready, or make the ramp generator have long rest spaces between ramps so that display is steady for a large proportion of the time.

24a 1 V
b 1 μA
c The capacitor.
d Yes
e 10 μC, 20 μC
f 0.1 V, 0.2 V
g Left hand positive.
h Falling steadily
i -0.01 V s^{-1}
j Fall at 0.02 V s^{-1}.
k V_{out} moves with uniform gradients from (0 s, 0 V) to (2 s, -0.02 V) to (7 s, -0.17 V) to (8 s, -0.15 V)
l All rates of change multiplied by 10, V values 0 V, -0.2 V, -1.7 V, -1.5 V.

28a 0.2 mA
b 2 V
c $+2$ V
d $+2$ V
e $V_{out} = 3V_{in}$
f In place of the 1:2 resistance ratio of the diagram, it would need a 1:9 ratio.
g Straight line runs from (0 Ω, $+6$ V) to (30 kΩ, 0 V). X is at (20 kΩ, 2 V).
h All V values half those in **g**.

35ai $V_X = (V_{out} + 3)/2$,
ii $V_Y = 5/2$ V
b $V_{out} = 2V$
c $V_X = (V_{out} + V_A)/2$, $V_Y = V_B/2$, whence $V_{out} = V_B - V_A$
d Two intersecting straight lines AC and BD. A is (0 Ω, 3 V), B is (0 Ω, 5 V), C is (2 MΩ, 2 V), D is (2 MΩ, 0 V), lines intersect at X ≡ Y (1 MΩ, 2.5 V)
e A is (0, 1), B is (0, 3), C is (1.5, 4), D is (1.5, 0), intersecting at X ≡ Y (0.5, 2); $V_{out} = 4$ V.

39a They are equal.
b $dV/dt = -(1/CR)V$, $V = V'e^{-t/CR}$ $(V = V'$ when $t = 0)$.
c 1.84 V
d 0.68 V
e 2.27×10^{-4} V

40g $V = 0.1e^{10t}$
i $0.34\,$V

41b $1600\,$Hz (2 significant figures).

44ai $Z/1000$
ii $S - Z/10$
b $Z/S = 9.9(0)$
c $Z/S = 9.99$

d $G = \dfrac{1}{\beta + 1/A}$ or $\dfrac{A}{A\beta + 1}$

or $\dfrac{A/\beta}{A + 1/\beta}$

e $G = 1/\beta$: depends only on β.

45 The answers to this question depend upon interpretation of what is being controlled: level, or inflow.
Feedback: position of ball controls inflow.
Reference signal: setting of ball relative to valve position, or intended water level.
Error signal: discrepancy between ball level required to stop flow, and present level.
Input: could mean reference signal, or water input.
Output: could mean rate of flow into tank, or water outflow.
Disturbance: change of water pressure and therefore flow rate, or drop in level when water is being used.

49a

No.	3	4	5	6	7	8	9	10	11
m/g	90	100	110	110	100	90	90	100	110

Table Q2

b Reducing the correction by $50\,\%$ will give damped oscillation, but not immediate correction. Moving the sensor one place to the left will give stable correction.

UNIT J
Electromagnetic waves

7 Minima of intensity are detected at 0.30, 0.64 rad, etc.

8b $0.23\,$m

9 Solving these should not be taken too seriously; it can be quite fun and quite a valuable exercise in detective work. See figure Q3 for some clues.

CLUES

Aperture

Diffraction pattern

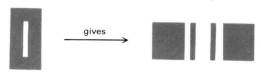

gives

gives

Figure Q3

14a $\theta = 0.008\,$rad
b About $1.6 \times 10^{18}\,$m (160 light years).

17a $0.6 \times 10^{-3}\,$rad
b $8 \times 10^{17}\,$km
c $1.5\,$km

18b Maxima occur at angles θ where $\sin \theta = \left[\dfrac{(2n + 1)}{4}\right] 0.015$, and where $n = 0, 1, 2, 3$, etc.

22 About $3400\,$Hz.

24a $1.6 \times 10^{-6}\,$m
b $420\,$nm

25a $30°$

26c $n\lambda = sx_n/L$ or $\lambda = sx_1/L$.

27a Nearly $5 \times 10^{-7}\,$m.

28c $5 \times 10^{-6}\,$m

31a $10^{-4}\,$m

32a $\theta_1 = 24°$
b $\theta_2 = 53°$

35 $c = 2.8(5) \times 10^8\,$m s^{-1}

37b $0.3\,$m

38b $2.5 \times 10^8\,$m s^{-1}

40a $5 \times 10^{-15}\,$W

43b $3 \times 10^8\,$m s^{-1}

UNIT K
Energy and entropy

1a By random collisions, a water molecule gets enough energy to break the bonds holding it to other water molecules or to the fabric, and moves into the air nearby. If there is a breeze, water molecules are swept away, reducing the number near the wet clothes and so reducing the chance that any will go back into the wet clothes.
b Water molecules in ice are bonded in a regular lattice, with permanent neighbours. As the ice melts, a molecule is still closely surrounded by others (the density actually increases) but has shifting neighbours, and itself moves about.
c The water already has tannin and other molecules from the tea dispersed rather uniformly through it. When milk is stirred in fat, casein, and other molecules, previously close together, become dispersed so that there is a roughly equal average distance between molecules of the same kind, and the chance of having a neighbour of a given kind is proportional to the total number of that kind of molecule in the mixture.
d Energy leaves the radiator in two ways, by emission of photons of infra-red radiation, and by giving extra energy to nearby air molecules.

2 $W \approx 8 \times 10^{67}$; $\ln W \approx 156$;
$k \ln W \approx 2 \times 10^{-21}\,$J K^{-1}.
$\Delta S = k \ln W - k \ln 1 = 2 \times 10^{-21}\,$J K^{-1}.

4a 10^7
b 4^{10^7}
c $1.9 \times 10^{-16}\,$J K^{-1}

6a Figure Q4 shows two examples.

Figure Q4

b N

9 $2^{100} \approx 10^{30}$; 1 chance in 10^{30}.

11a $2^{100} \approx 10^{30}$
b $\lg 2^{100} = 100 \lg 2 \approx 30$; so $2^{100} \approx 10^{30}$.
c 10^{24} s
d 3×10^6

12a About 4×10^{-4} m³ (0.4 litres).
b 3×10^{21}
c 3×10^{21} digits; 3×10^{18} m; 300 light years. Betelgeuse (alpha Orionis).

14 $\ln 10 = 2.302$
$\ln 10.5 = 2.351$
$\ln 10.5 - \ln 10 = 0.049$; compared with
$0.05 = 0.5/10$
$\ln (x + dx) - \ln x \approx dx/x$ if $dx \ll x$.

17a Cycle pump: about 0.2 m long; cross-section about 2×10^{-4} m²; volume $\approx 4 \times 10^{-5}$ m³.
b About 10^{21} molecules in 4×10^{-5} m³.
c See figure Q5.

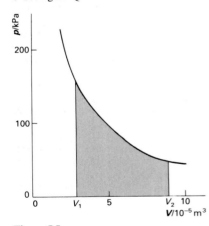

Figure Q5

d Area from $V_1 = 3 \times 10^{-5}$ m³ to
$V_2 = 9 \times 10^{-5}$ m³ ≈ 4.5 J.
e $\ln V_1 = -10.41$; $\ln V_2 = -9.32$;
$\ln (V_2/V_1) = 1.09$
$\Delta S \approx 1.5 \times 10^{-2}$ J K⁻¹
f $T\Delta S \approx 4.5$ J
g The gas would become hotter when compressed; its internal energy would increase. To keep the temperature constant, the gas must give energy to the surroundings, which it can do if it briefly

becomes a little hotter than the surroundings.

19 Two examples are shown in figure Q6. More energy means more ways to share.

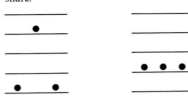

Figure Q6

22 See figure Q7 (below). Both are 'equal ratio' distributions, therefore in (b), where more energy is being shared by the same number of particles, more are on higher levels, fewer are on the very lowest level.

23 See table Q3

Level	$f = 0.5$ Number	$f = 0.25$ Number	$f = 0.75$ Number
0	256	256	256
1	128	64	192
2	64	16	144
3	32	4	108
4	16	1	81
5	8		≈ 61
6	4	less	≈ 45
7	2	than 1	≈ 34
8	1		≈ 26

Table Q3

25a X is hotter.
b $W_X' = \frac{2}{3} W_X$
$W_Y' = \frac{3}{1} W_Y$
$W_X' W_Y' = 2 W_X W_Y$

26a -9.6×10^{-24} J K⁻¹
b -9.6×10^{-22} J K⁻¹
c -9.6×10^{-21} J K⁻¹
d -9.6×10^{-3} J K⁻¹
e -9.6 J K⁻¹

28a $-\ln x = \ln 1/x$, so if $x < 1$, $\ln x$ is negative and $-\ln x$ is positive.
b $-2k \ln f$
c Q/ε
d $n = Q/\varepsilon$, so $\Delta S = -(Q/\varepsilon)k \ln f$.
If $\ln f = -\varepsilon/kT$, $\Delta S = Q/T$.

29a

f	$-\ln f$
1	0
0.5	$+0.69$
0.1	$+2.3$
0.01	$+4.6$

Table Q4

b If f is small, $\ln f$ is large and negative, $-\ln f$ is large and positive.
c Increases.
d Infinite.
e Zero.

31a

E/kT	$e^{-E/kT}$
1	0.37
2	0.14
5	0.0067
10	4.5×10^{-5}
20	2.1×10^{-9}
50	1.9×10^{-22}
100	3.7×10^{-44}

Table Q5

b 14

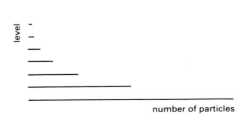

(a)   (b)

Figure Q7

33 See figure Q8. The Boltzmann factor increases very rapidly with temperature.

34a 41 kJ mol^{-1}
b $6.8 \times 10^{-20} \text{ J molecule}^{-1}$
c $3.4 \times 10^{-20} \text{ J bond}^{-1}$
d $4.1 \times 10^{-21} \text{ J}$; 8.3; 2.5×10^{-4}.

36a $\ln r_1 = \ln C - E/kT_1$
$\ln r_2 = \ln C - E/kT_2$

$$\ln\left(\frac{r_2}{r_1}\right) = \ln r_2 - \ln r_1 = \frac{E}{k}\left(\frac{1}{T_1} - \frac{1}{T_2}\right)$$

b i $1.4 \times 10^{-19} \text{ J}$
ii 4.5

39 The current increases by a factor of about 5 between $T = 900 \text{ K}$ and $T = 1000 \text{ K}$. $\Phi \approx 2 \times 10^{-19} \text{ J}$.

40 The bouncing ball passes kinetic energy to the molecules of the ball and floor, making ball and floor warmer, and sharing the energy out amongst many more particles than before.

   Mixing a drink means that particles can exchange places with unlike particles in many more ways than before. Dissolving sugar in water is in essence the same.

   Air escaping from a tyre occupies a larger volume, so that the molecules can be arranged in many more ways than before.

43a 85 %
b 5.2 %. The temperature difference is maintained by the world climate, and affects large masses of water, so that a substantial amount of renewable energy might be extracted, provided that doing so did not materially affect the temperature gradient.

47a

Liquid	ΔH_{evap} /kJ mol^{-1}	T/K	ΔS_{evap} /J K^{-1} mol^{-1}
carbon disulphide	27.2	319	85.3
trichloromethane	29.3	335	87.5
hexane	28.8	342	84.2
octane	34.9	399	87.5
sulphuric acid	50.2	617	81.4
water	40.6	373	108.8

Table Q6

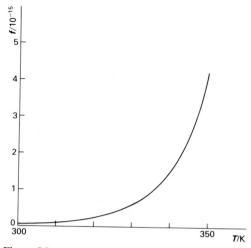

Figure Q8

47b About 60 J K^{-1}.
c About 70 %. If there is structure in the liquid and not in the vapour, the entropy increase on evaporation must be larger than that due to the volume change above.
d The entropy change for water is larger (by some 20 J K^{-1}) than for the other liquids. If there is more structure in the water, this might explain some of the excess. Methanol, $\Delta S = 104 \text{ J K}^{-1}$, is more like water than the other liquids.

48

	Steam condensing	Water freezing	Material more magnetized
a energy of surroundings increase because:	bonds form	bonds form	molecular magnet aligned along field has less energy
b entropy of surroundings:	increases	increases	increases
c entropy of substance:	decreases	decreases	decreases
d effect of raising temperature:	more steam	more liquid water	less magnetized

Table Q7

UNIT L
Waves, particles, and atoms

1 $1.6 \times 10^{-19} \text{ J}$

2 $5.8 \times 10^{15} \text{ Hz}$

4 $6.4 \times 10^{-34} \text{ J s}$

6 See table Q8.

	BBC Radio 4	Microwaves	Visible light	Gamma rays
λ	1500 m	3×10^{-2} m	6×10^{-7} m	1×10^{-12} m
f	2.0×10^5 Hz	1×10^{10} Hz	5×10^{14} Hz	3×10^{20} Hz
E	$\begin{cases} 1.3 \times 10^{-28} \text{ J} \\ 8.2 \times 10^{-10} \text{ eV} \end{cases}$	7×10^{-24} J 4×10^{-5} eV	3×10^{-19} J 2 eV	2×10^{-13} J 1×10^6 eV

Table Q8

8 About 1.5×10^{20} photons per second; 1.5×10^{10} photons per cycle of oscillation ($f \approx 10^{10}$ Hz).

9 About 2×10^7 W.

The gamma ray source emits far fewer than 10^{20} photons in a second. (The strength of radioactive sources is given in disintegrations per second or becquerel (Bq). A school gamma ray source may have an activity of around 0.2 MBq. This means that about 2×10^5 gamma ray photons are emitted per second.)

11a Energy levels A and B.
b 582 nm
c Emitted.

13 A

16a 4.567×10^{14} Hz
b 0.458×10^{-18} J

17 1.63×10^{-18} J; 1.94×10^{-18} J; 2.04×10^{-18} J; 2.09×10^{-18} J. (Note that since h is given to 3 significant figures, the energies cannot be given more precisely, even though frequencies are given to 5 significant figures.)

18a $-Gm/r$
b $\sqrt{Gm/r}$
c $Gm/2r$
d $-Gm/2r$

19a -2.18×10^{-18} J
b -0.55×10^{-18} J; -0.24×10^{-18} J; -0.14×10^{-18} J; -0.09×10^{-18} J.

21a 0.3 W
b About 2.3×10^{16} photons per second.
c About one in 50 000 (the area of your eye pupil divided by total area of sphere 0.3 m radius).
d About 5×10^{11} photons enter your eye per second; time between photons is about 2×10^{-12} seconds.
e About 6×10^{-4} m.
f About 6 m.

22 *Behaviour:* interference, diffraction, photoelectric effect, reflection, refraction, polarization.
Models: wave model (superposition effects: diffraction, interference, polarization); particle model (photoelectric effect). Both models can explain reflection and refraction. Models which refer to objects and phenomena we can see aren't adequate to explain matter on a very small scale.

25 $\sin\theta_1/\sin\theta_2 = s_2/s_1$; does not depend on λ.

26a 0.167
b 0.167

27a 1.73; 1.74; 1.65. Average $= 1.71$.
b $1:1.71$
c Smaller spacing.
d Decrease; wavelength decreases as energy is increased.

28a $1:1.73$
b $1:1.73$ agrees well enough with **27b**.
c Horizontal rows (wider spacing) give smaller rings (D_1).

30a $\sqrt{V}$
b $D \propto \sin\theta \propto \lambda$

31 $D\sqrt{V}$ should be constant. Values are 410; 427; 413; 424; 436; 419; 435; 429. (Since values of V were estimated from the size of a spark gap and so are not accurately known, the agreement is quite good.)

32a 0.205×10^{-10} m
b $\frac{1}{2}mv^2 = Ve$
c $mv = \sqrt{2mVe}$
d $h = 7.78 \times 10^{-34}$ J s (the accepted value is 6.6×10^{-34} J s).
e Yes; both are J s.

33a Slope is $\dfrac{\lambda}{1/\sqrt{V}} = \lambda\sqrt{V} = \dfrac{h}{mv} \times \sqrt{V}$
$= \dfrac{h}{\sqrt{2mVe}} \times \sqrt{V} = \dfrac{h}{\sqrt{2me}}$

b From the graph the slope is approximately $2 \times 10^{-10}/0.15 = 13 \times 10^{-10}$
So $h \approx 13 \times 10^{-10} \times \sqrt{2me}$
$\approx 7.1 \times 10^{-34}$ J s.

35 $\lambda \approx 10^{-34}$ m

37a Wavelengths of 420 MeV and 183 MeV electrons are 2.96×10^{-15} m and 6.79×10^{-15} m respectively.
b Estimates of nuclear diameters:
C 4.7×10^{-15} m
O 5.2×10^{-15} m
V 9.1×10^{-15} m

39 Points to make include:
Mistake or ambiguity: they still behave as 'very tiny billiard balls', and as waves *as well*.

Explanation: neither model complete; need both ideas to understand behaviour of matter on a very small scale. Most scientists accept the need for two models,

but some are unhappy with this and search for 'a better idea'.

40 Points to make include:
Light: some behaviour (superposition) explained on wave model; other behaviour (photoelectric effect) needs particle model.
Particles: small particles (*e.g.* electrons, but also neutrons, protons, etc.) show wave-like behaviour (electron, neutron diffraction). Wavelength $\lll$ wavelength of light.
Duality: neither model complete – need both, depending on behaviour to be 'explained'.

43a 4×10^{-10} m
b Largest
c 1.65×10^{-24} kg m s^{-1}
d No
e 1.5×10^{-18} J
f Minimum.
g Electrical attraction between proton and electron.
h 2.3×10^{-18} J
i No

44a Wavelength: ten times smaller; momentum: ten times larger; kinetic energy: hundred times larger.
b 23×10^{-18} J
c No, because kinetic energy would be 150×10^{-18} J.

45a Electron's kinetic energy will decrease by factor of 100; electrical potential energy will decrease in magnitude by factor of 10. Total energy
$= 0.015 \times 10^{-18}$ J $- 0.23 \times 10^{-18}$ J
$= -0.215 \times 10^{-18}$ J.

Total energy is more (*i.e.* a smaller negative quantity) than for the atoms with radius 1×10^{-10} m.
b Total energy (for atom with radius 0.1×10^{-10} m) is (150×10^{-18}) J $-$ (23×10^{-18}) J $= 127 \times 10^{-18}$ J.

46a $\dfrac{h}{4r}$

b $\dfrac{h^2}{32mr^2}$

c $-\dfrac{e^2}{4\pi\varepsilon_0 r}$

d $E = \dfrac{h^2}{32mr^2} - \dfrac{e^2}{4\pi\varepsilon_0 r}$

e $\dfrac{dE}{dr} = -\dfrac{h^2}{16mr^3} + \dfrac{e^2}{4\pi\varepsilon_0 r^2}$

f $r = \dfrac{4\pi\varepsilon_0 h^2}{16me^2}$

$\quad = 1.3 \times 10^{-10}\,\text{m}$

50a Tension in the spring; mass per unit length of the spring.
b Speed decreases because tension is less near the lower end (less weight to support).
c Similarity: electron standing waves in atoms have variable wavelength.

Difference: electron standing wave in atom shows chance of finding electron, it does not represent displacement of a material object like a spring.

51 (c)

52 E

53i Explanation: some properties of electrons are only understood by thinking of them as waves, but this does not mean they *are* waves.

Support: electron diffraction (experimental evidence); success of wave mechanics in explaining, for example, energy levels of hydrogen atom (theory, evidence).
ii Explanation: electron confined to a box must be a standing wave (model). If size of box is about 10^{-10} m, then, because at least one half-wavelength loop must fit in the box, wavelength can't be more than 2×10^{-10} m. This puts a lower limit to momentum (since momentum $\propto 1/\text{wavelength}$) and to kinetic energy ($[\text{momentum}]^2/2m$). Smaller box means shorter wavelength, so higher momentum and kinetic energy (theory, model, calculations).

Support: atoms have finite size (evidence, calculations); nuclear forces which hold neutrons, protons in the nucleus, are much stronger as they must be able to confine a particle to a much smaller box (evidence, model, calculations).
iii Explanation: if the total energy is not negative the electron will fly away from the nucleus (*cf.* satellite orbiting a planet, etc.). Wave mechanics shows that kinetic energy of electron exceeds $10\,\text{eV}$ if it is confined within a space much smaller than 10^{-10} m (theory, model, calculation).

Support: calculations of this kind correctly predict the size of atoms (calculations, evidence).
iv Explanation: atoms cannot have any arbitrary amount of energy: only specific, well-defined amounts called energy levels are allowed. The values of energy which the atom can have are $c/1, c/4, c/9, \ldots, c/n^2$.

Value of c: $-2.18 \times 10^{-18}\,\text{J}$ (evidence, theory, calculations).

Support: measurement of frequencies of spectral lines; (evidence, calculations, theory).
v Explanation: electron is standing wave because it is confined. Standing wave must have a whole number of half-wavelength loops, so only certain wavelengths are possible. Since kinetic energy depends on wavelength, only discrete values of kinetic energy are possible. This model predicts energy $\propto n^2$; in fact energy $\propto 1/n^2$.

Support: momentum $\propto 1/\text{wavelength}$, and kinetic energy $\propto (\text{momentum})^2$. Wave with 2 loops has half the wavelength, so four times the kinetic energy of one-loop standing wave. Three-loop standing wave has 9 times, etc. The $1/n^2$ rule arises because potential as well as kinetic energies contribute to total energy of atom; also because the standing waves with more loops occupy more space (model, theory, and evidence.)

54a Average momentum $= \sqrt{2mE}$
b Average wavelength $= h/\sqrt{2mE}$
c $E \propto -1/r_0$
d $n \propto r_0/\lambda$
e $E \propto -1/n^2$

REFERENCE MATERIAL

Textbooks and further reading

Textbooks that are useful throughout the course are listed here. Other books and other references that are particularly relevant to specific Units are listed individually.

AKRILL, T. B., BENNET, G. A. G., and MILLAR, C. J. *Physics.* Edward Arnold, 1979.
BOLTON, W. *Patterns in physics.* McGraw Hill, 1974.
DUNCAN, T. *Physics: a textbook for advanced level students.* Murray, 1982.
OR

{ DUNCAN, T. *Advanced physics: fields, waves, and atoms.* 2nd edn. Murray, 1981.
DUNCAN, T. *Advanced physics: materials and mechanics.* 2nd edn. Murray, 1981.

WENHAM, E. J., DORLING, G. W., SNELL, J. A. N., and TAYLOR, B. *Physics: concepts and models.* 2nd edn. Addison-Wesley, 1984.

Unit H Magnetic fields and a.c.

Textbooks for reference
BENNET, G. A. G. *Electricity and modern physics.* 2nd edn. Arnold, 1974.
NUFFIELD REVISED PHYSICS *Pupils' text year 5.* Longman, 1980.

Further reading
CARO, D. E., MCDONNELL, J. A., and SPICER, B. M. *Modern physics.* 3rd edn. Edward Arnold, 1978.
MORGAN, D. V. and HOWES, M. J. Wykeham Science Series No. 20. *Solid state electronic devices.* Wykeham, 1972.
STAFFORD, G. H. A Rutherford Appleton Laboratory Monograph. *The use of high energy machines in particle physics.* Rutherford Appleton Laboratories, 1980. (Out of print.)
WILSON, R. R. and LITTAUER, R. Science Study Series No. 15. *Accelerators: machines of nuclear physics.* Heinemann, 1962.
WRIGHT, J. P. *The vital spark.* Heinemann, 1974. (Out of print.)

Unit I Linear electronics, feedback and control

Further reading
BOLTON, W. *Engineering instrumentation and control.* Butterworth, 1980.

BRAUN, E. and MACDONALD, S. *Revolution in miniature: history and impact of semiconductor electronics.* 2nd edn. Cambridge University Press, 1982.
CLOSE, K. J. and YARWOOD, J. *Electronics.* University Tutorial Press, 1976.
ELECTRONIC SYSTEMS TEACHING PROGRAMME ESP700 Book 4 *Feedback systems.* Feedback Instruments Ltd.
ENGINEERING CONCEPTS CURRICULUM PROJECT *The man-made world.* McGraw-Hill, 1971.
ENGINEERING SCIENCE PROJECT *Electronics, systems, and analogues.* Macmillan, 1975. (Out of print.)
HARDY, R. N. Studies in Biology No. 63. *Homeostasis.* 2nd edn. Edward Arnold, 1983.
MARSTON, R. M. *110 operational amplifier projects.* Hayden, 1975.
NUFFIELD ADVANCED PHYSICS Students' book *Unit 6 Electronics and reactive circuits.* Penguin, 1971.
NUFFIELD REVISED ADVANCED BIOLOGY *Study guide I.* Longman, 1985.
PLANT, M. *Operational amplifier applications.* NCST Trent Polytechnic, 1974.
PROJECT TECHNOLOGY Handbook 14 *Simple computer and control logic.* Heinemann/Schools Council, 1972.
RAMSEY, D. C. *Engineering instrumentation and control.* Stanley Thornes, 1981.
ROBERTS, M. B. V. *Biology, a functional approach.* 2nd edn. Nelson, 1976.
Science in Society Book M *Engineering 1.* Heinemann/ASE, 1983.

Unit J Electromagnetic waves

On optics
FRENCH, A. P. MIT Introductory Physics Series. *Electromagnetic waves and optics.* Nelson, 1968.
FRENCH, A. P. MIT Introductory Science Series. *Vibrations and waves.* Van Nostrand Reinhold (U.K.) Co. Ltd., 1982.

On images
CANNON, T. M. and HUNT, B. R. 'Image processing by computer'. *Scientific American* Volume **245**(4), Oct. 1981.
TAYLOR, C. A. Wykeham Science Series, *Images.* Wykeham, 1978.

On historical background
MASON, P. *The light fantastic.* Pelican Books, 1981

On radioastronomy
HENBEST, N. 'Jodrell under Merlin's spell'. *New Scientist* Volume **96**, 1332, Nov. 1982.
KELLERMANN, K. I. 'Intercontinental radio astronomy'. *Scientific American* Volume **226**(2), Feb. 1972.
READHEAD, A. C. S. 'Radioastronomy by very-long-baseline interferometry'. *Scientific American* Volume **246**(6), June 1982.

On electromagnetic waves
BENNET, G. A. G. *Electricity and modern physics.* 2nd edn. Edward Arnold, 1975.
WHELAN, P. M. and HODGSON, M. J. *Essential principles of physics.* Murray, 1978.

On relativity
BONDI, H. *Relativity and common sense: a new approach to Einstein.* Heinemann, 1964.
EPSTEIN, L. C. *Relativity visualized.* Insight Press, San Francisco, 1985. (Available through Adam Hilger Ltd., Bristol.)
HOFFMANN, B. *Relativity and its roots.* A *Scientific American* Book. W. H. Freeman and Co., 1983.
LANDAU, L. D. and RUMER, G. B. *What is relativity?* Oliver and Boyd, 1960.
SANDAGE, A. R. 'The red shift'. *Scientific American* Volume **195**(3), Sept. 1956. (Offprint No. 240.)
SHANKLAND, R. S. 'The Michelson-Morley experiment'. *Scientific American* Volume **211**(5), Nov. 1964. (Offprint No. 327.)

Unit K Energy and entropy

ANGRIST, S. W. and HEPLER, L. G. *Order and chaos.* Basic Books, 1967.
ATKINS, P. W. *The creation.* W. H. Freeman, 1981.
CRAWLEY, G. M. *Energy.* Collier–Macmillan, 1975.
DAVIES, P. C. W. *The accidental Universe.* Cambridge University Press, 1982.
DAVIES, P. C. W. *The runaway Universe.* Cambridge University Press, 1982.
NUFFIELD REVISED ADVANCED CHEMISTRY *Students' books 1 and 2.* Longman, 1984.

PSSC *College Physics.* 5th edn. Raytheon, 1981.

Energy and power. (A *Scientific American* book.) W. H. Freeman, 1971.

WEINBERG, S. *The first three minutes.* Fontana, 1983. (First published by André Deutsch, 1977.)

Unit L Waves, particles, and atoms

In addition to the general list of text books on page 348, the following are particularly useful for this Unit. Particular sections or chapters in several of them are referred to in the Reading section 'Waves and particles' on page 309.

BENNET, G. A. G. *Electricity and modern physics.* 2nd edn. Edward Arnold, 1974.

BORN, M. *The restless Universe.* Dover, 1951.

CARO, D. E., MCDONNEL, J. A., and SPICER, B. M. *Modern physics: an introduction to atomic and nuclear physics.* 3rd edn. Arnold, 1978.

CONN, G. K. T. and TURNER, H. D. *The evolution of the nuclear atom.* Iliffe, 1965.

FEYNMAN, R. P., LEIGHTON, R. B., and SANDS, M. The Feynman lectures on physics *Volume 1: Mainly mechanics, radiation, and heat.* Addison–Wesley, 1963.

HOFFMANN, B. *The strange story of the quantum.* Penguin, 1970. (Also available in Dover Press edition.)

MILLIKAN, R. A. Phoenix Science Series. *The electron.* University of Chicago Press, 1963.

OPEN UNIVERSITY Science Foundation Course S101 Unit 9 *Light: waves or particles?* Open University Press, 1979.

PROJECT PHYSICS Text and Reader *Unit 5, Models of the atom.* Holt, Rinehart, and Winston, 1971.

PSSC *College physics.* 5th edn. Raytheon, 1981.

PSSC *Physics.* 3rd edn. Heath, 1971.

ROGERS, E. M. *Physics for the inquiring mind.* Oxford University Press, 1960.

ROTHMAN, M. A. *The laws of physics.* Penguin, 1966.

TAYLOR, R. J. Unilever Educational Booklet Advanced Series No. 5. *Water.* 2nd edn. Unilever, 1969.

TOLANSKY, S. *Revolution in optics.* Penguin, 1968.

TOULMIN, S. E. and GOODFIELD, J. *The architecture of matter.* Hutchinson, 1962.

WRIGHT, S. (ed.) *Classical scientific papers – physics.* Mills and Boon, 1964. (Out of print.)

DATA; FORMULAE AND RELATIONSHIPS; SYMBOLS

Data

(Values are given to three significant figures, except where more – or less – are useful)

Physical constants

speed of light	c	$3.00 \times 10^8 \, \mathrm{m \, s^{-1}}$
permittivity of free space	ε_0	$8.85 \times 10^{-12} \, \mathrm{C^2 \, N^{-1} \, m^{-2}}$ (or $\mathrm{F \, m^{-1}}$)
electric force constant	$\dfrac{1}{4\pi\varepsilon_0}$	$8.98 \times 10^9 \, \mathrm{N \, m^2 \, C^{-2}}$ ($\approx 9 \times 10^9 \, \mathrm{N \, m^2 \, C^{-2}}$)
permeability of free space	μ_0	$4\pi \times 10^{-7} \, \mathrm{N \, A^{-2}}$ (or $\mathrm{H \, m^{-1}}$)
charge on electron	e	$-1.60 \times 10^{-19} \, \mathrm{C}$
mass of electron	m_e	$9.11 \times 10^{-31} \, \mathrm{kg} = 0.000\,55 \, \mathrm{u}$
mass of proton	m_p	$1.673 \times 10^{-27} \, \mathrm{kg} = 1.007\,3 \, \mathrm{u}$
mass of neutron	m_n	$1.675 \times 10^{-27} \, \mathrm{kg} = 1.008\,7 \, \mathrm{u}$
mass of alpha particle	m_α	$6.646 \times 10^{-27} \, \mathrm{kg} = 4.001\,5 \, \mathrm{u}$
Avogadro constant	L, N_A	$6.02 \times 10^{23} \, \mathrm{mol^{-1}}$
Planck constant	h	$6.63 \times 10^{-34} \, \mathrm{J \, s}$
Boltzmann constant	k	$1.38 \times 10^{-23} \, \mathrm{J \, K^{-1}}$
molar gas constant	R	$8.31 \, \mathrm{J \, mol^{-1} \, K^{-1}}$
gravitational force constant	G	$6.67 \times 10^{-11} \, \mathrm{N \, m^2 \, kg^{-2}}$

Other data

standard temperature and pressure (s.t.p.)		$273 \, \mathrm{K} \, (0\,^\circ\mathrm{C})$, $1.01 \times 10^5 \, \mathrm{Pa}$ (1 atmosphere)
molar volume of a gas at s.t.p.	V_m	$2.24 \times 10^{-2} \, \mathrm{m^3}$
gravitational field strength at Earth's surface (in the U.K.)	g	$9.81 \, \mathrm{N \, kg^{-1}}$
mass of Earth		$5.98 \times 10^{24} \, \mathrm{kg}$
GM for Earth		$\approx 4 \times 10^{14} \, \mathrm{N \, m^2 \, kg^{-1}}$
mass of Moon		$7.35 \times 10^{22} \, \mathrm{kg}$
average separation of Earth and Moon		$3.82 \times 10^8 \, \mathrm{m}$
mean radius of Earth		$6.37 \times 10^6 \, \mathrm{m}$
mean radius of Moon		$1.74 \times 10^6 \, \mathrm{m}$

Conversion factor

unified atomic mass unit $\qquad$ 1 u $\qquad$ $= 1.661 \times 10^{-27}\,\text{kg}$

Numerical constants

the number e, the base of natural logarithms $\quad$ e $\qquad$ 2.718 ...

ratio of circumference to diameter of circle $\quad$ π $\qquad$ 3.14 ... $(\approx \sqrt{10})$

Formulae and relationships
Motion and forces

$$\text{linear momentum} = mv \qquad \text{(mass } m, \text{ velocity } v)$$

$$\text{force} = \text{rate of change of momentum}$$

$$F = ma \qquad \text{if mass is constant (force } F, \text{ acceleration } a)$$

$$\text{impulse} = F\Delta t$$

$$\text{translational kinetic energy} = \tfrac{1}{2}mv^2$$

$$\text{gravitational potential energy difference} = mg\Delta h \qquad \text{(uniform field strength } g, \text{ height } \Delta h)$$

$$\text{energy transformed (work)} = \text{component of force} \times \text{displacement}$$

components of force in two perpendicular directions:

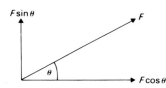

$$\text{moment of force about a point} = \text{force} \times \text{perpendicular distance from point to line of action of force}$$

static equilibrium conditions: $\qquad$ $\Sigma F = 0$

$$\Sigma \text{ moments} = 0$$

limiting friction $\qquad$ $F = \mu N$ $\qquad$ (coefficient of friction μ, normal force N)

circular motion $\qquad$ $a = v^2/r$ $\qquad$ (acceleration a, speed v, radius r)

$$F = mv^2/r \qquad \text{(centripetal force } F, \text{ mass } m)$$

Solids

For a material in tension

Hooke's Law: $\qquad$ $F = kx$ $\qquad$ (tension F, spring constant k, extension x)

$$\text{stress} = \text{tension/cross-sectional area}$$

$$\text{strain} = \text{extension/original length}$$

$$\text{Young modulus} = \text{stress/strain}$$

$$\text{elastic strain energy} = \tfrac{1}{2}kx^2$$

$$\text{elastic strain energy per unit volume} = \tfrac{1}{2}\,\text{stress} \times \text{strain}$$

Gases

Ideal gas equation

for n moles

$$pV = nRT$$

(pressure p, volume V, molar gas constant R, temperature T)

for one mole

$$pV_m = RT$$

(molar volume V_m)

Kinetic theory of gases

$$pV = \tfrac{1}{3}Nm\overline{c^2}$$

(number of molecules N, mass of molecule m, mean square speed $\overline{c^2}$)

$$p = \tfrac{1}{3}\rho\overline{c^2}$$

(density ρ)

mean kinetic energy of translation of one mole of an ideal gas $= \tfrac{3}{2}RT$

Electricity

flow

$$I = AvnQ$$

(current I, area A, velocity of carriers v, carrier density n, charge Q)

resistance

$$R = V/I$$

(resistance R, potential difference V)

$$R = \rho l/A$$

(resistivity ρ, length l, area A)

$$R = R_1 + R_2 + \dots$$

(resistors in series)

$$1/R = 1/R_1 + 1/R_2 + \dots$$

(resistors in parallel)

charge

$$\Delta Q = I\Delta t$$

(charge Q, time t)

capacitance

$$C = Q/V$$

(capacitance C)

$$\text{energy stored} = \tfrac{1}{2}QV$$

$$1/C = 1/C_1 + 1/C_2 + \dots$$

(capacitors in series)

$$C = C_1 + C_2 + \dots$$

(capacitors in parallel)

discharge of capacitor

$$Q = Q_0\,e^{-t/RC}$$

(initial charge Q_0, time t, time constant RC)

Oscillations

Simple harmonic motion

equation of motion

$$a = -(k/m)s$$

(acceleration a, force per unit displacement k, mass m, displacement s)

displacement–time relation

$$s = A\cos\omega t$$
$$\omega^2 = k/m$$
$$T = 2\pi/\omega$$

(amplitude A, angular frequency ω, time t)

(periodic time T)

$$= 2\pi\sqrt{\frac{m}{k}}$$

$$f = 1/T = \omega/2\pi$$

(frequency f)

$$f = \frac{1}{2\pi}\sqrt{\frac{k}{m}}$$

$$v_{max} = \omega A$$

(maximum velocity v_{max})

$$a_{max} = \omega v_{max} = \omega^2 A$$

(maximum acceleration a_{max})

$$\text{kinetic energy} = \tfrac{1}{2}mv^2$$
$$\text{potential energy} = \tfrac{1}{2}ks^2$$
$$\text{total energy} = \tfrac{1}{2}kA^2$$

Quality factor	$Q = 2\pi \dfrac{\text{energy stored in oscillator}}{\text{energy lost per cycle}}$	

Waves

Wave speeds

for all waves	$c = f\lambda$	(wave speed c, frequency f, wavelength λ)
compression wave in mass–spring system	$c = x\sqrt{\dfrac{k}{m}}$	(spacing x, force per unit displacement k, mass m)
sound in a solid	$c = \sqrt{\dfrac{E}{\rho}}$	(Young modulus E, density ρ)
transverse wave on string	$c = \sqrt{\dfrac{T}{\mu}}$	(tension T, mass per unit length μ)
electromagnetic waves in free space	$c = 1/\sqrt{\varepsilon_0\mu_0}$	(permittivity of free space ε_0, permeability of free space μ_0)

Diffraction
narrow slit	$n\lambda = b\sin\theta$	(order n, slit width b, angles of minima θ)
Rayleigh criterion	$\theta \geqslant \lambda/b$	
diffraction grating	$n\lambda = s\sin\theta$	(grating spacing s, angles of maxima θ)
Young's double slits	$\lambda/x \approx s/L$	(fringe separation x, slit spacing s, distance from slits to fringes L)

Field and potential

All fields

	$E = -dV/dr$ $(\approx -\Delta V/\Delta r)$	(field strength E, potential gradient dV/dr)
electric field	$E = F/Q$	(electric field strength E, force F, charge Q)
uniform field between parallel plates	$E = V/d$ $= \sigma/\varepsilon_0$	(potential difference V, separation d) (charge density σ, permittivity of free space ε_0)
parallel plate capacitor	$C = \varepsilon_0\varepsilon_r A/d$	(capacitance C, relative permittivity ε_r, area A, separation d)
point charges	$F = \dfrac{1}{4\pi\varepsilon_0}\dfrac{Q_1 Q_2}{r^2}$	(charges Q_1, Q_2, separation r)
	$E = \dfrac{1}{4\pi\varepsilon_0}\dfrac{Q}{r^2}$	(electric field strength E)
	$V = \dfrac{1}{4\pi\varepsilon_0}\dfrac{Q}{r}$	(electric potential V)
gravitational field	$g = F/m$	(gravitational field strength g, force F, mass m)
	$F = -Gm_1 m_2/r^2$	(gravitational constant G, masses m_1, m_2, separation of centres r)
	$g = -GM/r^2$	(mass of Earth, or other body, M)

$$V_g = -GM/r \qquad \text{(gravitational potential } V_g\text{)}$$
$$\Delta V_g = GM(1/r_1 - 1/r_2) \qquad \text{(gravitational potential difference } \Delta V_g\text{)}$$
uniform gravitational field $\qquad \Delta V_g = g\Delta h \qquad \text{(height } h\text{)}$

Atomic and nuclear physics

Radioactive decay

$$dN/dt = -\lambda N \qquad \text{(number } N\text{, decay constant } \lambda\text{)}$$
$$N = N_0 e^{-\lambda t} \qquad \text{(initial number } N_0\text{)}$$

$$T_{\frac{1}{2}} = \frac{\ln 2}{\lambda} \qquad \text{(half-life } T_{\frac{1}{2}}\text{)}$$

$$= \frac{0.693}{\lambda}$$

mass-energy relationship $\qquad \Delta E = c^2 \Delta m \qquad$ (energy E, mass m, speed of light c)

energy–frequency relationship $\qquad E = hf \qquad$ (photon energy E, Planck constant h,
for photons $\qquad\qquad\qquad\qquad\qquad$ frequency f)

wavelength–momentum relationship $\qquad \lambda = h/p \qquad$ (wavelength λ, momentum p)
for particles

Electromagnetism

Magnetic fields

force on a current carrying $\qquad F = BIl \qquad$ (flux density B, current I,
conductor $\qquad\qquad\qquad\qquad\qquad\qquad$ length l)

force on a moving charge $\qquad F = BQv \qquad$ (charge Q, velocity perpendicular
$\qquad\qquad\qquad\qquad\qquad\qquad\qquad\qquad$ to field v)

flux densities
  inside a long solenoid $\qquad B = \mu_0 NI/l \qquad$ (permeability of free space μ_0,
$\qquad\qquad\qquad\qquad\qquad\qquad\qquad\qquad$ turns N, length l)

  near a long straight wire $\qquad B = \mu_0 I/2\pi r \qquad$ (radial distance r)
  at centre of circular coil $\qquad B = \mu_0 NI/2r \qquad$ (radius of coil r)

magnetic circuit

$$\text{reluctance} = l/\mu_0\mu_r A \qquad \text{(length } l\text{, relative permeability } \mu_r,$$
$$\text{area } A\text{)}$$

$$\text{flux} = \text{current turns/reluctance}$$

Induction

$$\text{induced e.m.f.} = \text{rate of change of flux linked}$$
$$\mathscr{E} = Nd\Phi/dt \qquad \text{(induced e.m.f. } \mathscr{E}\text{, rate of change of}$$
$$\text{flux } d\Phi/dt\text{, number of turns linked } N\text{)}$$

$$\mathscr{E} = MdI/dt \qquad \text{(e.m.f. in secondary } \mathscr{E}\text{,}$$
$$\text{mutual inductance } M\text{)}$$

$$V = L\,dI/dt \qquad \text{(p.d. across coil } V\text{, self inductance } L\text{)}$$

Transformers

$$\mathscr{E}_s = V_p \times N_s/N_p \qquad \text{(e.m.f. in secondary } \mathscr{E}_s\text{, p.d.}$$
$$\text{across primary } V_p\text{, turns } N_p, N_s\text{)}$$

$$I_p V_p > I_s \mathscr{E}_s \qquad \text{(currents } I_p, I_s\text{)}$$

| Alternating current | $I_{\text{r.m.s.}} = I_0/\sqrt{2}$ | (root mean square current $I_{\text{r.m.s.}}$, peak current I_0) |
| Electrical oscillation | $2\pi f = \omega = 1/\sqrt{LC}$ | (resonant frequency f, angular frequency ω, inductance L, capacitance C) |

Energy and entropy

Energy transfer

$$\text{efficiency} = \frac{\text{useful energy output}}{\text{total energy input}}$$

$$\text{efficiency of heat engine} = 1 - \frac{T_2}{T_1}$$
(temperature of source T_1, temperature of sink T_2)

$$\Delta T = \phi \mathscr{R}$$
(temperature difference ΔT, rate of thermal transfer of energy ϕ, thermal resistance $\mathscr{R}$)

$$\mathscr{R} = l/kA$$
(area A, length l, thermal conductivity k)

$$X = \mathscr{R}A$$
(thermal resistance coefficient X)

Entropy

$$\Delta S = (\Delta Q/T)_{\text{reversible}}$$
(entropy change ΔS, energy transferred thermally and reversibly ΔQ)

$$\Delta S = k\,\Delta\ln W$$
(number of ways W, Boltzmann constant k)

$$\Delta S = Nk\ln(V_2/V_1)$$
(number of particles N, volume change from V_1 to V_2; for ideal gas)

$$p\,dV = T\,dS$$
(pressure p, volume V; for ideal gas, reversible isothermal change)

Boltzmann factor

$$f = e^{-\varepsilon/kT}$$
(Boltzmann factor f, difference between energies of particle ε)

$$\text{rate} \propto e^{-E_A/kT}$$
(activation energy E_A)

Electrical circuit symbols

Some of the symbols used in circuit diagrams are shown below:

Wires, junctions, terminals

crossing of wires,
no electrical contact

junction

double junction	
terminal	
aerial	
earth	
frame or chassis connection	
Lamps signal lamp	
lamp for illumination	
Transducers microphone	
earphone	
loudspeaker	
motor	
Amplifier (or non-inverting gate)	
Logic gates Invert or NOT gate	
OR gate	
NOR gate	
AND gate	
NAND gate	
Exclusive OR (XOR) gate	

Capacitors

general symbol

polarized (electrolytic) capacitor

Inductors

general symbol

inductor with core

transformer with ferromagnetic core

Batteries

primary or secondary cell *(The short thick bar represents the negative terminal)*

battery with tappings

Diodes

diode/rectifier

light sensitive diode

light emitting diode (L.E.D.)

Measuring instruments

voltmeter

ammeter

galvanometer

Switches, relays

normally open switch

normally closed switch

relay coil and contact

Resistors

general symbol

variable resistor

variable resistor with preset
adjustment

potentiometer

resistor with inherent
variability (*e.g.* thermistor)

light-dependent resistor

fuse

INDEX

X-ray diffraction by, 232
water waves, diffraction, 152, 185–6, 214
wave detectors, 153
wave functions, 305–7
wave mechanics, 301–7, 313–14
waveguide, 164, 166
wavelength, of electrons, 300
    of light, measurement: using diffraction grating, 156, 198–9; using Young's fringes, 160
    of X-rays, measurement, 161, 202
weber (unit), 8
Wheatstone bridge, *see* bridge circuit

Wilson, R. W., 267
wires, field near, 36, 37
    induced e.m.f. in moving, 6–7, 38, 42
    to measure resistance of strained, 122
    X-ray diffraction by, 297

X

X-ray camera, 231
X-ray diffraction, 156, 162, 203, 230–32
    by polythene, 297
    by water, 232
    by wires, 297

by zinc sulphide, 162, 230–32
X-rays, measurement of wavelength, 161, 202

Y

Young, Thomas, 171, 292
Young's double-slit experiment, 160–61, 199–201

Z

zinc sulphide, X-ray diffraction by, 162, 230–32